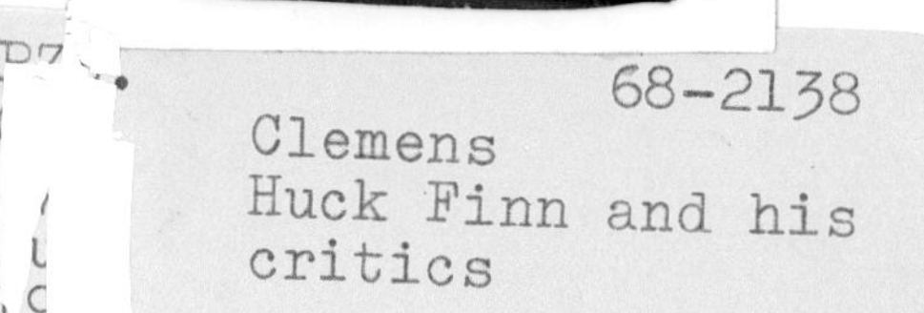

MAR 6 '69		JUN	2004
APR 11 '69			
APR 28 '69		JUL 09	
APR 30 '69			
		JUL X X 2015	

HUCK FINN AND HIS CRITICS

Richard Lettis C. W. POST COLLEGE

Robert F. McDonnell OHIO UNIVERSITY

William E. Morris OHIO UNIVERSITY

THE MACMILLAN COMPANY *New York*

Seventh Printing, 1968

Library of Congress catalog card number: 62-14372

The Macmillan Company, New York
Collier-Macmillan Canada, Ltd., Toronto, Ontario

Printed in the United States of America

TABLE OF CONTENTS

Table of Contents

INTRODUCTION

In most situations it is enough to take on one new task at a time, but this text challenges you to try two at once. When we say that these challenges are reading and writing, you will perhaps feel there is nothing "new" about them, for you have been doing both since first grade. But you have already learned in college English that there are different kinds of writing, and probably it has occurred to you that there is more than one way of reading. The challenges we present to you include three ways of reading (two of them new to you) and one way of writing. Until now, your writing has probably been the expression of your own feelings and ideas. In college, perhaps you have been writing essays—describing personal events, explaining public situations, and presenting your thoughts on problems that have troubled you. Chances are that in high school you wrote book reports, accounts of novels and what you found in them. In this text you are faced with a similar problem, though something more will be expected of you as well. You are asked to read the novel *Huckleberry Finn*, and you are asked to acquire a command of its content, to record your thoughts and feelings—your responses to it. But in addition, you are asked to improve and qualify your own responses by careful reading of others who have also read *Huckleberry Finn* and have written down their thoughts and feelings about it. In other words, you must not only have and be able to record your responses, but you must do what you can to improve them by utilizing the responses of others. And when you have done this, you are asked to present *your* reader with a record of the results of your experiences; the record is called a research paper.

The writing of such a paper has complicated technical aspects which we leave to your writing handbook to explain; but the reading requires our comment. Obviously, there are going to be several kinds of reading necessary to the preparation of your investigative essay. Each kind is equally important. First you will read the novel. You will read it in the "usual" way, as you would read any novel, getting interested in the characters, becoming excited by the scenes and situations, wanting to find out what happens next. If you cannot read *Huckleberry Finn* in this way, you had better not dream of writing a research paper on it; there is nothing here for you.

Since we have picked this novel for our text, obviously we feel that you should be able to enjoy it. But why? It is about a boy, after all—a kid in his early 'teens. And he is not much of a boy at that: the son of a drunkard and of a mother we hear nothing about. He is not "real," of course, and the time during which he was supposed to have lived is more than a hundred years ago, and not of much concern to us, with our own modern problems. And though plenty of things happen in the novel, they don't seem to add up to much—where does it all take us? Where is the defeated bad guy? If Huck is a hero, what has he accomplished?

If you have read the novel before, probably you are giving answers already. If Huck is a child, he is what we all have been, and pity the man who has lived so long that he has lost interest in his past, or thinks he can learn nothing from it. If Huck's origin is humble and obscure, his life is exciting and significant, his character attractive and compelling. And if he is not real in the historical sense, if he "lived" many years ago, there is yet a reality in him that no history text can capture, there is a timelessness which enables us, with a few external changes, to put him into our own environment. As for the significance of the novel, that we leave to you and the critics to discover.

But we hope you will attempt to discover it for yourself before you turn to the critics for aid. If you read them first, the response you give to the novel will be largely their response; the significance you find in it will be the significance they have told you to find. You will want to make use of their opinions to broaden and strengthen your own opinions, but unless you acquire your opinions first, you will become a mere carbon paper for the ideas of others. No good investigative essay comes out of such an approach.

Therefore we suggest that you read *Huckleberry Finn* a second time before you consult the critics. It is such a good book that you will enjoy the second reading as much as the first, but now your appreciation of what happens to whom will be seconded by your critical interests—by your analysis of the characters and scenes, for example, and by your decision as to whether "what happens next" works well within the novel. As you analyze the characters you will want to evaluate them from several standpoints. Why do you find them interesting? Do they seem real—that is, do they act in a believable manner, with consistency and with proper motivation for their actions? Are they distinguishable from each other in speech, manner, and personality? Do the main characters seem complete, fully developed ("round," as one critic has put it, as opposed to "flat" characters who seem to represent human qualities rather than to be human beings)? And are their actions also believable, and worked into some sort of useful pattern—a plot? Do opposing forces meet in the plot to present some kind of conflict? How is this conflict made useful to the novel? Does it reach an acceptable climax (a point, not necessarily the peak of excitement or action in the plot, but always the peak of the intensification of problems, and the place where these problems must begin to resolve)? How much expository material is needed to help us understand the background of the characters and the action? How well has this material been handled—for example, has it been worked into the novel easily and believably, or does it seem forced and awkward?

Character and plot will lead you to consider other problems. Who tells the story? What are the advantages and limitations of his doing so? For example, how does the selection of the narrator of the story affect the style in which it will be told? Is the style here effective communication? Is it pleasing to read? Does it suit the subject matter it presents? To what extent is imagery (figurative language such as the metaphor and simile) a part of the style? Are symbols of importance—does the author seem to make characters, events, or objects represent things beyond themselves? (Think, for example, of the river, the raft, Miss Watson, or the Boggs-Sherburn incident.) Are the incidents in which all the above are presented realistic—that is, are they "the way life really is," or do they seem to be the result of a man's imagination, his memory, or his wishful thinking? And what is the final impression of all these things upon you; how does Mark Twain seem to look at life? Class discussion will augment these brief suggestions of things to look for in the novel, but your thinking about them while you read *Huckleberry Finn* will help your instructor to help you.

At this point you will have done two kinds of reading. If you had read the novel only for pleasure (no one should suggest there is anything wrong with that), the first kind would have sufficed, but in order to understand *why Huckleberry Finn* was such good reading you have had to employ the second. Now this second kind of reading will lead you, in your attempt to know *Huckleberry Finn*, to a third: literary criticism. Here you can check your impressions, your analyses, your interpretations and criticisms, against those of others. It will be encouraging for you, we think, to find that these critics, these experts on the business of literature, do not present pat and final answers to which you must conform your own ideas and responses. Instead, they disagree, sometimes widely and almost violently, on how they feel about *Huckleberry Finn*. That they do so suggests that if there are final and pat answers to literary problems, there is at least a long and difficult road to travel to reach them, and every man may try his hand at making his own path. You will certainly hold the opinions of these experts in some esteem, as you would respect the ideas of any trained individual. But you need not be overwhelmed by them, for they too are searching for answers, and though their attempts may help you, they cannot dominate you unless you have failed to experience any real response to the novel in your first and second readings. The critics, therefore, will not instruct you in how you should talk about *Huckleberry Finn*; they will simply help you in your progress toward that end.

When you have completed this third kind of reading, you will be ready for the new kind of writing, a research paper on *Huckleberry Finn*. It will be a record of your intelligent reading of the novel and of some critics who have written about the novel. It will seek to fuse this reading into a coherent and useful explanation of some aspect of the novel which you set before your reader. Its purpose will be to provide him with as much help as you can give, drawn from all the kinds of reading you have done, in his own attempt to understand *Huckleberry Finn*.

To help you write such a paper, we here present the novel and the criticism, plus a few aids. We have presented the essays just as you would find them in the journals from which they were taken, with a minimum of abridgment or correction. In referring to these articles in your paper, you will use the bibliographical information of the journal, not of this text. To this end the page numbers of the original have been included in the text (in slash marks: /15/) at the end of the material taken from that page. Bibliographical information (author, name of journal or book, volume and number of issue, date, etc.) is presented on the first page of each article. At the end of the article, we have presented a list of problems suggested by it; these are by no means exhaustive, but are intended to illustrate the kinds of problems you can search for. At the end of the text are further suggestions for topics for research, both inside and outside this text.

We wish to thank Miss Patricia Grlicky for her conscientious assistance in the task of compilation of this material.

R. L.
R. F. McD.
W. E. M.

The Adventures of Huckleberry Finn

SAMUEL L. CLEMENS

Notice

Persons attempting to find a motive in this narrative will be prosecuted; persons attempting to find a moral in it will be banished; persons attempting to find a plot in it will be shot.

By Order of the Author,
Per G.G., Chief of Ordnance.

Explanatory

In this book a number of dialects are used, to wit: the Missouri Negro dialect; the extremest form of the backwoods Southwestern dialect; the ordinary "Pike County" dialect; and four modified varieties of this last. The shadings have not been done in a haphazard fashion, or by guesswork; but painstakingly, and with the trustworthy guidance and support of personal familiarity with these several forms of speech.

I make this explanation for the reason that without it many readers would suppose that all these characters were trying to talk alike and not succeeding.

The Author.

I Civilizing Huck—Miss Watson—Tom Sawyer Waits

You don't know about me without you have read a book by the name of *The Adventures of Tom Sawyer;* but that ain't no matter. That book was made by Mr. Mark Twain, and he told the truth, mainly. There was things which he stretched, but mainly he told the truth. That is nothing. I never seen anybody but lied one time or another, without it was Aunt Polly, or the widow, or maybe Mary. Aunt Polly—Tom's Aunt Polly, she is—and Mary, and the Widow Douglas is all told about in that book, which is mostly a true book, with some stretchers, as I said before.

Now the way that the book winds up is this: Tom and me found the money that the robbers hid in the cave, and it made us rich. We got six thousand dollars apiece—all gold. It was an awful sight of money when it was piled up. Well, Judge Thatcher he took it and put it out at interest, and it fetched us a dollar a day apiece all the year around—more than a body could tell what to do with. The Widow Douglas she took me for her son, and allowed she would sivilize me; but it was rough living in the house all the time, considering how dismal regular and decent the widow was in all her ways; and so when I couldn't stand it no longer I lit out. I got into my old rags and my sugar-hogshead again, and was free and satisfied. But Tom Sawyer he hunted me up and said he was going to start a band of robbers, and I might join if I would go back to the widow and be respectable. So I went back.

The widow she cried over me, and called me a poor lost lamb, and she called me a lot of other names, too, but she never meant no harm by it. She put me in them new clothes again, and I couldn't do nothing but sweat and sweat, and feel all cramped up. Well, then, the old thing commenced again. The widow rung a bell for supper, and you had to come to time. When you got to the table you couldn't go right to eating, but you had to wait for the widow to tuck down her head and grumble a little over the victuals, though there warn't really anything the matter with them—that is, nothing only everything was cooked by itself. In a barrel of odds and ends it is different;

things get mixed up, and the juice kind of swaps around, and the things go better.

After supper she got out her book and learned me about Moses and the Bulrushers, and I was in a sweat to find out all about him; but by and by she let it out that Moses had been dead a considerable long time; so then I didn't care no more about him, because I don't take no stock in dead people.

Pretty soon I wanted to smoke, and asked the widow to let me. But she wouldn't. She said it was a mean practice and wasn't clean, and I must try to not do it any more. That is just the way with some people. They get down on a thing when they don't know nothing about it. Here she was a-bothering about Moses, which was no kin to her, and no use to anybody, being gone, you see, yet finding a power of fault with me for doing a thing that had some good in it. And she took snuff, too; of course that was all right, because she done it herself.

Her sister, Miss Watson, a tolerable slim old maid, with goggles on, had just come to live with her, and took a set at me now with a spelling-book. She worked me middling hard for about an hour, and then the widow made her ease up. I couldn't stood it much longer. Then for an hour it was deadly dull, and I was fidgety. Miss Watson would say, "Don't put your feet up there, Huckleberry"; and "Don't scrunch up like that, Huckleberry—set up straight"; and pretty soon she would say, "Don't gap and stretch like that, Huckleberry—why don't you try to behave?" Then she told me all about the bad place, and I said I wished I was there. She got mad then, but I didn't mean no harm. All I wanted was to go somewheres; all I wanted was a change, I warn't particular. She said it was wicked to say what I said; said she wouldn't say it for the whole world; *she* was going to live so as to go to the good place. Well, I couldn't see no advantage in going where she was going, so I made up my mind I wouldn't try for it. But I never said so, because it would only make trouble, and wouldn't do no good.

Now she had got a start, and she went on and told me all about the good place. She said all a body would have to do there was to go around all day long with a harp and sing, forever and ever. So I didn't think much of it. But I never said so. I asked her if she reckoned Tom Sawyer would go there, and she said not by a considerable sight. I was glad about that, because I wanted him and me to be together.

Miss Watson she kept pecking at me, and it got tiresome and lonesome. By and by they fetched the niggers in and had prayers, and then everybody was off to bed. I went up to my room with a piece of candle, and put it on the table. Then I set down in a chair by the window and tried to think of something cheerful, but it warn't no use. I felt so lonesome I most wished I was dead. The stars were shining, and the leaves rustled in the woods ever so mournful; and I heard an owl, away off, who-whooing about somebody that was dead, and a whippowill and a dog crying about somebody that was going to die; and the wind was trying to whisper something to me, and I couldn't make out what it was, and so it made the cold shivers run over me. Then away out in the woods I heard that kind of a sound that a ghost makes when it wants to tell about something that's on its mind and can't make itself understood, and so can't rest easy in its grave, and has to go about that way every night grieving. I got so downhearted and scared I did wish I had some company. Pretty soon a spider went crawling up my shoulder, and I flipped it off and it lit in the candle; and before I could budge it was all shriveled up. I didn't need anybody to tell me that that was an awful bad sign and would fetch me some bad luck, so I was scared and most shook the clothes off of me. I got up and turned around in my tracks three times and crossed my breast every time; and then I tied up a little lock of my hair with a thread to keep witches away. But I hadn't no confidence. You do that when you've lost a horseshoe that you've found, instead of nailing it up over the door, but I hadn't ever heard anybody say it was any way to keep off bad luck when you'd killed a spider.

I set down again, a-shaking all over, and got out my pipe for a smoke; for the house was all as still as death now, and so the widow wouldn't know. Well, after a long time I heard the clock away off in the town go boom—boom—boom—twelve licks; and all still again—stiller than ever. Pretty soon I heard a twig snap down in the dark amongst the trees—something was a-stirring. I set still and listened. Directly I could just barely hear a "*me-yow! me-yow!*" down there. That was good! Says I, "*me-yow! me-yow!*" as soft as I could, and then I put out the light and scrambled out of the window on to the shed. Then I slipped down to the ground and crawled in among the trees, and, sure enough, there was Tom Sawyer waiting for me.

2 *The Boys Escape Jim—Tom Sawyer's Gang—Deep-laid Plans*

We went tiptoeing along a path amongst the trees back toward the end of the widow's garden, stooping down so as the branches wouldn't scrape our heads. When we was passing by the kitchen I fell over a root and made a noise. We scrouched down and laid still. Miss Watson's big nigger, named Jim, was setting in the kitchen door; we could see him pretty clear, because there was a light behind him. He got up and stretched his neck out about a minute, listening. Then he says:

"Who dah?"

He listened some more; then he came tiptoeing down and stood right between us; we could 'a' touched him, nearly. Well, likely it was minutes and minutes that there warn't a sound, and we all there so close together. There was a place on my ankle that got to itching, but I dasn't scratch it; and then my ear begun to itch; and next my back, right between my shoulders. Seemed like I'd die if I couldn't scratch. Well, I've noticed that thing plenty times since. If you are with the quality, or at a funeral, or trying to go to sleep when you ain't sleepy—if you are anywheres where it won't do for you to scratch, why you will itch all over in upward of a thousand places. Pretty soon Jim says:

"Say, who is you? Whar is you? Dog my cats ef I didn' hear sumf'n. Well, I know what I's gwyne to do: I's gwyne to set down here and listen tell I hears it agin."

So he set down on the ground betwixt me and Tom. He leaned his back up against a tree, and stretched his legs out till one of them most touched one of mine. My nose begun to itch. It itched till the tears come into my eyes. But I dasn't scratch. Then it begun to itch on the inside. Next I got to itching underneath. I didn't know how I was going to set still. This miserableness went on as much as six or seven minutes; but it seemed a sight longer than that. I was itching in eleven different places now. I reckoned I couldn't stand it more'n a minute longer, but I set my teeth hard and got ready to try. Just then Jim begun to breathe heavy; next he begun to snore—and then I was pretty soon comfortable again.

Tom he made a sign to me—kind of a little noise with his mouth—and we went creeping away on our hands and knees. When we was ten foot off Tom whispered to me, and wanted to tie Jim to the tree for fun. But I said no; he might wake and make a disturbance, and then they'd find out I warn't in. Then Tom said he hadn't got candles enough, and he would slip in the kitchen and get some more. I didn't want him to try. I said Jim might wake up and come. But Tom wanted to resk it; so we slid in there and got three candles, and Tom laid five cents on the table for pay. Then we got out, and I was in a sweat to get away; but nothing would do Tom but he must crawl to where Jim was, on his hands and knees, and play something on him. I waited, and it seemed a good while, everything was so still and lonesome.

As soon as Tom was back we cut along the path, around the garden fence, and by and by fetched up on the steep top of the hill the other side of the house. Tom said he slipped Jim's hat off of his head and hung it on a limb right over him, and Jim stirred a little, but he didn't wake. Afterward Jim said the witches bewitched him and put him in a trance, and rode him all over the state, and then set him under the trees again, and hung his hat on a limb to show who done it. And next time Jim told it he said they rode him down to New Orleans; and, after that, every time he told it he spread it more and more, till by and by he said they rode him all over the world, and tired him most to death, and his back was all over saddle-boils. Jim was monstrous proud about it, and he got so he wouldn't hardly notice the other niggers. Niggers would come miles to hear Jim tell about it, and he was more looked up to than any nigger in that country. Strange niggers would stand with their mouths open and look him all over, same as if he was a wonder. Niggers is always talking about witches in the dark by the kitchen fire; but whenever one was talking and letting on to know all about such things, Jim would happen in and say, "Hm! What you know 'bout witches?" and that nigger was corked up and had to take a back seat. Jim always kept that five-center piece around his neck with a string, and said it was a charm the devil give to him with his own hands, and told him he could cure anybody with it and fetch witches whenever he wanted to just by saying something to it; but he never told what it was he said to it. Niggers would come from all around there and give Jim anything they had, just for a sight of that five-center piece; but they wouldn't touch it, because the devil had had his hands on it. Jim was most ruined for a servant, because he got stuck up on account of having seen the devil and been rode by witches.

Well, when Tom and me got to the edge of the hilltop we looked away down into the village and could see three or four lights twinkling, where there was sick folks, maybe; and the stars over us was sparkling ever so fine; and down by the village was the river, a whole mile broad, and awful still and grand. We went down the hill and found Joe Harper and Ben Rogers, and two or three more of the boys, hid in the old tanyard. So we unhitched a skiff and pulled down the river two mile and a half, to the big scar on the hillside, and went ashore.

We went to a clump of bushes, and Tom made everybody swear to keep the secret, and then showed them a hole in the hill, right in the thickest part of the bushes. Then we lit the candles, and crawled in on our hands and knees. We went about two hundred yards, and then the cave opened up. Tom poked about amongst the passages, and pretty soon ducked under a wall where you wouldn't 'a' noticed that there was a hole. We went along a narrow place and got into a kind of room, all damp and sweaty and cold, and there we stopped. Tom says:

"Now, we'll start this band of robbers and call it Tom Sawyer's Gang. Everybody that wants to join has got to take an oath, and write his name in blood."

Everybody was willing. So Tom got out a sheet of paper that he had wrote the oath on, and read it. It swore every boy to stick to the band, and never tell any of the secrets; and if anybody done anything to any boy in the band, whichever boy was ordered to kill that person and his family must do it, and he mustn't eat and he mustn't sleep till he had killed them and hacked a cross in their breasts, which was the sign of the band. And nobody that didn't belong to the band could use that mark, and if he did he must be sued; and if he done it again he must be killed. And if anybody that belonged to the band told the secrets, he must have his throat cut, and then have his carcass burnt up and the ashes scattered all around, and his name blotted off the list with blood and never mentioned again by the gang, but have a curse put on it and be forgot forever.

Everybody said it was a real beautiful oath, and asked Tom if he got it out of his own head. He said some of it, but the rest was out of pirate-books and robber-books, and every gang that was high-toned had it.

Some thought it would be good to kill the *families* of boys that told the secrets. Tom said it was a good idea, so he took a pencil and wrote it in. Then Ben Rogers says:

"Here's Huck Finn, he hain't got no family; what you going to do 'bout him?"

"Well, hain't he got a father?" says Tom Sawyer.

"Yes, he's got a father, but you can't never find him these days. He used to lay drunk with the hogs in the tanyard, but he hain't been seen in these parts for a year or more."

They talked it over, and they was going to rule me out, because they said every boy must have a family or somebody to kill, or else it wouldn't be fair and square for the others. Well, nobody could think of anything to do—everybody was stumped, and set still. I was most ready to cry; but all at once I thought of a way, and so I offered them Miss Watson—they could kill her. Everybody said:

"Oh, she'll do. That's all right. Huck can come in."

Then they all stuck a pin in their fingers to get blood to sign with, and I made my mark on the paper.

"Now," says Ben Rogers, "what's the line of business of this Gang?"

"Nothing only robbery and murder," Tom said.

"But who are we going to rob?—houses, or cattle, or—"

"Stuff! stealing cattle and such things ain't robbery; it's burglary," says Tom Sawyer. "We ain't burglars. That ain't no sort of style. We are highwaymen. We stop stages and carriages on the road, with masks on, and kill the people and take their watches and money."

"Must we always kill the people?"

"Oh, certainly. It's best. Some authorities think different, but mostly it's considered best to kill them—except some that you bring to the cave here, and keep them till they're ransomed."

"Ransomed? What's that?"

"I don't know. But that's what they do. I've seen it in books; and so of course that's what we've got to do."

"But how can we do it if we don't know what it is?"

"Why, blame it all, we've *got* to do it. Don't I tell you it's in the books? Do you want to go to doing different from what's in the books, and get things all muddled up?"

"Oh, that's all very fine to *say*, Tom Sawyer, but how in the nation are these fellows going to be ransomed if we don't know how to do it to them?—that's the thing *I* want to get at. Now, what do you *reckon* it is?"

"Well, I don' know. But per'aps if we keep them till they're ransomed, it means that we keep them till they're dead."

"Now, that's something *like*. That'll answer. Why couldn't you said that before? We'll keep them till they're ransomed to death; and a bothersome lot they'll be, too—eating up everything, and always trying to get loose."

"How you talk, Ben Rogers. How can they get loose when there's a guard over them, ready to shoot them down if they move a peg?"

"A guard! Well, that *is* good. So somebody's got to set up all night and never get any sleep, just so as to watch them. I think that's foolishness. Why can't a body take a club and ransom them as soon as they get here?"

"Because it ain't in the books so—that's why. Now, Ben Rogers, do you want to do things regular, or don't you?—that's the idea. Don't you reckon that the people that made the books knows what's the correct thing to do? Do you reckon *you* can learn 'em anything? Not by a good deal. No, sir, we'll just go on and ransom them in the regular way."

"All right. I don't mind; but I say it's a fool way, anyhow. Say, do we kill the women, too?"

"Well, Ben Rogers, if I was as ignorant as you I wouldn't let on. Kill the women? No; nobody ever saw anything in the books like that. You fetch them to the cave, and you're always as polite as pie to them; and by and by they fall in love with you, and never want to go home any more."

"Well, if that's the way I'm agreed, but I don't take no stock in it. Mighty soon we'll have the cave so cluttered up with women, and fellows waiting to be ransomed, that there won't be no place for the robbers. But go ahead, I ain't got nothing to say."

Little Tommy Barnes was asleep now, and when they waked him up he was scared, and cried, and said he wanted to go home to his ma, and didn't want to be a robber any more.

So they all made fun of him, and called him crybaby, and that made him mad, and he said he would go straight and tell all the secrets. But Tom give him five cents to keep quiet, and said we would all go home and meet next week, and rob somebody and kill some people.

Ben Rogers said he couldn't get out much, only Sundays, and so he wanted to begin next Sunday; but all the boys said it would be wicked to do it on Sunday, and that settled the thing. They agreed to get together and fix a day as soon as they could, and then we elected Tom Sawyer first captain and Joe Harper second captain of the Gang, and so started home.

I clumb up the shed and crept into my window just before day was breaking. My new clothes was all greased up and clayey, and I was dog-tired.

3 *A Good Going-over—Grace Triumphant—"One of Tom Sawyer's Lies"*

Well, I got a good going-over in the morning from old Miss Watson on account of my clothes; but the widow she didn't scold, but only cleaned off the grease and clay, and looked so sorry that I thought I would behave awhile if I could. Then Miss Watson she took me in the closet and prayed, but nothing come of it. She told me to pray every day, and whatever I asked for I would get it. But it warn't so. I tried it. Once I got a fish-line, but no hooks. It warn't any good to me without hooks. I tried for the hooks three or four times, but somehow I couldn't make it work. By and by, one day, I asked Miss Watson to try for me, but she said I was a fool. She never told me why, and I couldn't make it out no way.

I set down one time back in the woods, and had a long think about it. I says to myself, if a body can get anything they pray for, why don't Deacon Winn get back the money he lost on pork? Why can't the widow get back her silver snuff-box that was stole? Why can't Miss Watson fat up? No, says I to myself, there ain't nothing in it. I went and told the widow about it, and she said the thing a body could get by praying for it was "spiritual gifts." This was too many for me, but she told me what she meant—I must help other people, [illegible]verything I could for other people, and look out for them all [illegible]ne, and never think about myself. This was including Miss [illegible]on, as I took it. I went out in the woods and turned it over in m[illegible] mind a long time, but I couldn't see no advantage about it—except for the other people; so at last I reckoned I wouldn't worry about it any more, but just let it go. Sometimes the widow would take me one side and talk about Providence in a way to make a body's mouth water; but maybe next day Miss Watson would take hold and knock it all down again. I judged I could see that there was two Providences, and a poor chap would stand considerable show with the widow's Providence, but if Miss Watson's got him there warn't no help for him any more. I thought it all out, and reckoned I would belong to the widow's if he wanted me, though I couldn't make out how he was a-going to be any better off then than what he was before, seeing I was so ignorant, and so kind of low-down and ornery.

Pap he hadn't been seen for more than a year, and that was comfortable for me; I didn't want to see him no more. He used to always whale me when he was sober and could get his hands on me; though I used to take to the woods most of the time when he was around. Well, about this time he was found in the river drownded, about twelve mile above town, so people said. They judged it was him, anyway; said this drownded man was just his size, and was ragged, and had uncommon long hair, which was all like pap; but they couldn't make nothing out of the face, because it had been in the water so long it warn't much like a face at all. They said he was floating on his back in the water. They took him and buried him on the bank. But I warn't comfortable long, because I happened to think of something. I knowed mighty well that a drownded man don't float on his back, but on his face. So I knowed, then, that this warn't pap, but a woman dressed up in a man's clothes. So I was uncomfortable again. I judged the old man would turn up again by and by, though I wished he wouldn't.

We played robber now and then about a month, and then I resigned. All the boys did. We hadn't robbed nobody, hadn't killed any people, but only just pretended. We used to hop out of the woods and go charging down on hog-drivers and women in carts taking garden stuff to market, but we never hived any of them. Tom Sawyer called the hogs "ingots," and he called the turnips and stuff "julery," and we would go to the cave and powwow over what we had done, and how many people we had killed and marked. But I couldn't see no profit in it. One time Tom sent a boy to run about town with a blazing stick, which he called a slogan (which was the sign for the Gang to get together), and then he said he had got secret news by his spies that next day a whole parcel of Spanish merchants and rich A-rabs was going to camp in Cave Hollow with two hundred elephants, and six hundred camels, and over a thousand "sumter" mules, all loaded down with di'monds, and they didn't have only a guard of four hundred soldiers, and so we would lay in ambuscade, as he called it, and kill the lot and scoop the things. He said we must slick up our swords and guns, and get ready. He never could go after even a turnip-cart but he must have the swords and guns all scoured up for it, though they was only lath and broomsticks, and you might scour at them till you rotted, and then they warn't worth a mouthful of ashes more than what they was before. I didn't believe we could lick such a crowd of Spaniards and A-rabs, but I wanted to see the camels and elephants, so I was on hand next day, Saturday, in the ambuscade; and when we got the word we rushed out of the woods and down the hill. But there warn't no Spaniards and A-rabs, and there warn't no camels nor no elephants. It warn't anything but a Sunday-school picnic, and only a primer class at that. We busted it up, and chased the children up the hollow; but we never got anything but some doughnuts and jam, though Ben Rogers got a rag doll, and Joe Harper got a hymn-book and a tract; and then the teacher charged in, and made us drop everything and cut. I didn't see no di'monds, and I told Tom Sawyer so. He said there was loads of them there, anyway; and he said there was A-rabs there, too, and elephants and things. I said, why couldn't we see them, then? He said if I warn't so ignorant, but had read a book called *Don Quixote*, I would know without asking. He said it was all done by enchantment. He said there was hundreds of soldiers there, and elephants and treasure, and so on, but we had enemies which he called magicians, and they had turned the whole thing into an infant Sunday-school, just out of spite. I said, all right; then the thing for us to do was to go for the magicians. Tom Sawyer said I was a numskull.

"Why," said he, "a magician could call up a lot of genies, and they would hash you up like nothing before you could say Jack Robinson. They are as tall as a tree and as big around as a church."

"Well," I says, "s'pose we got some genies to help *us*—can't we lick the other crowd then?"

"How you going to get them?"

"I don't know. How do *they* get them?"

"Why, they rub an old tin lamp or an iron ring, and then the genies come tearing in, with the thunder and lightning a-ripping around and the smoke a-rolling, and everything they're told to do they up and do it. They don't think nothing of pulling a shot-tower up by the roots, and belting a Sunday-school superintendent over the head with it—or any other man."

"Who makes them tear around so?"

"Why, whoever rubs the lamp or the ring. They belong to whoever rubs the lamp or the ring, and they've got to do whatever he says. If he tells them to build a palace forty miles long out of di'-monds, and fill it full of chewing-gum, or whatever you want, and fetch an emperor's daughter from China for you to marry, they've got to do it—and they've got to do it before sun-up next morning, too. And more: they've got to waltz that palace around over the country wherever you want it, you understand."

"Well," says I, "I think they are a pack of flatheads for not keeping the palace themselves 'stead of fooling them away like that. And what's more—if I was one of them I would see a man in Jericho before I would drop my business and come to him for the rubbing of an old tin lamp."

"How you talk, Huck Finn. Why, you'd *have* to come when he rubbed it, whether you wanted to or not."

"What! and I as high as a tree and as big as a church? All right, then; I *would* come; but I lay I'd make that man climb the highest tree there was in the country."

"Shucks, it ain't no use to talk to you, Huck Finn. You don't seem to know anything, somehow—perfect saphead."

I thought all this over for two or three days, and then I reckoned I would see if there was anything in it. I got an old tin lamp and an iron ring, and went out in the woods and rubbed and rubbed till I sweat like an Injun, calculating to build a palace and sell it; but it warn't no use, none of the genies come. So then I judged that all that stuff was only just one of Tom Sawyer's lies. I reckoned he believed in the A-rabs and the elephants, but as for me I think different. It had all the marks of a Sunday-school.

4 Huck and the Judge—Superstition

Well, three or four months run along, and it was well into the winter now. I had been to school most all the time and could spell and read and write just a little, and could say the multiplication table up to six times seven is thirty-five, and I don't reckon I could ever get any further than that if I was to live forever. I don't take no stock in mathematics, anyway.

At first I hated the school, but by and by I got so I could stand it. Whenever I got uncommon tired I played hookey, and the hiding I got next day done me good and cheered me up. So the longer I went to school the easier it got to be. I was getting sort of used to the widow's ways, too, and they warn't so raspy on me. Living in a house and sleeping in a bed pulled on me pretty tight mostly, but before the cold weather I used to slide out and sleep in the woods sometimes, and so that was a rest to me. I liked the old ways best, but I was getting so I liked the new ones, too, a little bit. The widow said I was coming along slow but sure, and doing very satisfactory. She said she warn't ashamed of me.

One morning I happened to turn over the salt-cellar at breakfast. I reached for some of it as quick as I could to throw over my left shoulder and keep off the bad luck, but Miss Watson was in ahead of me, and crossed me off. She says, "Take your hands away, Huckleberry; what a mess you are always making!" The widow put in a good word for me, but that warn't going to keep off the bad luck, I knowed that well enough. I started out, after breakfast, feeling worried and shaky, and wondering where it was going to fall on me, and what it was going to be. There is ways to keep off some kinds of bad luck, but this wasn't one of them kind; so I never tried to do anything, but just poked along low-spirited and on the watch-out.

I went down to the front garden and clumb over the stile where you go through the high board fence. There was an inch of new snow on the ground, and I seen somebody's tracks. They had come up from the quarry and stood around the stile awhile, and then went on around the garden fence. It was funny they hadn't come in, after standing around so. I couldn't make it out. It was very curious, some-

w. I was going to follow around, but I stooped down to look at the tracks first. I didn't notice anything at first, but next I did. There was a cross in the left boot-heel made with big nails, to keep off the devil.

I was up in a second and shinning down the hill. I looked over my shoulder every now and then, but I didn't see nobody. I was at Judge Thatcher's as quick as I could get there. He said:

"Why, my boy, you are all out of breath. Did you come for your interest?"

"No, sir," I says; "is there some for me?"

"Oh, yes, a half-yearly is in last night—over a hundred and fifty dollars. Quite a fortune for you. You had better let me invest it along with your six thousand, because if you take it you'll spend it."

"No, sir," I says, "I don't want to spend it. I don't want it at all—nor the six thousand, nuther. I want you to take it; I want to give it to you—the six thousand and all."

He looked surprised. He couldn't seem to make it out. He says:

"Why, what can you mean, my boy?"

I says, "Don't you ask me no questions about it, please. You'll take it—won't you?"

He says:

"Well, I'm puzzled. Is something the matter?"

"Please take it," says I, "and don't ask me nothing—then I won't have to tell no lies."

He studied awhile, and then he says:

"Oho-o! I think I see. You want to *sell* all your property to me—not give it. That's the correct idea."

Then he wrote something on a paper and read it over, and says:

"There; you see it says 'for a consideration.' That means I have bought it of you and paid you for it. Here's a dollar for you. Now you sign it."

So I signed it, and left.

Miss Watson's nigger, Jim, had a hair-ball as big as your fist, which had been took out of the fourth stomach of an ox, and he used to do magic with it. He said there was a spirit inside of it, and it knowed everything. So I went to him that night and told him pap was here again, for I found his tracks in the snow. What I wanted to know was, what he was going to do, and was he going to stay? Jim got out his hair-ball and said something over it, and then he held it up and dropped it on the floor. It fell pretty solid, and only rolled about an inch. Jim tried it again, and then another time, and it acted just the same. Jim got down on his knees, and put his ear against it and listened. But it warn't no use; he said it wouldn't talk. He said sometimes it wouldn't talk without money. I told him I had an old slick counterfeit quarter that warn't no good because the brass showed through the silver a little, and it wouldn't pass nohow, even if the brass didn't show, because it was so slick it felt greasy, and so that would tell on it every time. (I reckoned I wouldn't say nothing about the dollar I got from the judge.) I said it was pretty bad money, but maybe the hair-ball would take it, because maybe it wouldn't know the difference. Jim smelt it and bit it and rubbed it, and said he would manage so the hair-ball would think it was good. He said he would split open a raw Irish potato and stick the quarter in between and keep it there all night, and next morning you couldn't see no brass, and it wouldn't feel greasy no more, and so anybody in town would take it in a minute, let alone a hair-ball. Well, I knowed a potato would do that before, but I had forgot it.

Jim put the quarter under the hair-ball, and got down and listened again. This time he said the hair-ball was all right. He said it would tell my whole fortune if I wanted it to. I says, go on. So the hair-ball talked to Jim, and Jim told it to me. He says:

"Yo' ole father doan' know yit what he's a-gwyne to do. Sometimes he spec he'll go 'way, en den ag'in he spec he'll stay. De bes' way is to res' easy en let de ole man take his own way. Dey's two angels hoverin' roun' 'bout him. One uv 'em is white en shiny, en t'other one is black. De white one gits him to go right a little while, den de black one sail in en bust it all up. A body can't tell yit which one gwyne to fetch him at de las'. But you is all right. You gwyne to have considable trouble in yo' life, en considable joy. Sometimes you gwyne to git hurt, en sometimes you gwyne to git sick; but every time you's gwyne to git well ag'in. Dey's two gals flyin' 'bout you in yo' life. One uv 'em's light en t'other one is dark. One is rich en t'other is po'. You's gwyne to marry de po' one fust en de rich one by en by. You wants to keep 'way fum de water as much as you kin, en don't run no resk, 'kase it's down in de bills dat you's gwyne to git hung."

When I lit my candle and went up to my room that night there sat pap—his own self!

5 *Huck's Father—The Fond Parent—Reform*

I had shut the door to. Then I turned around, and there he was. I used to be scared of him all the time, he tanned me so much. I reckoned I was scared now, too; but in a minute I see I was mistaken—that is, after the first jolt, as you may say, when my breath sort of hitched, he being so unexpected; but right away after I see I warn't scared of him worth bothring about.

He was most fifty, and he looked it. His hair was long and tangled and greasy, and hung down, and you could see his eyes shining through like he was behind vines. It was all black, no gray; so was his long, mixed-up whiskers. There warn't no color in his face, where his face showed; it was white; not like another man's white, but a white to make a body sick, a white to make a body's flesh crawl—a tree-toad white, a fish-belly white. As for his clothes—just rags, that was all. He had one ankle resting on t'other knee; the boot on that foot was busted, and two of his toes stuck through, and he worked them now and then. His hat was laying on the floor—an old black slouch with the top caved in, like a lid.

I stood a-looking at him; he sat there a-looking at me, with his chair tilted back a little. I set the candle down. I noticed the window was up; so he had clumb in by the shed. He kept a-looking me all over. By and by he says:

"Starchy clothes—very. You think you're a good deal of a big-bug, *don't* you?"

"Maybe I am, maybe I ain't," I says.

"Don't you give me none o' your lip," says he. "You've put on considerable many frills since I been away. I'll take you down a peg before I get done with you. You're educated, too, they say—can read and write. You think you're better'n your father, now, don't you, because he can't? I'll take it out of you. Who told you you might meddle with such hifalut'n foolishness, hey?—who told you you could?"

"The widow. She told me."

"The widow, hey?—and who told the widow she could put in her shovel about a thing that ain't none of her business?"

"Nobody never told her."

"Well, I'll learn her how to meddle. And looky here—you drop that school, you hear? I'll learn people to bring up a boy to put on airs over his own father and let on to be better'n what *he* is. You lemme catch you fooling around that school again, you hear? Your mother couldn't read, and she couldn't write, nuther, before she died. None of the family couldn't before *they* died. *I* can't; and here you're a-swelling yourself up like this. I ain't the man to stand it—you hear? Say, lemme hear you read."

I took up a book and begun something about General Washington and the wars. When I'd read about a half a minute, he fetched the book a whack with his hand and knocked it across the house. He says:

"It's so. You can do it. I had my doubts when you told me. Now looky here; you stop that putting on frills. I won't have it. I'll lay for you, my smarty; and if I catch you about that school I'll tan you good. First you know you'll get religion, too. I never see such a son."

He took up a little blue and yaller picture of some cows and a boy, said says:

"What's this?"

"It's something they give me for learning my lessons good."

He tore it up, and says:

"I'll give you something better—I'll give you a cowhide."

He set there a-mumbling and a-growling a minute, and then he says:

"*Ain't* you a sweet-scented dandy, though? A bed; and bedclothes; and a look'n'-glass; and a piece of carpet on the floor—and your own father got to sleep with the hogs in the tanyard. I never see such a son. I bet I'll take some o' these frills out o' you before I'm done with you. Why, there ain't no end to your airs—they say you're rich. Hey? —how's that?"

"They lie—that's how."

"Looky here—mind how you talk to me; I'm a-standing about all I can stand now—so don't gimme no sass. I've been in town two days, and I hain't heard nothing but about you bein' rich. I heard about it away down the river, too. That's why I come. You git me that money to-morrow—I want it."

"I hain't got no money."

"It's a lie. Judge Thatcher's got it. You git it. I want it."

"I hain't got no money, I tell you. You ask Judge Thatcher; he'll tell you the same."

"All right. I'll ask him; and I'll make him pungle, too, or I'll know the reason why. Say, how much you got in your pocket? I want it."

"I hain't got only a dollar, and I want that to—"

"It don't make no difference what you want it for—you just shell it out."

He took it and bit it to see if it was good, and then he said he was going downtown to get some whiskey; said he hadn't had a drink all day. When he had got out on the shed he put his head in again, and cussed me for putting on frills and trying to be better than him; and when I reckoned he was gone he come back and put his head in again, and told me to mind about that school, because he was going to lay for me and lick me if I didn't drop that.

Next day he was drunk, and he went to Judge Thatcher's and bullyragged him, and tried to make him give up the money; but he couldn't, and then he swore he'd make the law force him.

The judge and the widow went to law to get the court to take me away from him and let one of them be my guardian; but it was a new judge that had just come, and he didn't know the old man; so he said courts mustn't interfere and separate families if they could help it; said he'd druther not take a child away from its father. So Judge Thatcher and the widow had to quit on the business.

That pleased the old man till he couldn't rest. He said he'd cowhide me till I was black and blue if I didn't raise some money for him. I borrowed three dollars from Judge Thatcher, and pap took it and got drunk, and went a-blowing around and cussing and whooping and carrying on; and he kept it up all over town, with a tin pan, till most midnight; then they jailed him, and next day they had him before court, and jailed him again for a week. But he said *he* was satisfied; said he was boss of his son, and he'd make it warm for *him.*

When he got out the new judge said he was a-going to make a man of him. So he took him to his own house, and dressed him up clean and nice, and had him to breakfast and dinner and supper with the family, and was just old pie to him, so to speak. And after supper he talked to him about temperance and such things till the old man cried, and said he'd been a fool, and fooled away his life; but now he was a-going to turn over a new leaf and be a man nobody wouldn't be ashamed of, and he hoped the judge would help him and not look down on him. The judge said he could hug him for them words; so *he* cried, and his wife she cried again; pap said he'd been a man that had always been misunderstood before, and the judge said he believed it. The old man said that what a man wanted that was down was sympathy, and the judge said it was so; so they cried again. And when it was bedtime the old man rose up and held out his hand, and says:

"Look at it, gentlemen and ladies all; take a-hold of it; shake it. There's a hand that was the hand of a hog; but it ain't so no more; it's the hand of a man that's started in on a new life, and'll die before he'll go back. You mark them words—don't forget I said them. It's a clean hand now; shake it—don't be afeard."

So they shook it, one after the other, all around, and cried. The judge's wife she kissed it. Then the old man he signed a pledge—made his mark. The judge said it was the holiest time on record, or something like that. Then they tucked the old man into a beautiful room, which was the spare room, and in the night some time he got powerful thirsty and clumb out on to the porch roof and slid down a stanchion and traded his new coat for a jug of forty-rod, and clumb back again and had a good old time; and toward daylight he crawled out again, drunk as a fiddler, and rolled off the porch and broke his left arm in two places, and was most froze to death when somebody found him after sun-up. And when they come to look at that spare room they had to take soundings before they could navigate it.

The judge he felt kind of sore. He said he reckoned a body could reform the old man with a shotgun, maybe, but he didn't know no other way.

6 *He Went for Judge Thatcher—Huck Decides to Leave—Political Economy—Thrashing Around*

Well, pretty soon the old man was up and around again, and then he went for Judge Thatcher in the courts to make him give up that money, and he went for me, too, for not stopping school. He catched me a couple of times and thrashed me, but I went to school just the same, and dodged him or outrun him most of the time. I didn't want to go to school much before, but I reckoned I'd go now to spite pap. That law trial was a slow business—appeared like they warn't ever going to get started on it; so every now and then I'd borrow two or three dollars off of the judge for him, to keep from getting a cowhiding. Every time he got money he got drunk; and every time he got drunk he raised Cain around town; and every time he raised Cain he got jailed. He was just suited—this kind of thing was right in his line.

He got to hanging around the widow's too much, and so she told him at last that if he didn't quit using around there she would make trouble for him. Well, *wasn't* he mad? He said he would show who was Huck Finn's boss. So he watched out for me one day in the spring, and catched me, and took me up the river about three mile in a skiff, and crossed over to the Illinois shore where it was woody and there warn't no houses but an old log hut in a place where the timber was so thick you couldn't find it if you didn't know where it was.

He kept me with him all the time, and I never got a chance to run off. We lived in that old cabin, and he always locked the door and put the key under his head nights. He had a gun which he had stole, I reckon, and we fished and hunted, and that was what we lived on. Every little while he locked me in and went down to the store, three miles, to the ferry, and traded fish and game for whisky, and fetched it home and got drunk and had a good time, and licked me. The widow she found out where I was by and by, and she sent a man over to try to get hold of me; but pap drove him off with the gun, and it warn't long after that till I was used to being where I was, and liked it—all but the cowhide part.

It was kind of lazy and jolly, laying off comfortable all day, smoking and fishing, and no books nor study. Two months or more run along, and my clothes got to be all rags and dirt, and I didn't see how I'd ever got to like it so well at the widow's, where you had to wash, and eat on a plate, and comb up, and go to bed and get up regular, and be forever bothering over a book, and have old Miss Watson pecking at you all the time. I didn't want to go back no more. I had stopped cussing, because the widow didn't like it; but now I took to it again because pap hadn't no objections. It was pretty good times up in the woods there, take it all around.

But by and by pap got too handy with his hick'ry, and I couldn't stand it. I was all over welts. He got to going away so much, too, and locking me in. Once he locked me in and was gone three days. It was dreadful lonesome. I judged he had got drownded, and I warn't ever going to get out any more. I was scared. I made up my mind I would fix up some way to leave there. I had tried to get out of that cabin many a time, but I couldn't find no way. There warn't a window to it big enough for a dog to get through. I couldn't get up the chimbly; it was too narrow. The door was thick, solid oak slabs. Pap was pretty careful not to leave a knife or anything in the cabin when he was away; I reckon I had hunted the place over as much as a hundred times; well, I was 'most all the time at it, because it was about the only way to put in the time. But this time I found something at last; I found an old rusty wood-saw without any handle; it was laid in between a rafter and the clapboards of the roof. I greased it up and went to work. There was an old horse-blanket nailed against the logs at the far end of the cabin behind the table, to keep the wind from blowing through the chinks and putting the candle out. I got under the table and raised the blanket, and went to work to saw a section of the big bottom log out—big enough to let me through. Well, it was a good long job, but I was getting toward the end of it when I heard pap's gun in the woods. I got rid of the signs of my work, and dropped the blanket and hid my saw, and pretty soon pap come in.

Pap warn't in a good humor—so he was his natural self. He said he was downtown, and everything was going wrong. His lawyer said he reckoned he would win his lawsuit and get the money if they ever got started on the trial; but then there was ways to put it off a long time, and Judge Thatcher knowed how to do it. And he said people allowed there'd be another trial to get me away from him and give me to the widow for my guardian, and they guessed it would win this time. This shook me up considerable, because I didn't want to get back to the widow's any more and be so cramped up and sivilized, as they called it. Then the old man got to cussing, and cussed everything and everybody he could think of, and then cussed them all over again to make sure he hadn't skipped any, and after that he polished off with a kind of a general cuss all around, including a considerable parcel of people which he didn't know the names of, and so called them what's-his-name when he got to them, and went right along with his cussing.

He said he would like to see the widow get me. He said he would watch out, and if they tried to come any such game on him he knowed of a place six or seven mile off to stow me in, where they might hunt till they dropped and they couldn't find me. That made me pretty uneasy again, but only for a minute; I reckoned I wouldn't stay on hand till he got that chance.

The old man made me go to the skiff and fetch the things he had got. There was a fifty-pound sack of corn meal, and a side of bacon, ammunition, and a four-gallon jug of whisky, and an old book and two newspapers for wadding, beside some tow. I toted up a load, and went back and set down on the bow of the skiff to rest. I thought it all over, and I reckoned I would walk off with the gun and some lines, and take to the woods when I run away. I guessed I wouldn't stay in one place, but just tramp right across the country, mostly nighttimes, and hunt and fish to keep alive, and so get so far away that the old man nor the widow couldn't ever find me any more. I judged I would saw out and leave that night if pap got drunk enough, and I reckoned he would. I got so full of it I didn't notice how long I was staying till the old man hollered and asked me whether I was asleep or drownded.

I got the things all up to the cabin, and then it was about dark. While I was cooking supper, the old man took a swig or two and got sort of warmed up, and went to ripping again. He had been drunk over in town, and laid in the gutter all night, and he was a sight to look at. A body would 'a' thought he was Adam—he was just all mud. Whenever his liquor begun to work he most always went for the govment. This time he says:

"Call this a govment! why, just look at it an
Here's the law a-standing ready to take a man'
—a man's own son, which he has had all the trou
iety and all the expense of raising. Yes, just as that man
son raised at last, and ready to go to work and begin to do
for *him* and give him a rest, the law up and goes for him. And they call *that* govment! That ain't all, nuther. The law backs that old Judge Thatcher up and helps him to keep me out o' my property. Here's what the law does: The law takes a man worth six thousand dollars and up'ards, and jams him into an old trap of a cabin like this, and lets him go round in clothes that ain't fitten for a hog. They call that govment! A man can't get his rights in a govment like this. Sometimes I've a mighty notion to just leave the country for good and all. Yes, and I *told* 'em so; I told old Thatcher so to his face. Lots of 'em heard me, and can tell what I said. Says I, for two cents I'd leave the blamed country and never come a-near it ag'in. Them's the very words. I says, look at my hat—if you call it a hat—but the lid raises up and the rest of it goes down till it's below my chin, and then it ain't rightly a hat at all, but more like my head was shoved up through a jint o' stove-pipe. Look at it, says I—such a hat for me to wear—one of the wealthiest men in this town if I could git my rights.

"Oh, yes, this is a wonderful govment, wonderful. Why, looky here. There was a free nigger there from Ohio—a mulatter, most as white as a white man. He had the whitest shirt on you ever see, too, and the shiniest hat; and there ain't a man in that town that's got as fine clothes as what he had; and he had a gold watch and chain, and a silver-headed cane—the awfulest old gray-headed nabob in the state. And what do you think? They said he was a p'fessor in a college, and could talk all kinds of languages, and knowed everything. And that ain't the wust. They said he could *vote* when he was at home. Well, that let me out. Thinks I, what is the country a-coming to? It was 'lection day, and I was just about to go and vote myself if I warn't too drunk to get there; but when they told me there was a state in this country where they'd let that nigger vote, I drawed out. I says I'll never vote ag'in. Them's the very words I said; they all d me; and the country may rot for all me—I'll never vote ag'in as g as I live. And to see the cool way of that nigger—why, he ouldn't 'a' give me the road if I hadn't shoved him out o' the way. I says to the people, why ain't this nigger put up at auction and sold? —that's what I want to know. And what do you reckon they said? Why, they said he couldn't be sold till he'd been in the state six months, and he hadn't been there that long yet. There, now—that's a specimen. They call that a govment that can't sell a free nigger till he's been in the state six months. Here's a govment that calls itself a govment, and lets on to be a govment, and thinks it is a govment, and yet's got to set stock-still for six whole months before it can take a-hold of a prowling, thieving, infernal, white-shirted free nigger, and—"

Pap was a-going on so he never noticed where his old limber legs was taking him to, so he went head over heels over the tub of salt pork and barked both shins, and the rest of his speech was all the hottest kind of language—mostly hove at the nigger and the govment, though he give the tub some, too, all along, here and there. He hopped around the cabin considerable, first on one leg and then on the other, holding first one shin and then the other one, and at last he let out with his left foot all of a sudden and fetched the tub a rattling kick. But it warn't good judgment, because that was the boot that had a couple of his toes leaking out of the front end of it; so now he raised a howl that fairly made a body's hair raise, and down he went in the dirt, and rolled there, and held his toes; and the cussing he done then laid over anything he had ever done previous. He said so his own self afterwards. He had heard old Sowberry Hagan in his best days, and he said it laid over him, too; but I reckon that was sort of piling it on, maybe.

After supper pap took the jug, and said he had enough whisky there for two drunks and one delirium tremens. That was always his word. I judged he would be blind drunk in about an hour, and then I would steal the key, or saw myself out, one or t'other. He drank and drank, and tumbled down on his blankets by and by; but luck didn't run my way. He didn't go sound asleep, but was uneasy. He groaned and moaned and thrashed around this way and that for a long time. At last I got so sleepy I couldn't keep my eyes open all I could do, and so before I knowed what I was about I was sound asleep, and the candle burning.

I don't know how long I was asleep, but all of a sudden there was an awful scream and I was up. There was pap looking wild, and skipping around every which way and yelling about snakes. He said they was crawling up his legs; and then he would give a jump and scream and say one had bit him on the cheek—but I couldn't see no snakes. He started and run round and round the cabin, hollering "Take him off! take him off! he's biting me on the neck!" I never see a man look so wild in the eyes. Pretty soon he was all fagged out, and fell down panting; then he rolled over and over wonderful fast, kicking things every which way, and striking and grabbing at the air with his hands, and screaming and saying there was devils a-hold of him. He wore out by and by, and laid still awhile, moaning. Then he laid stiller, and didn't make a sound. I could hear the owls and the wolves away off in the woods, and it seemed terrible still. He was laying over by the corner. By and by he raised up part way and listened, with his head to one side. He says, very low:

"Tramp—tramp—tramp; that's the dead; tramp—tramp—tramp; they're coming after me; but I won't go. Oh, they're here! don't touch me—don't! hands off—they're cold; let go. Oh, let a poor devil alone!"

Then he went down on all fours and crawled off, begging them to let him alone, and he rolled himself up in his blanket and wallowed in under the old pine table, still a-begging; and then he went to crying. I could hear him through the blanket.

By and by he rolled out and jumped up on his feet looking wild, and he see me and went for me. He chased me round and round the place with a clasp-knife, calling me the Angel of Death, and saying he would kill me, and then I couldn't come for him no more. I begged, and told him I was only Huck; but he laughed *such* a screechy laugh, and roared and cussed, and kept on chasing me up. Once when I turned short and dodged under his arm he made a grab and got me by the jacket between my shoulders, and I thought I was gone; but I slid out of the jacket quick as lightning, and saved myself. Pretty soon he was all tired out, and dropped down with his back against the door, and said he would rest a minute and then kill me. He put his knife under him, and said he would sleep and get strong, and then he would see who was who.

So he dozed off pretty soon. By and by I got the old split-bottom chair and clumb up as easy as I could, not to make any noise, and got down the gun. I slipped the ramrod down it to make sure it was loaded, and then I laid it across the turnip-barrel, pointing towards pap, and set down behind it to wait for him to stir. And how slow and still the time did drag along.

7 *Laying for Him—Locked in the Cabin—Sinking the Body—Resting*

"Git up! What you 'bout?"

I opened my eyes and looked around, trying to make out where I was. It was after sun-up, and I had been sound asleep. Pap was standing over me looking sour—and sick, too. He says:

"What you doin' with this gun?"

I judged he didn't know nothing about what he had been doing, so I says:

"Somebody tried to get in, so I was laying for him."

"Why didn't you roust me out?"

"Well, I tried to, but I couldn't budge you."

"Well, all right. Don't stand there palavering all day, but out with you and see if there's a fish on the lines for breakfast. I'll be along in a minute."

He unlocked the door, and I cleared out up the riverbank. I noticed some pieces of limbs and such things floating down, and a sprinkling of bark; so I knowed the river had begun to rise. I reckoned I would have great times now if I was over at the town. The June rise used to be always luck for me; because as soon as that rise begins here comes cordwood floating down, and pieces of log rafts—sometimes a dozen logs together; so all you have to do is to catch them and sell them to the woodyards and the sawmill.

I went along up the bank with one eye out for pap and t'other one out for what the rise might fetch along. Well, all at once here comes a canoe; just a beauty, too, about thirteen or fourteen foot long, riding high like a duck. I shot head-first off of the bank like a frog, clothes and all on, and struck out for the canoe. I just expected there'd be somebody laying down in it, because people often done that to fool folks, and when a chap had pulled a skiff out most to it they'd raise up and laugh at him. But it warn't so this time. It was a drift-canoe sure enough, and I clumb in and paddled her ashore. Thinks I, the old man will be glad when he sees this—she's worth ten dollars. But when I got to shore pap wasn't in sight yet, and as I was running her into a little creek like a gully, all hung over with vines and willows, I struck another idea: I judged I'd hide her good, and then, 'stead of taking to the woods when I run off, I'd go down the river about fifty mile and camp in one place, and not have a rough time tramping on foot.

It was pretty close to the shanty, and I thought I heard the old man coming all the time; but I got her hid; and then I out and looked around a bunch of willows, and there was the old man down the path a piece just drawing a bead on a bird with his gun. So he hadn't seen anything.

When he got along I was hard at it taking up a "trot" line. He abused me a little for being so slow; but I told him I fell in the river, and that was what made me so long. I knowed he would see I was wet, and then he would be asking questions. We got five catfish off the lines and went home.

While we laid off after breakfast to sleep up, both of us being about wore out, I got to thinking that if I could fix up some way to keep pap and the widow from trying to follow me, it would be a certainer thing than trusting to luck to get far enough off before they missed me; you see, all kinds of things might happen. Well, I didn't see no way for a while, but by and by pap raised up a minute to drink another barrel of water, and he says:

"Another time a man comes a-prowling round here you roust me out, you hear? That man warn't here for no good. I'd a shot him. Next time you roust me out."

Then he dropped down and went to sleep again; what he had been saying give me the very idea I wanted. I says to myself, I can fix it now so nobody won't think of following me.

About twelve o'clock we turned out and went along up the bank. The river was coming up pretty fast, and lots of driftwood going by on the rise. By and by along comes part of a log raft—nine logs fast together. We went out with the skiff and towed it ashore. Then we had dinner. Anybody but pap would 'a' waited and seen the day through, so as to catch more stuff; but that warn't pap's style. Nine logs was enough for one time; he must shove right over to town and sell. So he locked me in and took the skiff, and started off towing the raft about half past three. I judged he wouldn't come back that night. I waited till I reckoned he had got a good start; then I out with my saw, and went to work on that log again. Before he was t'other side of the river I was out of the hole; him and his raft was just a speck on the water away off yonder.

I took the sack of corn meal and took it to where the canoe was hid, and shoved the vines and branches apart and put it in; then I done the same with the side of bacon; then the whisky-jug. I took all the coffee and sugar there was, and all the ammunition; I took the wadding; I took the bucket and gourd; took a dipper and a tin cup, and my old saw and two blankets, and the skillet and the coffee-pot. I took fish-lines and matches and other things—everything that was worth a cent. I cleaned out the place. I wanted an ax, but there wasn't any, only the one out at the woodpile, and I knowed why I was going to leave that. I fetched out the gun, and now I was done.

I had wore the ground a good deal crawling out of the hole and dragging out so many things. So I fixed that as good as I could from the outside by scattering dust on the place, which covered up the smoothness and the sawdust. Then I fixed the piece of log back into its place, and put two rocks under it and one against it to hold it there, for it was bent up at that place and didn't quite touch ground. If you stood four or five foot away and didn't know it was sawed, you wouldn't never notice it; and besides this was the back of the cabin, and it warn't likely anybody would go around there.

It was all grass clear to the canoe, so I hadn't left a track. I followed around to see. I stood on the bank and looked out over the river. All safe. So I took the gun and went up a piece into the woods, and was hunting around for some birds when I see a wild pig; hogs soon went wild in them bottoms after they had got away from the prairie-farms. I shot this fellow and took him into camp.

I took the ax and smashed in the door. I beat it and hacked it considerable a-doing it. I fetched the pig in, and took him back nearly to the table and hacked into his throat with the ax, and laid him down on the ground to bleed; I say ground becaue it *was* ground—hard packed, and no boards. Well, next I took an old sack and put a lot of big rocks in it—all I could drag—and I started it from the pig, and dragged it to the door and through the woods down to the river and dumped it in, and down it sunk, out of sight. You could easy see that something had been dragged over the ground. I did wish Tom Sawyer was there; I knowed he would take an interest in this kind of business, and throw in the fancy touches. Nobody could spread himself like Tom Sawyer in such a thing as that.

Well, last I pulled out some of my hair, and blooded the ax good, and stuck it on the back side, and slung the ax in the corner. Then I took up the pig and held him to my breast with my jacket (so he couldn't drip) till I got a good piece below the house and then dumped him into the river. Now I thought of something else. So I went and got the bag of meal and my old saw out of the canoe, and fetched them to the house. I took the bag to where it used to stand, and ripped a hole in the bottom of it with the saw, for there warn't no knives and forks on the place—pap done everything with his clasp-knife about the cooking. Then I carried the sack about a hundred yards across the grass and through the willows east of the house, to a shallow lake that was five mile wide and full of rushes—and ducks too, you might say, in the season. There was a slough or a creek leading out of it on the other side that went miles away, I don't know where, but it didn't go to the river. The meal sifted out and made a little track all the way to the lake. I dropped pap's whetstone there too, so as to look like it had been done by accident. Then I tied up the rip in the meal-sack with a string, so it wouldn't leak no more, and took it and my saw to the canoe again.

It was about dark now; so I dropped the canoe down the river under some willows that hung over the bank, and waited for the moon to rise. I made fast to a willow; then I took a bite to eat, and by and by laid down in the canoe to smoke a pipe and lay out a plan. I says to myself, they'll follow the track of that sackful of rocks to the shore and then drag the river for me. And they'll follow that meal track to the lake and go browsing down the creek that leads out of it to find the robbers that killed me and took the things. They won't ever hunt the river for anything but my dead carcass. They'll soon get tired of that, and won't bother no more about me. All right; I can stop anywhere I want to. Jackson's Island is good enough for me; I know that island pretty well, and nobody ever comes there. And then I can paddle over to town nights, and slink around and pick up things I want. Jackson's Island's the place.

I was pretty tired, and the first thing I knowed I was asleep. When I woke up I didn't know where I was for a minute. I set up and looked around, a little scared. Then I remembered. The river looked miles and miles across. The moon was so bright I could 'a' counted the drift-logs that went a-slipping along, black and still, hundreds of yards out from shore. Everything was dead quiet, and it looked late, and *smelt* late. You know what I mean—I don't know the words to put it in.

I took a good gap and a stretch, and was just going to unhitch and start when I heard a sound away over the water. I listened. Pretty soon I made it out. It was that dull kind of a regular sound that comes from oars working in rowlocks when it's a still night. I peeped out through the willow branches, and there it was—a skiff, away across the water. I couldn't tell how many was in it. It kept a-coming, and when it was abreast of me I see there warn't but one man in it. Thinks I, maybe it's pap, though I warn't expecting him. He dropped below me with the current, and by and by he came a-swinging up shore in the easy water, and he went by so close I could 'a' reached out the gun and touched him. Well, it *was* pap, sure enough—and sober, too, by the way he laid his oars.

I didn't lose no time. The next minute I was a-spinning down-stream soft, but quick, in the shade of the bank. I made two mile and a half, and then struck out a quarter of a mile or more toward the middle of the river, because pretty soon I would be passing the ferry-landing, and people might see me and hail me. I got out amongst the driftwood, and then laid down in the bottom of the canoe and let her float. I laid there, and had a good rest and a smoke out of my pipe, looking away into the sky; not a cloud in it. The sky looks ever so deep when you lay down on your back in the moonshine; I never knowed it before. And how far a body can hear on the water such nights! I heard people talking at the ferry-landing. I heard what they said, too—every word of it. One man said it was getting towards the long days and the short nights now. T'other one said *this* warn't one of the short ones, he reckoned—and then they laughed, and he said it over again, and they laughed again; then they waked up another fellow and told him, and laughed, but he didn't laugh; he ripped out something brisk, and said let him alone. The first fellow said he 'lowed to tell it to his old woman—she would think it was pretty good; but he said that warn't nothing to some things he had said in his time. I heard one man say it was nearly three o'clock, and he hoped daylight wouldn't wait more than about a week longer. After that the talk got further and further away, and I couldn't make out the words any more; but I could hear the mumble, and now and then a laugh, too, but it seemed a long ways off.

I was away below the ferry now. I rose up, and there was Jackson's Island, about two mile and a half down-stream, heavy-timbered and standing up out of the middle of the river, big and dark and solid, like a steamboat without any lights. There warn't any signs of the bar at the head—it was all under water now.

It didn't take me long to get there. I shot past the head at a ripping rate, the current was so swift, and then I got into the dead water and landed on the side towards the Illinois shore. I run the canoe into a deep dent in the bank that I knowed about; I had to part the willow branches to get in; and when I made fast nobody could 'a' seen the canoe from the outside.

I went up and set down on a log at the head of the island, and looked out on the big river and the black driftwood and away over to the town, three mile away, where there was three or four lights twinkling. A monstrous big lumber-raft was about a mile upstream, coming along down, with a lantern in the middle of it. I watched it come creeping down, and when it was most abreast of where I stood I heard a man say, "Stern oars, there! heave her head to stabboard!" I heard that just as plain as if the man was by my side.

There was a little gray in the sky now; so I stepped into the woods, and laid down for a nap.

8 *Sleeping in the Woods—Raising the Dead—Exploring the Island—Finding Jim—Jim's Escape—Signs—Balum*

The sun was up so high when I waked that I judged it was after eight o'clock. I laid there in the grass and the cool shade thinking about things, and feeling rested and ruther comfortable and satisfied. I could see the sun out at one or two holes, but mostly it was big trees all about, and gloomy in there amongst them. There was freckled places on the ground where the light sifted down through the leaves, and the freckled places swapped about a little, showing there was a little breeze up there. A couple of squirrels set on a limb and jabbered at me very friendly.

I was powerful lazy and comfortable—didn't want to get up and cook breakfast. Well, I was dozing off again when I thinks I hears a deep sound of "boom!" away up the river. I rouses up, and rests on my elbow and listens; pretty soon I hears it again. I hopped up, and went and looked out at a hole in the leaves, and I see a bunch of smoke laying on the water a long ways up—about abreast the ferry. And there was the ferryboat full of people floating along down. I knowed what was the matter now. "Boom!" I see the white smoke squirt out of the ferryboat's side. You see, they was firing cannon over the water, trying to make my carcass come to the top.

I was pretty hungry, but it warn't going to do for me to start a fire, because they might see the smoke. So I set there and watched the cannon-smoke and listened to the boom. The river was a mile wide there, and it always looks pretty on a summer morning—so I was having a good enough time seeing them hunt for my remainders if I only had a bite to eat. Well, then I happened to think how they always put quicksilver in loaves of bread and float them off, because they always go right to the drownded carcass and stop there. So, says I, I'll keep a lookout, and if any of them's floating around after me I'll give them a show. I changed to the Illinois edge of the island to see what luck I could have, and I warn't disappointed. A big double loaf come along, and I most got it with a long stick, but my foot slipped and she floated out further. Of course I was where the current set in the closest to the shore—I knowed enough for that. But by and by along comes another one, and this time I won. I took out the plug and shook out the little dab of quicksilver, and set my teeth in it. It was "baker's bread"—what the quality eat; none of your low-down corn-pone.

I got a good place amongst the leaves, and set there on a log, munching the bread and watching the ferryboat, and very well satisfied. And then something struck me. I says, now I reckon the widow or the parson or somebody prayed that this bread would find me, and here it has gone and done it. So there ain't no doubt but there is something in that thing—that is, there's something in it when a body like the widow or the parson prays, but it don't work for me, and I reckon it don't work for only just the right kind.

I lit a pipe and had a good long smoke, and went on watching. The ferryboat was floating with the current, and I allowed I'd have a chance to see who was aboard when she come along, because she would come in close, where the bread did. When she'd got pretty well along down towards me, I put out my pipe and went to where I fished out the bread, and laid down behind a log on the bank in a little open place. Where the log forked I could peep through.

By and by she come along, and she drifted in so close that they could 'a' run out a plank and walked ashore. Most everybody was on the boat. Pap, and Judge Thatcher, and Bessie Thatcher, and Joe Harper, and Tom Sawyer, and his old Aunt Polly, and Sid and Mary, and plenty more. Everybody was talking about the murder, but the captain broke in and says:

"Look sharp, now; the current sets in the closest here, and maybe he's washed ashore and got tangled amongst the brush at the water's edge. I hope so, anyway."

I didn't hope so. They all crowded up and leaned over the rails, nearly in my face, and kept still, watching with all their might. I could see them first-rate, but they couldn't see me. Then the captain sung out: "Stand away!" and the cannon let off such a blast right before me that it made me deef with the noise and pretty near blind with the smoke, and I judged I was gone. If they'd 'a' had some bullets in, I reckon they'd 'a' got the corpse they was after. Well, I see I warn't hurt, thanks to goodness. The boat floated on and went out of sight around the shoulder of the island. I could hear the booming now and then, further and further off, and by and by, after an hour, I didn't hear it no more. The island was three mile long. I judged they had got to the foot, and was giving it up. But they didn't yet awhile. They turned around the foot of the island and started up the channel on the Missouri side, under steam, and booming once in a while as they went. I crossed over to that side and watched them. When they got abreast of the island they quit shooting and dropped over to the Missouri shore and went home to the town.

I knowed I was all right now. Nobody else would come a-hunting after me. I got my traps out of the canoe and made me a nice camp in the thick woods. I made a kind of a tent out of my blankets to put my things under so the rain couldn't get at them. I catched a catfish and haggled him open with my saw, and towards sundown I started my camp-fire and had supper. Then I set out a line to catch some fish for breakfast.

When it was dark I set by my camp-fire smoking and feeling pretty well satisfied; but by and by it got sort of lonesome, and so I went and set on the bank and listened to the current swashing along, and counted the stars and drift-logs and rafts that come down, and then went to bed; there ain't no better way to put in time when you are lonesome; you can't stay so, you soon get over it.

And so for three days and nights. No difference—just the same thing. But the next day I went exploring around down through the island. I was boss of it; it all belonged to me, so to say, and I wanted to know all about it; but mainly I wanted to put in the time. I found plenty strawberries, ripe and prime; and green summer grapes, and green razberries; and the green blackberries was just beginning to show. They would all come handy by and by, I judged.

Well, I went fooling along in the deep woods till I judged I warn't far from the foot of the island. I had my gun along, but I hadn't shot nothing; it was for protection; thought I would kill some game nigh home. About this time I mighty near stepped on a good-sized snake, and it went sliding off through the grass and flowers, and I after it, trying to get a shot at it. I clipped along, and all of a sudden I bounded right on to the ashes of a camp-fire that was still smoking.

My heart jumped up amongst my lungs. I never waited for to look further, but uncocked my gun and went sneaking back on my tiptoes as fast as ever I could. Every now and then I stopped a second amongst the thick leaves and listened, but my breath come so hard I couldn't hear nothing else. I slunk along another piece further, then listened again; and so on, and so on. If I see a stump, I took it for a man; if I trod on a stick and broke it, it made me feel like a person had cut one of my breaths in two and I only got half, and the short half, too.

When I got to camp I warn't feeling very brash, there warn't much sand in my craw; but I says, this ain't no time to be fooling around. So I got all my traps into my canoe again so as to have them out of sight, and I put out the fire and scattered the ashes around to look like an old last-year's camp, and then clumb a tree.

I reckon I was up in the tree two hours; but I didn't see nothing, I didn't hear nothing—I only *thought* I heard and seen as much as a thousand things. Well, I couldn't stay up there forever; so at last I got down, but I kept in the thick woods and on the lookout all the time. All I could get to eat was berries and what was left over from breakfast.

By the time it was night I was pretty hungry. So when it was good and dark I slid out from shore before moonrise and paddled over to the Illinois bank—about a quarter of a mile. I went out in the woods and cooked a supper, and I had about made up my mind I would stay there all night when I hear a *plunkety-plunk, plunkety-plunk,* and says to myself, horses coming; and next I hear people's voices. I got everything into the canoe as quick as I could, and then went creeping through the woods to see what I could find out. I hadn't got far when I hear a man say:

"We better camp here if we can find a good place; the horses is about beat out. Let's look around."

I didn't wait, but shoved out and paddled away easy. I tied up in the old place, and reckoned I would sleep in the canoe.

I didn't sleep much. I couldn't, somehow, for thinking. And every time I waked up I thought somebody had me by the neck. So the sleep didn't do me no good. By and by I says to myself, I can't live this way; I'm a-going to find out who it is that's here on the island with me; I'll find it out or bust. Well, I felt better right off.

So I took my paddle and slid out from shore just a step or two, and then let the canoe drop along down amongst the shadows. The moon was shining, and outside of the shadows it made it most as light as day. I poked along well on to an hour, everything still as rocks and sound asleep. Well, by this time I was most down to the foot of the island. A little ripply, cool breeze begun to blow, and that was as good as saying the night was about done. I give her a turn with the paddle and brung her nose to shore; then I got my gun and slipped out and into the edge of the woods. I sat down there on a log, and looked out through the leaves. I see the moon go off watch, and the darkness begin to blanket the river. But in a little while I see a pale streak over the treetops, and knowed the day was coming. So I took my gun and slipped off towards where I had run across that camp-fire, stopping every minute or two to listen. But I hadn't no luck somehow; I couldn't seem to find the place. But by and by, sure enough, I catched a glimpse of fire away through the trees. I went for it, cautious and slow. By and by I was close enough to have a look, and there laid a man on the ground. It most give me the fantods. He had a blanket around his head, and his head was nearly in the fire. I set there behind a clump of bushes in about six foot of him, and kept my eyes on him steady. It was getting gray daylight now. Pretty soon he gapped and stretched himself and hove off the blanket, and it was Miss Watson's Jim! I bet I was glad to see him. I says:

"Hello, Jim!" and skipped out.

He bounced up and stared at me wild. Then he drops down on his knees, and puts his hands together and says:

"Doan' hurt me—don't! I hain't ever done no harm to a ghos'. I alwuz liked dead people, en done all I could for 'em. You go en git in de river ag'in, whah you b'longs, en doan' do nuffn to Ole Jim, 'at 'uz alwuz yo' fren'."

Well, I warn't long making him understand I warn't dead. I was ever so glad to see Jim. I warn't lonesome now. I told him I warn't afraid of *him* telling the people where I was. I talked along, but he only set there and looked at me; never said nothing. Then I says:

"It's good daylight. Let's get breakfast. Make up your camp-fire good."

"What's de use er makin' up de camp-fire to cook strawbries en sich truck? But you got a gun, hain't you? Den we kin git sumfn better den strawbries."

"Strawberries and such truck," I says. "Is that what you live on?"

"I couldn't git nuffn else," he says.

"Why, how long you been on the island, Jim?"

"I come heah de night arter you's killed."

"What, all that time?"

"Yes-indeedy."

"And ain't you had nothing but that kind of rubbage to eat?"

"No, sah—nuffn else."

"Well, you must be most starved, ain't you?"

"I reck'n I could eat a hoss. I think I could. How long you ben on de islan'?"

"Since the night I got killed."

"No! W'y, what has you lived on? But you got a gun. Oh, yes, you got a gun. Dat's good. Now you kill sumfn en I'll make up de fire."

So we went over to where the canoe was, and while he built a fire in a grassy open place amongst the trees, I fetched meal and bacon and coffee, and coffee-pot and frying-pan, and sugar and tin cups, and the nigger was set back considerable, because he reckoned it was all done with witchcraft. I catched a good big catfish, too, and Jim cleaned him with his knife, and fried him.

When breakfast was ready we lolled on the grass and eat it smoking hot. Jim laid it in with all his might, for he was most about starved. Then when we had got pretty well stuffed, we laid off and lazied.

By and by Jim says:

"But looky here, Huck, who wuz it dat 'uz killed in dat shanty ef it warn't you?"

Then I told him the whole thing, and he said it was smart. He said Tom Sawyer couldn't get up no better plan than what I had. Then I says:

"How do you come to be here, Jim, and how'd you get here?"

He looked pretty uneasy, and didn't say nothing for a minute. Then he says:

"Maybe I better not tell."

"Why, Jim?"

"Well, dey's reasons. But you wouldn' tell on me ef I 'uz to tell you, would you, Huck?"

"Blamed if I would, Jim."

"Well, I b'lieve you, Huck. I—I *run off*."

"Jim!"

"But mind, you said you wouldn' tell—you know you said you wouldn' tell, Huck."

"Well, I did. I said I wouldn't, and I'll stick to it. Honest *injun*, I will. People would call me a low-down Abolitionist and despise me for keeping mum—but that don't make no difference. I ain't a-going to tell, and I aint a-going back there, anyways. So, now, le's know all about it."

"Well, you see, it 'uz dis way. Ole missus—dat's Miss Watson—she pecks on me all de time, en treats me pooty rough, but she alwuz said she wouldn' sell me down to Orleans. But I noticed dey wuz a nigger trader roun' de place considable lately, en I begin to git oneasy. Well, one night I creeps to de do' pooty late, an de do' warn't quite shet, en I hear old missus tell de widder she gwyne to sell me down to Orleans, but she didn' want to, but she could git eight hund'd dollars for me, en it 'uz sich a big stack o' money she couldn' resis'. De widder she try to git her to say she wouldn't do it, but I never waited to hear de res'. I lit out mighty quick, I tell you.

"I tuck out en shin down de hill, en 'spec to steal a skift 'long de sho' som'ers 'bove de town, but dey wuz people a-stirring yit, so I hid in de ole tumbledown cooper shop on de bank to wait for everybody to go 'way. Well, I wuz dah all night. Dey wuz somebody roun' all de time. 'Long 'bout six in de mawnin' skifts begin to go by, en 'bout eight er nine every skift dat went 'long wuz talkin' 'bout how yo' pap come over to de town en say you's killed. Dese las' skifts wuz full o' ladies and genlmen a-goin' over for to see de place. Sometimes dey'd pull up at de sho' en takes a res' be'fo' dey started acrost, so by de talk I got to know all 'bout de killin'. I 'uz powerful sorry you's killed, Huck, but I ain't no mo' now.

"I laid dah under de shavin's all day. I 'uz hungry, but I warn't afeard; bekase I knowed ole missus en de widder was goin' to start to de camp-meet'n' right arter breakfas' en be gone all day, en dey knows I goes off wid de cattle 'bout daylight, so dey wouldn' 'spec to see me roun' de place, en so dey wouldn't miss me tell arter dark in de evenin'. De yuther servants wouldn' miss me, kase dey'd shin out en take holiday soon as de ole folks 'uz out'n de way.

"Well, when it come dark I tuck out up de river road, en went 'bout two mile er more to whah dey warn't no houses. I'd made up my mine 'bout what I's a-gwyne to do. You see, ef I kep' on tryin' to git away afoot, de dogs 'ud track me; ef I stole a skift to cross over, dey'd miss dat skift, you see, en dey'd know 'bout whah I'd lan' on de yuther side, en whah to pick up my track. So I says, a raff is what I's arter; it doan' *make* no track.

"I see a light a-comin' roun' de p'int bymeby, so I wade' in en shove' a log ahead o' me en swum more'n half-way acrost de river, en got in 'mongst de driftwood, 'en kep' my head down low, en kinder swum agin de current tell de raff come along. Den I swum to de stern uv it en tuck a-holt. It clouded up en 'uz pooty dark for a little while. So I clumb up en laid down on de planks. De men 'uz all 'way yonder in de middle, whah de lantern wuz. De river wuz a-risin', en dey wuz a good current; so I reck'n'd 'at by fo' in de mawnin' I'd be twenty-five mile down de river, en den I'd slip in jis b'fo' daylight en swim asho', en take to de woods on de Illinois side.

"But I didn' have no luck. When we 'uz mos' down to de head er de islan' a man begin to come aft wid de lantern. I see it warn't no use fer to wait, so I slid overboard en struck out fer de islan'. Well, I had a notion I could lan' mos' anywhers, but I couldn't—bank too bluff. I 'uz mos' to de foot er de islan' b'fo' I foun' a good place. I went into de woods en jedged I wouldn' fool wid raffs no mo', long as dey move de lantern roun' so. I had my pipe en a plug er dog-leg en some matches in my cap, en dey warn't wet, so I 'uz all right."

"And so you ain't had no meat nor bread to eat all this time? Why didn't you get mud-turkles?"

"How you gwyne to git 'm? You can't slip up on um en grab um; en how's a body gwyne to hit um wid a rock? How could a body do it in de night? En I warn't gwyne to show myself on de bank in de daytime."

"Well, that's so. You've had to keep in the woods all the time, of course. Did you hear 'em shooting the cannon?"

"Oh, yes. I knowed dey was arter you. I see um go by heah—watched um thoo de bushes."

Some young birds come along, flying a yard or two at a time and lighting. Jim said it was a sign it was going to rain. He said it was a sign when young chickens flew that way, and so he reckoned it was the same way when young birds done it. I was going to catch some of them, but Jim wouldn't let me. He said it was death. He said his father laid mighty sick once, and some of them catched a bird, and his old granny said his father would die, and he did.

And Jim said you mustn't count the things you are going to cook for dinner, because that would bring bad luck. The same if you shook the table cloth after sundown. And he said if a man owned a beehive and that man died, the bees must be told about it before sun-up next morning, or else the bees would all weaken down and quit work and die. Jim said bees wouldn't sting idiots; but I didn't believe that, because I had tried them lots of times myself, and they wouldn't sting me.

I had heard about some of these things before, but not all of them. Jim knowed all kinds of signs. He said he knowed most everything. I said it looked to me like all the signs was about bad luck, and so I asked him if there warn't any good-luck signs. He says:

"Mighty few—an' *dey* ain't no use to a body. What you want to know when good luck's a-comin' for? Want to keep it off?" And he said: "Ef you's got hairy arms en a hairy breas', it's a sign dat you's a-gwyne to be rich. Well, dey's some use in a sign like dat, 'kase it's so fur ahead. You see, maybe you's got to be po' a long time fust, en so you might git discourage' en kill yo'sef 'f you didn't know by de sign dat you gwyne to be rich bymeby."

"Have you got hairy arms and a hairy breast, Jim?"

"What's de use to ax dat question? Don't you see I has?"

"Well, are you rich?"

"No, but I ben rich wunst, and gwyne to be rich ag'in. Wunst I had foteen dollars, but I tuck to specalat'n, en got busted out."

"What did you speculate in, Jim?"

"Well, fust I tackled stock."

"What kind of stock?"

"Why, live stock—cattle, you know. I put ten dollars in a cow. But I ain' gwyne to resk no mo' money in stock. De cow up 'n' died on my han's."

"So you lost the ten dollars."

"No, I didn't lose it all. I on'y los' 'bout nine of it. I sole de hide en taller for a dollar en ten cents."

"You had five dollars and ten cents left. Did you speculate any more?"

"Yes. You know that one-laigged nigger dat b'longs to old Misto Bradish? Well, he sot up a bank, en say anybody dat put in a dollar would git fo' dollars mo' at de en' er de year. Well, all de niggers went in, but dey didn't have much. I wuz de on'y one dat had much. So I stuck out for mo' dan fo' dollars, en I said 'f I didn' git it I'd start a bank mysef. Well, o' course dat nigger want' to keep me out er de business, bekase he says dey warn't business 'nough for two banks, so he say I could put in my five dollars en he pay me thirty-five at de en' er de year.

"So I done it. Den I reck'n'd I'd inves' de thirty-five dollars right off en keep things a-movin'. Dey wuz a nigger name' Bob, dat had ketched a wood-flat, en his marster didn' know it; en I bought it off'n him en told him to take de thirty-five dollars when de en' er de year come; but somebody stole de wood-flat dat night, en nex' day de one-laigged nigger say de bank's busted. So dey didn' none uv us git no money."

"What did you do with the ten cents, Jim?"

"Well, I 'uz gwyne to spen' it, but I had a dream, en de dream tole me to give it to a nigger name' Balum— Balum's Ass dey call him for short; he's one er dem chuckleheads, you know. But he's lucky, dey say, en I see I warn't lucky. De dream say let Balum inves' de ten cents en he'd make a raise for me. Well, Balum he tuck de money, en when he wuz in church he hear de preacher say dat whoever give to de po' len' to de Lord, en boun' to git his money back a hund'd times. So Balum he tuck en give de ten cents to de po', en laid low to see what wuz gwyne to come of it."

"Well, what did come of it, Jim?"

"Nuffn never come of it. I couldn' manage to k'leck dat money no way; en Balum he couldn'. I ain' gwyne to len' no mo' money 'dout I see de security. Boun' to git yo' money back a hund'd times, de preacher says! Ef I could git de ten *cents* back, I'd call it squah, en be glad er de chanst."

"Well, it's all right anyway, Jim, long as you're going to be rich again some time or other."

"Yes; en I's rich now, come to look at it. I owns myself, en I's wuth eight hun'd dollars. I wisht I had de money, I wouldn' want no mo'."

9 *The Cave—The Floating House*

I wanted to go and look at a place right about the middle of the island that I'd found when I was exploring; so we started and soon got to it, because the island was only three miles long and a quarter wide.

This place was a tolerable long, steep hill or ridge about forty foot high. We had a rough time getting to the top, the sides was so steep and the bushes so thick. We tramped and clumb around all over it, and by and by found a good big cavern in the rock, most up to the top on the side towards Illinois. The cavern was as big as two or three rooms bunched together, and Jim could stand up straight in it. It was cool in there. Jim was for putting our traps in there right away, but I said we didn't want to be climbing up and down all the time.

Jim said if we had the canoe hid in a good place, and had all the traps in the cavern, we could rush there if anybody was to come to the island, and they would never find us without dogs. And, besides, he said them little birds had said it was going to rain, and did I want the things to get wet?

So we went back and got the canoe, and paddled up abreast the cavern, and lugged all the traps up there. Then we hunted up a place close by to hide the canoe in, amongst the thick willows. We took some fish off of the lines and set them again, and begun to get ready for dinner.

The door of the cavern was big enough to roll a hogshead in, and on one side of the door the floor stuck out a little bit, and was flat and a good place to build a fire on. So we built it there and cooked dinner.

We spread the blankets inside for a carpet, and eat our dinner in there. We put all the other things handy at the back of the cavern. Pretty soon it darkened up, and begun to thunder and lighten; so the birds was right about it. Directly it begun to rain, and it rained like all fury, too, and I never see the wind blow so. It was one of these regular summer storms. It would get so dark that it looked all blue-black outside, and lovely; and the rain would thrash along by so thick that the trees off a little ways looked dim and spider-webby; and here would come a blast of wind that would bend the trees down and turn up the pale underside of the leaves; and then a perfect ripper of a gust would follow along and set the branches to tossing their arms as if they was just wild; and next, when it was just about the bluest and blackest—*fst!* it was as bright as glory, and you'd have a little glimpse of tree-tops a-plunging about away off yonder in the storm, hundreds of yards further than you could see before; dark as sin again in a second, and now you'd hear the thunder let go with an awful crash, and then go rumbling, grumbling, tumbling, down the sky towards the under side of the world, like rolling empty barrels down-stairs—where it's long stairs and they bounce a good deal, you know.

"Jim, this is nice," I says. "I wouldn't want to be nowhere else but here. Pass me along another hunk of fish and some hot corn-bread."

"Well, you wouldn't 'a' ben here 'f it hadn't 'a' ben for Jim. You'd 'a' ben down dah in de woods widout any dinner, en gittin' mos' drownded, too; dat you would, honey. Chickens knows when it's gwyne to rain, en so do de birds, chile."

The river went on raising and raising for ten or twelve days, till at last it was over the banks. The water was three or four foot deep on the island in the low places and on the Illinois bottom. On that side it was a good many miles wide, but on the Missouri side it was the same old distance across—a half a mile—because the Missouri shore was just a wall of high bluffs.

Daytimes we paddled all over the island in the canoe. It was mighty cool and shady in the deep woods, even if the sun was blazing outside. We went winding in and out amongst the trees and sometimes the vines hung so thick we had to back away and go some other way. Well, on every old broken-down tree you could see rabbits and snakes and such things; and when the island had been overflowed a day or two they got so tame, on account of being hungry, that you could paddle right up and put your hand on them if you wanted to; but not the snakes and turtles—they would slide off in the water. The ridge our cavern was in was full of them. We could 'a' had pets enough if we'd wanted them.

One night we catched a little section of a lumber-raft—nice pine planks. It was twelve foot wide and about fifteen or sixteen foot long, and the top stood above water six or seven inches—a solid, level floor.

Another night when we was up at the head of the island, just before daylight, here comes a frame-house down, on the west side. She was a two-story, and tilted over considerable. We paddled out and got aboard—clumb in at an up-stairs window. But it was too dark to see yet, so we made the canoe fast and set in her to wait for daylight.

The light begun to come before we got to the foot of the island. Then we looked in at the window. We could make out a bed, and a table, and two old chairs, and lots of things around about on the floor, and there was clothes hanging against the wall. There was something laying on the floor in the far corner that looked like a man. So Jim says:

"Hello, you!"

It didn't budge. So I hollered again, and then Jim says:

"De man ain't asleep—he's dead. You hold still—I'll go en see."

He went, and bent down and looked, and says:

"It's a dead man. Yes, indeedy; naked, too. He's ben shot in de back. I reck'n he's ben dead two er three days. Come in, Huck, but doan' look at his face—it's too gashly."

I didn't look at him at all. Jim throwed some old rags over him, but he needn't done it; I didn't want to see him. There was heaps of old greasy cards scattered around over the floor, and old whisky-bottles, and a couple of masks made out of blackcloth; and all over the walls was the ignorantest kind of words and pictures made with charcoal. There was two old dirty calico dresses, and a sun-bonnet, and some women's underclothes hanging against the wall, and some men's clothing, too. We put the lot into the canoe—it might come good. There was a boy's old speckled straw hat on the floor; I took that, too. And there was a bottle that had had milk in it, and it had a rag stopper for a baby to suck. We would 'a' took the bottle, but it was broke. There was a seedy old chest, and an old hair trunk with the hinges broke. They stood open, but there warn't nothing left in them that was any account. The way things was scattered about we reckoned the people left in a hurry, and warn't fixed so as to carry off most of their stuff.

We got an old tin lantern, and a butcher-knife without any handle, and a bran-new Barlow knife worth two bits in any store, and a lot of tallow candles, and a tin candlestick, and a gourd, and a tin cup, and a ratty old bedquilt off the bed, and a reticule with needles and pins and beeswax and buttons and thread and all such truck in it, and a hatchet and some nails, and a fish-line as thick as my little finger with some monstrous hooks on it, and a roll of buckskin, and a leather dog-collar, and a horseshoe, and some vials of medicine that didn't have no label on them; and just as we was leaving I found a tolerable good currycomb, and Jim he found a ratty old fiddle-bow, and a wooden leg. The straps was broke off of it, but, barring that, it was a good enough leg, though it was too long for me and not long enough for Jim, and we couldn't find the other one, though we hunted all around.

And so, take it all around, we made a good haul. When we was ready to shove off we was a quarter of a mile below the island, and it was pretty broad day; so I made Jim lay down in the canoe and cover up with the quilt, because if he set up people could tell he was a nigger a good ways off. I paddled over to the Illinois shore, and drifted down most a half a mile doing it. I crept up the dead water under the bank, and hadn't no accidents and didn't see nobody. We got home all safe.

10 The Find—Old Hank Bunker— In Disguise

After breakfast I wanted to talk about the dead man and guess out how he come to be killed, but Jim didn't want to. He said it would fetch bad luck; and besides, he said, he might come and ha'nt us; he said a man that warn't buried was more likely to go a-ha'nting around than one that was planted and comfortable. That sounded pretty reasonable, so I didn't say no more; but I couldn't keep from studying over it and wishing I knowed who shot the man, and what they done it for.

We rummaged the clothes we'd got, and found eight dollars in silver sewed up in the lining of an old blanket overcoat. Jim said he reckoned the people in that house stole the coat, because if they'd 'a' knowed the money was there they wouldn't 'a' left it. I said I reckoned they killed him, too; but Jim didn't want to talk about that. I says:

"Now you think it's bad luck; but what did you say when I fetched in the snake-skin that I found on the top of the ridge day before yesterday? You said it was the worst bad luck in the world to touch a snake-skin with my hands. Well, here's your bad luck! We've raked in all this truck and eight dollars besides. I wish we could have some bad luck like this every day, Jim."

"Never you mind, honey, never you mind. Don't you git too peart. It's a-comin'. Mind I tell you, it's a-comin'."

It did come, too. It was a Tuesday that we had that talk. Well, after dinner Friday we was laying around in the grass at the upper end of the ridge, and got out of tobacco. I went to the cavern to get some, and found a rattlesnake in there. I killed him, and curled him up on the foot of Jim's blanket, ever so natural, thinking there'd be some fun when Jim found him there. Well, by night I forgot all about the snake, and when Jim flung himself down on the blanket while I struck a light the snake's mate was there, and bit him.

He jumped up yelling, and the first thing the light showed was the varmint curled up and ready for another spring. I laid him out in a second with a stick, and Jim grabbed pap's whisky-jug and begun to pour it down.

He was barefooted, and the snake bit him right on the heel. That all comes of my being such a fool as to not remember that wherever you leave a dead snake its mate always comes there and curls around it. Jim told me to chop off the snake's head and throw it away, and then skin the body and roast a piece of it. I done it, and he eat it and said it would help cure him. He made me take off the rattles and tie them around his wrist, too. He said that that would help. Then I slid out quiet and throwed the snakes clear away amongst the bushes; for I warn't going to let Jim find out it was all my fault, not if I could help it.

Jim sucked and sucked at the jug, and now and then he got out of his head and pitched around and yelled; but every time he come to himself he went to sucking at the jug again. His foot swelled up pretty big, and so did his leg; but by and by the drunk begun to come, and so I judged he was all right; but I'd druther been bit with a snake than pap's whisky.

Jim was laid up for four days and nights. Then the swelling was all gone and he was around again. I made up my mind I wouldn't ever take a-holt of a snake-skin again with my hands, now that I see what had come of it. Jim said he reckoned I would believe him next time. And he said that handling a snake-skin was such awful bad luck that maybe we hadn't got to the end of it yet. He said he druther see the new moon over his left shoulder as much as a thousand times than take up a snake-skin in his hand. Well, I was getting to feel that way myself, though I've always reckoned that looking at the new moon over your left shoulder is one of the carelessest and foolishest things a body can do. Old Hank Bunker done it once, and bragged about it; and in less than two years he got drunk and fell off of the shottower, and spread himself out so that he was just a kind of a layer, as you may say; and they slid him edgeways between two barn doors for a coffin, and buried him so, so they say, but I didn't see it. Pap told me. But anyway it all come of looking at the moon that way, like a fool.

Well, the days went along, and the river went down between its banks again; and about the first thing we done was to bait one of the big hooks with a skinned rabbit and set it and catch a catfish that was as big as a man, being six foot two inches long, and weighed over two hundred pounds. We couldn't handle him, of course; he would 'a' flung us into Illinois. We just set there and watched him rip and tear around till he drownded. We found a brass button in his stomach and a round ball, and lots of rubbage. We split the ball open with the hatchet, and there was a spool in it. Jim said he'd had it there a long time, to coat it over so and make a ball of it. It was as big a fish as was ever catched in the Mississippi, I reckon. Jim said he hadn't ever seen a bigger one. He would 'a' been worth a good deal over at the village. They peddle out such a fish as that by the pound in the market-house there; everybody buys some of him; his meat's as white as snow and makes a good fry.

Next morning I said it was getting slow and dull, and I wanted to get a stirring-up some way. I said I reckoned I would slip over the river and find out what was going on. Jim liked that notion; but he said I must go in the dark and look sharp. Then he studied it over and said, couldn't I put on some of them old things and dress up like a girl? That was a good notion, too. So we shortened up one of the calico gowns, and I turned up my trouser-legs to my knees and got into it. Jim hitched it behind with the hooks, and it was a fair fit. I put on the sun-bonnet and tied it under my chin, and then for a body to look in and see my face was like looking down a joint of stove-pipe. Jim said nobody would know me, even in the daytime, hardly. I practised around all day to get the hang of the things, and by and by I could do pretty well in them, only Jim said I didn't walk like a girl; and he said I must quit pulling up my gown to get at my britches-pocket. I took notice, and done better.

I started up the Illinois shore in the canoe just after dark.

I started across to the town from a little below the ferry-landing, and the drift of the current fetched me in at the bottom of the town. I tied up and started along the bank. There was a light burning in a little shanty that hadn't been lived in for a long time, and I wondered who had took up quarters there. I slipped up and peeped in at the window. There was a woman about forty year old in there knitting by a candle that was on a pine table. I didn't know her face; she was a stranger, for you couldn't start a face in that town that I didn't know. Now this was lucky, because I was weakening; I was getting afraid I had come; people might know my voice and find me out. But if this woman had been in such a little town two days she could tell me all I wanted to know; so I knocked at the door, and made up my mind I wouldn't forget I was a girl.

II Huck and the Woman—The Search—Prevarication—Going to Goshen

"Come in," says the woman, and I did. She says: "Take a cheer."

I done it. She looked me all over with her little shiny eyes, and says:

"What might your name be?"

"Sarah Williams."

"Where 'bouts do you live? In this neighborhood?"

"No'm. In Hookerville, seven mile below. I've walked all the way and I'm all tired out."

"Hungry, too, I reckon. I'll find you something."

"No'm, I ain't hungry. I was so hungry I had to stop two miles below here at a farm; so I ain't hungry no more. It's what make me so late. My mother's down sick, and out of money and everything, and I come to tell my uncle Abner Moore. He lives at the upper end of the town, she says. I hain't ever been here before. Do you know him?"

"No; but I don't know everybody yet. I haven't lived here quite two weeks. It's a considerable ways to the upper end of the town. You better stay here all night. Take off your bonnet."

"No," I says; "I'll rest awhile, I reckon, and go on. I ain't afeard of the dark."

She said she wouldn't let me go by myself, but her husband would be in by and by, maybe in a hour and a half, and she'd send him along with me. Then she got to talking about her husband, and about her relations up the river, and her relations down the river, and about how much better off they used to was, and how they didn't know but they'd made a mistake coming to our town, instead of letting well alone—and so on and so on, till I was afeared I had made a mistake coming to her to find out what was going on in the town; but by and by she dropped on to pap and the murder, and then I was pretty willing to let her clatter right along. She told about me and Tom Sawyer finding the twelve thousand dollars (only she got it twenty) and all about pap and what a hard lot he was, and what a hard lot I was, and at last she got down to where I was murdered. I says:

"Who done it? We've heard considerable about these goings-on down in Hookerville, but we don't know who 'twas that killed Huck Finn."

"Well, I reckon there's a right smart chance of people *here* that 'd like to know who killed him. Some think old Finn done it himself."

"No—is that so?"

"Most everybody thought it at first. He'll never know how nigh he come to getting lynched. But before night they changed around and judged it was done by a runaway nigger named Jim."

"Why *he*—"

I stopped. I reckoned I better keep still. She run on, and never noticed I had put in at all:

"The nigger run off the very night Huck Finn was killed. So there's a reward out for him—three hundred dollars. And there's a reward out for old Finn, too—two hundred dollars. You see, he come to town the morning after the murder, and told about it, and was out with 'em on the ferryboat hunt, and right away after he up and left. Before night they wanted to lynch him, but he was gone, you see. Well, next day they found out the nigger was gone; they found out he hadn't been seen sence ten o'clock the night the murder was done. So then they put it on him, you see; and while they was full of it, next day, back comes old Finn, and went boo-hooing to Judge Thatcher to get money to hunt for the nigger all over Illinois with. The judge gave him some, and that evening he got drunk, and was around till after midnight with a couple of mighty hard-looking strangers, and then went off with them. Well, he hain't come back sence, and they ain't looking for him back till this thing blows over a little, for people thinks now that he killed his boy and fixed things so folks would think robbers done it, and then he'd get Huck's money without having to bother a long time with a lawsuit. People do say he warn't any too good to do it. Oh, he's sly, I reckon. If he don't come back for a year he'll be all right. You can't prove anything on him, you know; everything will be quieted down then, and he'll walk in Huck's money as easy as nothing."

"Yes, I reckon so, 'm. I don't see nothing in the way of it. Has everybody quit thinking the nigger done it?"

"Oh, no, not everybody. A good many thinks he done it. But they'll get the nigger pretty soon now, and maybe they can scare it out of him."

"Why, are they after him yet?"

"Well, you're innocent, ain't you! Does three hundred dollars lay around every day for people to pick up? Some folks think the nigger ain't far from here. I'm one of them—but I hain't talked it around. A few days ago I was talking with an old couple that lives next door in the log shanty, and they happened to say hardly anybody ever goes to that island over yonder that they call Jackson's Island. Don't anybody live there? says I. No, nobody, says they. I didn't say any more, but I done some thinking. I was pretty near certain I'd seen smoke over there, about the head of the island, a day or two before that, so I says to myself, like as not that nigger's hiding over there; anyway, says I, it's worth the trouble to give the place a hunt. I hain't seen any smoke sence, so I reckon maybe he's gone, if it was him; but husband's going over to see—him and another man. He was gone up the river; but he got back to-day, and I told him as soon as he got here two hours ago."

I had got so uneasy I couldn't set still. I had to do something with my hands; so I took up a needle off of the table and went to threading it. My hands shook, and I was making a bad job of it. When the woman stopped talking I looked up, and she was looking at me pretty curious and smiling a little. I put down the needle and thread, and let on to be interested—and I was, too—and says:

"Three hundred dollars is a power of money. I wish my mother could get it. Is your husband going over there to-night?"

"Oh, yes. He went up-town with the man I was telling you of, to get a boat and see if they could borrow another gun. They'll go over after midnight."

"Couldn't they see better if they was to wait till daytime?"

"Yes. And couldn't the nigger see better, too? After midnight he'll likely be asleep, and they can slip around through the woods and hunt up his camp-fire all the better for the dark, if he's got one."

"I didn't think of that."

The woman kept looking at me pretty curious, and I didn't feel a bit comfortable. Pretty soon she says:

"What did you say your name was, honey?"

"M—Mary Williams."

Somehow it didn't seem to me that I said it was Mary before, so I didn't look up—seemed to me I said it was Sarah; so I felt sort of cornered, and was afeard maybe I was looking it, too. I wished the woman would say something more; the longer she set still the uneasier I was. But now she says:

"Honey, I thought you said it was Sarah when you first come in?"

"Oh, yes'm, I did. Sarah Mary Williams. Sarah's my first name. Some calls me Sarah, some calls me Mary."

"Oh, that's the way of it?"

"Yes'm."

I was feeling better then, but I wished I was out of there, anyway. I couldn't look up yet.

Well, the woman fell to talking about how hard times was, and how poor they had to live, and how the rats were as free as if they owned the place, and so forth and so on, and then I got easy again.

She was right about the rats. You'd see one stick his nose out of a hole in the corner every little while. She said she had to have things handy to throw at them when she was alone, or they wouldn't give her no peace. She showed me a bar of lead twisted up into a knot, and said she was a good shot with it generly, but she'd wrenched her arm a day or two ago, and didn't know whether she could throw true now. But she watched for a chance, and directly banged away at a rat; but she missed him wide, and said, "Ouch!" it hurt her arm so. Then she told me to try for the next one. I wanted to be getting away before the old man got back, but of course I didn't let on. I got the thing, and the first rat that showed his nose I let drive, and if he'd 'a' stayed where he was he'd 'a' been a tolerable sick rat. She said that was first-rate, and she reckoned I would hive the next one. She went and got the lump of lead and fetched it back, and brought along a hank of yarn which she wanted me to help her with. I held up my two hands and she put the hank over them, went on talking about her and her husband's matters. But she broke off to say:

"Keep your eye on the rats. You better have the lead in your lap, handy."

So she dropped the lump into my lap just at that moment, and I clapped my legs together on it and she went on talking. But only about a minute. Then she took off the hank and looked me straight in the face, and very pleasant, and says:

"Come, now, what's your real name?"

"Wh-hat, mum?"

"What's your real name? Is it Bill, or Tom, or Bob?—or what is it?"

I reckon I shook like a leaf, and I didn't know hardly what to do. But I says:

"Please to don't poke fun at a poor girl like me, mum. If I'm in the way here, I'll—"

"No, you won't. Set down and stay where you are. I ain't going to hurt you, and I ain't going to tell on you, nuther. You just tell me your secret, and trust me. I'll keep it; and, what's more, I'll help you. So'll my old man if you want him to. You see, you're a runaway 'prentice, that's all. It ain't anything. There ain't no harm in it. You've been treated bad, and you made up your mind to cut. Bless you, child, I wouldn't tell on you. Tell me all about it now, that's a good boy."

So I said it wouldn't be no use to try to play it any longer, and I would just make a clean breast and tell her everything, but she mustn't go back on her promise. Then I told her my father and mother was dead, and the law had bound me out to a mean old farmer in the country thirty mile back from the river, and he treated me so bad I couldn't stand it no longer; he went away to be gone a couple of days, and so I took my chance and stole some of his daughter's old clothes and cleared out, and I had been three nights coming the thirty miles. I traveled nights, and hid daytimes and slept, and the bag of bread and meat I carried from home lasted me all the way, and I had a-plenty. I said I believed my uncle Abner Moore would take care of me, and so that was why I struck out for this town of Goshen.

"Goshen, child? This ain't Goshen. This is St. Petersburg. Goshen's ten miles further up the river. Who told you this was Goshen?"

"Why, a man I met at daybreak this morning, just as I was going to turn into the woods for my regular sleep. He told me when the roads forked I must take the right hand, and five miles would fetch me to Goshen."

"He was drunk, I reckon. He told you just exactly wrong."

"Well, he did act like he was drunk, but it ain't no matter now. I got to be moving along. I'll fetch Goshen before daylight."

"Hold on a minute. I'll put you up a snack to eat. You might want it."

So she put me up a snack, and says:

"Say, when a cow's laying down, which end of her gets up first? Answer up prompt now—don't stop to study over it. Which end gets up first?"

"The hind end, mum."

"Well, then, a horse?"

"The for'rard end, mum."

"Which side of a tree does the moss grow on?"

"North side."

"If fifteen cows is browsing on a hillside, how many of them eats with their heads pointed the same direction?"

"The whole fifteen, mum."

"Well, I reckon you *have* lived in the country. I thought maybe you was trying to hocus me again. What's your real name, now?"

"George Peters, mum."

"Well, try to remember it, George. Don't forget and tell me it's Elexander before you go, and then get out by saying it's George Elexander when I catch you. And don't go about women in that old calico. You do a girl tolerable poor, but you might fool men, maybe. Bless you, child, when you set out to thread a needle don't hold the thread still and fetch the needle up to it; hold the needle still and poke the thread at it; that's the way a woman most always does, but a man always does t'other way. And when you throw at a rat or anything, hitch yourself up a-tiptoe and fetch your hand up over your head as awkward as you can, and miss your rat about six or seven foot. Throw stiff-armed from the shoulder, like there was a pivot there for it to turn on, like a girl; not from the wrist and elbow, with your arm out to one side, like a boy. And, mind you, when a girl tries to catch anything in her lap she throws her knees apart; she don't clap them together, the way you did when you catched the lump of lead. Why, I spotted you for a boy when you was threading the needle; and I contrived the other things just to make certain. Now trot along to your uncle, Sarah Mary William George Elexander Peters, and if you get into trouble you send word to Mrs. Judith Loftus, which is me, and I'll do what I can to get you out of it. Keep the river road all the way, and next time you tramp take shoes and socks with you. The river road's a rocky one, and your feet'll be in a condition when you get to Goshen, I reckon."

I went up the bank about fifty yards, and then I doubled on my tracks and slipped back to where my canoe was, a good piece below the house. I jumped in, and was off in a hurry. I went up-stream far enough to make the head of the island, and then started across. I took off the sun-bonnet, for I didn't want no blinders on then. When I was about the middle I heard the clock begin to strike, so I stops and listens; the sound come faint over the water but clear—eleven. When I struck the head of the island I never waited to blow, though I was most winded, but I shoved right into the timber where my old camp used to be, and started a good fire there on a high and dry spot.

Then I jumped in the canoe and dug out for our place, a mile and a half below, as hard as I could go. I landed, and slopped through the timber and up the ridge and into the cavern. There Jim laid, sound asleep on the ground. I roused him out and says:

"Git up and hump yourself, Jim! There ain't a minute to lose. They're after us!"

Jim never asked no questions, he never said a word; but the way he worked for the next half an hour showed about how he was scared. By that time everything we had in the world was on our raft, and she was ready to be shoved out from the willow cove where she was hid. We put out the camp-fire at the cavern the first thing, and didn't show a candle outside after that.

I took the canoe out from the shore a little piece, and took a look; but if there was a boat around I couldn't see it, for stars and shadows ain't good to see by. Then we got out the raft and slipped along down in the shade, past the foot of the island dead still—never saying a word.

12 Slow Navigation—Borrowing Things—Boarding the Wreck—The Plotters—Hunting for the Boat

It must 'a' been close on to one o'clock when we got below the island at last, and the raft did seem to go mighty slow. If a boat was to come along we was going to take to the canoe and break for the Illinois shore; and it was well a boat didn't come, for we hadn't ever thought to put the gun in the canoe, or a fishing-line, or anything to eat. We was in ruther too much of a sweat to think of so many things. It warn't good judgment to put *everything* on the raft.

If the men went to the island I just expect they found the camp-fire I built, and watched it all night for Jim to come. Anyways, they stayed away from us, and if my building the fire never fooled them it warn't no fault of mine. I played it as low down on them as I could.

When the first streak of day began to show we tied up to a tow-head in a big bend on the Illinois side, and hacked off cottonwood branches with the hatchet, and covered up the raft with them so she looked like there had been a cave-in in the bank there. A tow-head is a sand-bar with cottonwoods on it thick as harrow-teeth.

We had mountains on the Missouri shore and heavy timber on the Illinois side, and the channel was down the Missouri shore at that place, so we warn't afraid of anybody running across us. We laid there all day, and watched the rafts and steamboats spin down the Missouri shore, and up-bound steamboats fight the big river in the middle. I told Jim all about the time I had jabbering with that woman; and Jim said she was a smart one, and if she was to start after us herself *she* wouldn't set down and watch a camp-fire—no, sir, she'd fetch a dog. Well, then, I said, why couldn't she tell her husband to fetch a dog? Jim said he bet she did think of it by the time the men was ready to start and he believed they must 'a' gone up-town to get a dog and so they lost all that time, or else we wouldn't be here on a towhead sixteen or seventeen mile below the village—no, indeedy, we would be in that same old town again. So I said I didn't care what was the reason they didn't get us as long as they didn't.

When it was beginning to come on dark we poked our heads out of the cottonwood thicket, and looked up and down and across; nothing in sight; so Jim took up some of the top planks of the raft and built a snug wigwam to get under in blazing weather and rainy, and to keep the things dry. Jim made a floor for the wigwam, and raised it a foot or more above the level of the raft, so now the blankets and all the traps was out of reach of steamboat waves. Right in the middle of the wigwam we made a layer of dirt about five or six inches deep with a frame around it for to hold it to its place; this was to build a fire on in sloppy weather or chilly; the wig-wam would keep it from being seen. We made an extra steering-oar, too, because one of the others might get broke on a snag or some-thing. We fixed up a short forked stick to hang the old lantern on, because we must always light the lantern whenever we see a steam-boat coming down-stream, to keep from getting run over; but we wouldn't have to light it for up-stream boats unless we see we was in what they call a "crossing"; for the river was pretty high yet, very low banks being still a little under water; so up-bound boats didn't always run the channel, but hunted easy water.

This second night we run between seven and eight hours, with a current that was making over four mile an hour. We catched fish and talked, and we took a swim now and then to keep off sleepiness. It was kind of solemn, drifting down the big, still river, laying on our backs looking up at the stars, and we didn't even feel like talking loud, and it warn't often that we laughed—only a little kind of a low chuckle. We had mighty good weather as a general thing, and nothing ever happened to us at all—that night, nor the next, nor the next.

Every night we passed towns, some of them away up on black hillsides, nothing but just a shiny bed of lights; not a house could you see. The fifth night we passed St. Louis, and it was like the whole world lit up. In St. Petersburg they used to say there was twenty or thirty thousand people in St. Louis, but I never believed it till I see that wonderful spread of lights at two o'clock that still night. There warn't a sound there; everybody was asleep.

Every night now I used to slip ashore toward ten o'clock at some little village, and buy ten or fifteen cents' worth of meal or bacon or other stuff to eat; and sometimes I lifted a chicken that warn't roosting comfortable, and took him along. Pap always said, take a chicken when you get a chance, because if you don't want him yourself you can easy find somebody that does, and a good deed ain't ever forgot, but I never see pap when he didn't want the chicken himself but that is what he used to say, anyway.

Mornings before daylight I slipped into cornfields and borrowed a watermelon, or a mushmelon, or a punkin, or some new corn, or things of that kind. Pap always said it warn't no harm to borrow things if you was meaning to pay them back some time; but the widow said it warn't anything but a soft name for stealing, and no decent body would do it. Jim said he reckoned the widow was partly right and pap was partly right; so the best way would be for us to pick out two or three things from the list and say we wouldn't borrow them any more—then he reckoned it wouldn't be no harm to borrow the others. So we talked it over all one night, drifting along down the river, trying to make up our minds whether to drop the watermelons, or the cantelopes, or the mushmelons, or what. But toward daylight we got it all settled satisfactory, and concluded to drop crabapples and p'simmons. We warn't feeling just right before that, but it was all comfortable now. I was glad the way it come out, too, because crabapples ain't ever good, and the p'simmons wouldn't be ripe for two or three months yet.

We shot a water-fowl now and then that got up too early in the morning or didn't go to bed early enough in the evening. Take it all around, we lived pretty high.

The fifth night below St. Louis we had a big storm after midnight, with a power of thunder and lightning, and the rain poured down in a solid sheet. We stayed in the wigwam and let the raft take care of itself. When the lightning glared out we could see a big straight river ahead, and high, rocky bluffs on both sides. By and by says I "Hel-*lo*, Jim, looky yonder!" It was a steamboat that had killed herself on a rock. We was drifting straight down for her. The lightning showed her very distinct. She was leaning over, with part of her upper deck above water, and you could see every little chimbly-guy clean and clear, and a chair by the big bell, with an old slouch hat hanging on the back of it, when the flashes come.

Well, it being away in the night and stormy, and all so mysterious-like, I felt just the way any other boy would 'a' felt when I seen that wreck laying there so mournful and lonesome in the middle of the river. I wanted to get aboard of her and slink around a little, and see what there was there. So I says:

"Le's land on her, Jim."

But Jim was dead against it at first. He says:

"I doan' want to go fool'n 'long er no wrack. We's doin' blame' well, en we better let blame' well alone, as de good book says. Like as not dey's a watchman on dat wrack."

"Watchman your grandmother," I says; "there ain't nothing to watch but the texas and the pilot-house; and do you reckon anybody's going to resk his life for a texas and a pilot-house such a night as this, when it's likely to break up and wash off down the river any minute?" Jim couldn't say nothing to that, so he didn't try. "And besides," I says, "we might borrow something worth having out of the captain's stateroom. Seegars, *I* bet you—and cost five cents apiece, solid cash. Steamboat captains is always rich, and get sixty dollars a month, and *they* don't care a cent what a thing costs, you know, long as they want it. Stick a candle in your pocket; I can't rest, Jim, till we give her a rummaging. Do you reckon Tom Sawyer would ever go by this thing? Not for pie, he wouldn't. He'd call it an adventure—that's what he'd call it; and he'd land on that wreck if it was his last act. And wouldn't he throw style into it?—wouldn't he spread himself, nor nothing?"

Jim he grumbled a little, but give in. He said we mustn't talk any more than we could help, and then talk mighty low. The lightning showed us the wreck again just in time, and we fetched the stabboard derrick, and made fast there.

The deck was high out here. We went sneaking down the slope of it to labbord, in the dark, towards the texas, feeling our way slow with our feet, and spreading our hands out to fend off the guys, for it was so dark we couldn't see no sign of them. Pretty soon we struck the forward end of the skylight, and clumb on to it; and the next step fetched us in front of the captain's door, which was open, and by Jimminy, away down through the texas-hall we see a light! and all in the same second we seem to hear low voices in yonder!

Jim whispered and said he was feeling powerful sick, and told me to come along. I says, all right, and was going to start for the raft; but just then I heard a voice wail out and say:

"Oh, please don't, boys; I swear I won't ever tell!"

Another voice said, pretty loud:

"It's a lie, Jim Turner. You've acted this way before. You always want more'n your share of the truck, and you've always got it, too, because you've swore 't if you didn't you'd tell. But this time you've said it jest one time too many. You're the meanest, treacherousest hound in this country."

By this time Jim was gone for the raft. I was just a-biling with curiosity; and I says to myself, Tom Sawyer wouldn't back out now, and so I won't either; I'm a-going to see what's going on here. So I dropped on my hands and knees in the little passage, and crept aft in the dark till there warn't but one stateroom betwixt me and the cross-hall of the texas. Then in there I see a man stretched on the floor and tied hand and foot, and two men standing over him, and one of them had a dim lantern in his hand, the other one had a pistol. This one kept pointing the pistol at the man's head on the floor, and saying:

"I'd *like* to! And I orter, too—a mean skunk!"

The man on the floor would shrivel up and say, "Oh, please don't, Bill; I hain't ever goin' to tell."

And every time he said that the man with the lantern would laugh and say:

" 'Deed you *ain't!* You never said no truer thing 'n that, you bet you." And once he said: "Hear him beg! and yit if we hadn't got the best of him and tied him he'd 'a' killed us both. And what *for?* Jist for noth'n'. Jist because we stood on our *rights*—that's what for. But I lay you ain't a-goin' to threaten nobody any more, Jim Turner. Put *up* that pistol, Bill."

Bill says:

"I don't want to, Jake Packard. I'm for killin' him—and didn't he kill old Hatfield jist the same way—and don't he deserve it?"

"But I don't *want* him killed, and I've got my reasons for it."

"Bless yo' heart for them words, Jake Packard! I'll never forgit you long's I live!" says the man on the floor, sort of blubbering.

Packard didn't take no notice of that, but hung up his lantern on a nail and started toward where I was, there in the dark, and motioned Bill to come. I crawfished as fast as I could about two yards, but the boat slanted so that I couldn't make very good time; so to keep from getting run over and catched I crawled into a stateroom on the upper side. The man came a-pawing along in the dark, and when Packard got to my stateroom, he says:

"Here—come in here."

And in he come, and Bill after him. But before they got in I was up in the upper berth, cornered, and sorry I come. Then they stood there, with their hands on the ledge of the berth, and talked. I couldn't see them, but I could tell where they was by the whisky they'd been having. I was glad I didn't drink whisky; but it wouldn't made much difference anyway, because most of the time they couldn't 'a' treed me because I didn't breathe. I was too scared. And, besides, a body *couldn't* breathe and hear such talk. They talked low and earnest. Bill wanted to kill Turner. He says:

"He's said he'll tell, and he will. If we was to give both our shares to him *now* it wouldn't make no difference after the row and the way we've served him. Shore's you're born, he'll turn state's evidence; now you hear *me*. I'm for putting him out of his troubles."

"So'm I," says Packard, very quiet.

"Blame it, I'd sorter begun to think you wasn't. Well, then, that's all right. Le's go and do it."

"Hold on a minute; I hain't had my say yit. You listen to me.

Shooting's good, but there's quieter ways if the things' *got* to be done. But what *I* say is this: it ain't good sense to go court'n around after a halter if you can git at what you're up to in some way that's jist as good and at the same time don't bring you into no resks. Ain't that so?"

"You bet it is. But how you goin' to manage it this time?"

"Well, my idea is this: we'll rustle around and gather up whatever pickin's we've overlooked in the staterooms, and shove for shore and hide the truck. Then we'll wait. Now I say it ain't a-goin' to be more'n two hours befo' this wrack breaks up and washes off down the river. See? He'll be drownded, and won't have nobody to blame for it but his own self. I reckon that's a considerable sight better 'n killin' of him. I'm unfavorable to killin' a man as long as you can git aroun' it; it ain't good sense, it ain't good morals. Ain't I right?"

"Yes, I reck'n you are. But s'pose she *don't* break up and wash off?"

"Well, we can wait the two hours anyway and see, can't we?"

"All right, then; come along."

So they started, and I lit out, all in a cold sweat, and scrambled forward. It was dark as pitch there; but I said, in a kind of a coarse whisper, "Jim!" and he answered up, right at my elbow, with a sort of a moan, and I says:

"Quick, Jim, it ain't no time for fooling around and moaning; there's a gang of murderers in yonder, and if we don't hunt up their boat and set her drifting down the river so these fellows can't get away from the wreck there's one of 'em going to be in a bad fix. But if we find their boat we can put *all* of 'em in a bad fix—for the sheriff 'll get 'em. Quick—hurry! I'll hunt the labboard side, you hunt the stabboard. You start at the raft, and—"

"Oh, my lordy, lordy! *Raf'?* Dey ain' no raf' no mo'; she done broke loose en gone!—en here we is!"

13 *Escaping from the Wreck—The Watchman—Sinking*

Well, I catched my breath and most fainted. Shut up on a wreck with such a gang as that! But it warn't no time to be sentimentering. We'd *got* to find that boat now—had to have it for ourselves. So we went a-quaking and shaking down the stabboard side, and slow work it was, too—seemed a week before we got to the stern. No sign of a boat. Jim said he didn't believe he could go any farther—so scared he hadn't hardly any strength left, he said. But I said, come on, if we get left on this wreck we are in a fix, sure. So on we prowled again. We struck for the stern of the texas, and found it, and then scrabbled along forwards on the skylight, hanging on from shutter to shutter, for the edge of the skylight was in the water. When we got pretty close to the cross-hall door there was the skiff, sure enough! I could just barely see her. I felt ever so thankful. In another second I would 'a' been aboard of her, but just then the door opened. One of the men stuck his head out only about a couple of foot from me, and I thought I was gone; but he jerked it in again, and says:

"Heave that blame lantern out o' sight, Bill!"

He flung a bag of something into the boat, and then got in himself and set down. It was Packard. Then Bill *he* come out and got in. Packard says, in a low voice:

"All ready—shove off!"

I couldn't hardly hang on to the shutters, I was so weak. But Bill says:

"Hold on—'d you go through him?"

"No. Didn't you?"

"No. So he's got his share o' the cash yet."

"Well, then, come along; no use to take truck and leave money."

"Say, won't he suspicion what we're up to?"

"Maybe he won't. But we got to have it anyway. Come along."

So they got out and went in.

The door slammed to because it was on the careened side; and in a half second I was in the boat, and Jim come tumbling after me. I out with my knife and cut the rope, and away we went!

We didn't touch an oar, and we didn't speak nor whisper, nor hardly even breathe. We went gliding swift along, dead silent, past the tip of the paddle-box, and past the stern; then in a second or two more we was a hundred yards below the wreck, and the darkness soaked her up, every last sign of her, and we was safe, and knowed it.

When we was three or four hundred yards down-stream we see the lantern show like a little spark at the texas door for a second, and we knowed by that that the rascals had missed their boat, and was beginning to understand that they was in just as much trouble now as Jim Turner was.

Then Jim manned the oars, and we took out after our raft. Now was the first time that I begun to worry about the men—I reckon I hadn't had time to before. I begun to think how dreadful it was, even for murderers, to be in such a fix. I says to myself, there ain't no telling but I might come to be a murderer myself yet, and then how would I like it? So says I to Jim:

"The first light we see we'll land a hundred yards below it or above it, in a place where it's a good hiding-place for you and the skiff, and then I'll go and fix up some kind of a yarn, and get somebody to go for that gang and get them out of their scrape, so they can be hung when their time comes."

But that idea was a failure; for pretty soon it begun to storm again, and this time worse than ever. The rain poured down, and never a light showed; everybody in bed, I reckon. We boomed along down the river, watching for lights, and watching for our raft. After a long time the rain let up, but the clouds stayed, and the lightning kept whimpering, and by and by a flash showed us a black thing ahead, floating, and we made for it.

It was the raft, and mighty glad was we to get aboard of it again. We seen a light now away down to the right, on shore. So I said I would go for it. The skiff was half full of plunder which that gang had stole there on the wreck. We hustled it on to the raft in a pile, and I told Jim to float along down, and show a light when he judged he had gone about two mile, and keep it burning till I come; and then I manned my oars and shoved for the light. As I got down towards it three or four more showed—up on a hillside

It was a village. I closed in above the shore light, and laid on my oars and floated. As I went by I see it was a lantern hanging on the jackstaff of a double-hull ferryboat. I skimmed around for the watchman, a-wondering whereabouts he slept; and by and by I found him roosting on the bitts forward, with his head down between his knees. I gave his shoulder two or three little shoves, and begun to cry.

He stirred up in a kind of a startlish way; but when he see it was only me he took a good gap and stretch, and then he says:

"Hello, what's up? Don't cry, bub. What's the trouble?"

I says:

"Pap, and mam, and sis, and—"

Then I broke down. He says:

"Oh, dang it now, *don't* take on so; we all has to have our troubles, and this 'n 'll come out all right. What's the matter with 'em?"

"They're—they're—are you the watchman of the boat?"

"Yes," he says, kind of pretty-well-satisfied like. "I'm the captain and the owner and the mate and the pilot and watchman and head deck-hand; and sometimes I'm the freight and passengers. I ain't as rich as old Jim Hornback, and I can't be so blame' generous and good to Tom, Dick, and Harry as what he is, and slam around money the way he does; but I've said many a time 't I wouldn't trade places with him; for, says I, a sailor's life's the life for me, and I'm derned if *I'd* live two mile out o' town, where there ain't nothing ever goin' on, not for all his spondulicks and as much more on top of it. Says I—"

I broke in and says:

"They're in an awful peck of trouble, and—"

"*Who* is?"

"Why, pap and mam and sis and Miss Hooker; and if you'd take your ferryboat and go up there—"

"Up where? Where are they?"

"On the wreck."

"What wreck?"

"Why, there ain't but one."

"What, you don't mean the *Walter Scott?*"

"Yes."

"Good land! what are they doin' *there*, for gracious sakes?"

"Well, they didn't go there a-purpose."

"I bet they didn't! Why, great goodness, there ain't no chance for 'em if they don't git off mighty quick! Why, how in the nation did they ever git into such a scrape?"

"Easy enough. Miss Hooker was a-visiting up there to the town—"

"Yes, Booth's Landing—go on."

"She was a-visiting there at Booth's Landing, and just in the edge of the evening she started over with her nigger woman in the horse-ferry to stay all night at her friend's house, Miss What-you-may-call-her—I disremember her name—and they lost their steering-oar, and swung around and went a-floating down, stern first, about two mile, and saddle-baggsed on the wreck, and the ferryman and the nigger woman and the horses was all lost, but Miss Hooker she made a grab and got aboard the wreck. Well, about an hour after dark we come along down in our trading-scow, and it was so dark we didn't notice the wreck till we was right on it; and so *we* saddle-baggsed; but all of us was saved but Bill Whipple—and oh, he *was* the best cretur!—I most wish 't it had been me, I do."

"My George! It's the beatenest thing I ever struck. And *then* what did you all do?"

"Well, we hollered and took on, but it's so wide there we couldn't make nobody hear. So pap said somebody got to get ashore and get help somehow. I was the only one that could swim, so I made a dash for it, and Miss Hooker she said if I didn't strike help sooner, come here and hunt up her uncle, and he'd fix the thing. I made the land about a mile below, and been fooling along ever since, trying to get people to do something, but they said, 'What, in such a night and such a current? There ain't no sense in it; go for the steam-ferry.' Now if you'll go and—"

"By Jackson, I'd *like* to, and, blame it, I don't know but I will; but who in the dingnation's a-going to *pay* for it? Do you reckon your pap—"

"Why *that's* all right. Miss Hooker she tole me, *particular*, that her uncle Hornback—"

"Great guns! is *he* her uncle? Looky here, you break for that light over yonder-way, and turn out west when you git there, and about a quarter of a mile out you'll come to the tavern; tell 'em to dart you out to Jim Hornback's, and he'll foot the bill. And don't you fool around any, because he'll want to know the news. Tell him

I'll have his niece all safe before he can get to town. Hump yourself, now; I'm a-going up around the corner here to roust out my engineer."

I struck for the light, but as soon as he turned the corner I went back and got into my skiff and bailed her out, and then pulled up shore in the easy water about six hundred yards, and tucked myself in among some wood-boats; for I couldn't rest easy till I could see the ferryboat start. But take it all around, I was feeling ruther comfortable on accounts of taking all this trouble for that gang, for not many would 'a' done it. I wished the widow knowed about it. I judged she would be proud of me for helping these rapscallions, because rapscallions and dead-beats is the kind the widow and good people takes the most interest in.

Well, before long here comes the wreck, dim and dusky, sliding along down! A kind of cold shiver went through me, and then I struck out for her. She was very deep, and I see in a minute there warn't much chance for anybody being alive in her. I pulled all around her and hollered a little, but there wasn't any answer; all dead still. I felt a little bit heavy-hearted about the gang, but not much, for I reckoned if they could stand it I could.

Then here comes the ferryboat; so I shoved for the middle of the river on a long down-stream slant; and when I judged I was out of eye-reach I laid on my oars, and looked back and see her go and smell around the wreck for Miss Hooker's remainders, because the captain would know her uncle Hornback would want them; and then pretty soon the ferryboat give it up and went for the shore, and I laid into my work and went a-booming down the river.

It did seem a powerful long time before Jim's light showed up; and when it did show it looked like it was a thousand mile off. By the time I got there the sky was beginning to get a little gray in the east; so we struck for an island, and hid the raft, and sunk the skiff, and turned in and slept like dead people.

14 *A General Good Time— The Harem—French*

By and by, when we got up, we turned over the truck the gang had stole off of the wreck, and found boots, and blankets, and clothes, and all sorts of other things, and a lot of books, and a spy-glass, and three boxes of seegars. We hadn't ever been this rich before in neither of our lives. The seegars was prime. We laid off all the afternoon in the woods talking, and me reading the books, and having a general good time. I told Jim all about what happened inside the wreck and at the ferryboat, and I said these kinds of things was adventures; but he said he didn't want no more adventures. He said that when I went in the texas and he crawled back to get on the raft and found her gone he nearly died, because he judged it was all up with *him* anyway it could be fixed; for if he didn't get saved he would get drownded; and if he did get saved, whoever saved him would send him back home so as to get the reward, and then Miss Watson would sell him South, sure. Well, he was right; he was most always right; he had an uncommon level head for a nigger.

I read considerable to Jim about kings and dukes and earls and such, and how gaudy they dressed, and how much style they put on, and called each other your majesty, and your grace, and your lordship, and so on, 'stead of mister; and Jim's eyes bugged out, and he was interested. He says:

"I didn' know dey was so many un um. I hain't hearn 'bout none un um, skasely, but ole King Sollermun, onless you counts dem kings dat's in a pack er k'yards. How much do a king git?"

"Get?" I says; "why, they get a thousand dollars a month if they want it; they can have just as much as they want; everything belongs to them."

"*Ain'* dat gay? En what dey got to do, Huck?"

"*They* don't do nothing! Why, how you talk! They just set around."

"No; is dat so?"

"Of course it is. They just set around—except, maybe when there's a war; then they go to the war. But other times they just lazy around; or go hawking—just hawking and sp— Sh!—d'you hear a noise?"

We skipped out and looked; but it warn't nothing but the flutter of a steamboat's wheel away down, coming around the point; so we come back.

"Yes," says I, "and other times, when things is dull, they fuss with the parlyment; and if everybody don't go just so he whacks their heads off. But mostly they hang round the harem."

"Roun' de which?"

"Harem."

"What's de harem?"

"The place where he keeps his wives. Don't you know about the harem? Solomon had one; he had about a million wives."

"Why, yes, dat's so; I—I'd done forgot it. A harem's a bo'd'n-house, I reck'n. Mos' likely dey has rackety times in de nussery. En I reck'n de wives quarrels considable; en dat 'crease de racket. Yit de say Sollermun de wises' man dat ever live'. I doan' take no stock in dat. Bekase why: would a wise man want to live in de mids' er sich a blim-blammin' all de time? No—'deed he wouldn't. A wise man 'ud take en buil' a biler-factry; en den he could shet *down* de biler-factry when he want to res'."

"Well, but he *was* the wisest man, anyway; because the widow she told me so, her own self."

"I doan' k'yer what de widder say, he *warn't* no wise man nuther. He had some er de dad-fetchedes' ways I ever see. Does you know 'bout dat chile dat he 'uz gwyne to chop in two?"

"Yes, the widow told me all about it."

"*Well*, den! Warn' dat de beatenes' notion in de worl'? You jes' take en look at it a minute. Dah's de stump, dah—dat's one er de women; heah's you—dat's de yuther one; I's Sollermun; en dish yer dollar bill's de chile. Bofe un you claims it. What does I do? Does I shin aroun' mongs' de neighbors en fine out which un you de bill *do* b'long to, en han' it over to de right one, all safe en soun', de way dat anybody dat had any gumption would? No; I take en whack de bill in *two*, en give half un it to you, en de yuther half to de yuther woman. Dat's de way Sollermun was gwyne to do wid de chile. Now I want to ast you: what's de use er dat half a bill?—

can't buy noth'n wid it. En what use is a half a chile? I wouldn' give a dern for a million un um."

"But hang it, Jim, you've clean missed the point—blame it, you've missed it a thousand mile."

"Who? Me? Go 'long. Doan' talk to *me* 'bout yo' pints. I reck'n I knows sense when I sees it; en dey ain' no sense in sich doin's as dat. De 'spute warn't 'bout a half a chile, de 'spute was 'bout a whole chile; en de man dat think he kin settle a 'spute 'bout a whole chile wid a half a chile doan' know enough to come in out'n de rain. Doan' talk to me 'bout Sollermun, Huck, I knows him by de back."

"But I tell you you don't get the point."

"Blame de pint! I reck'n I knows what I knows En mine you, de *real* pint is down furder—it's down deeper. It lays in de way Sollermun was raised. You take a man dat's got on'y one or two chillen; is dat man gwyne to be waseful o' chillen? No, he ain't; he can't 'ford it. *He* know how to value 'em. But you take a man dat's got 'bout five million chillen runnin' roun' de house, en it's diffunt. *He* as soon chop a chile in two as a cat. Dey's plenty mo'. A chile er two, mo' er less, warn't no consekens to Sollermun, dad fetch him!"

I never see such a nigger. If he got a notion in his head once, there warn't no getting it out again. He was the most down on Solomon of any nigger I ever see. So I went to talking about other kings, and let Solomon slide. I told about Louis Sixteenth that got his head cut off in France long time ago; and about his little boy the dolphin, that would 'a' been a king, but they took and shut him up in jail, and some say he died there.

"Po' little chap."

"But some says he got out and got away, and come to America."

"Dat's good! But he'll be pooty lonesome—dey ain' no kings here, is dey, Huck?"

"No."

"Den he cain't git no situation. What he gwyne to do?"

"Well, I don't know. Some of them gets on the police, and some of them learns people how to talk French."

"Why, Huck, doan' de French people talk de same way we does?"

"*No*, Jim; you couldn't understand a word they said—not a single word."

"Well, now, I be ding-busted! How do dat come?"

"*I* don't know; but it's so. I got some of their jabber out of a book. S'pose a man was to come to you and say *Polly-voo-franzy*—what would you think?"

"I wouldn' think nuffn; I'd take en bust him over de head—dat is, if he warn't white. I wouldn' 'low no nigger to call me dat."

"Shucks, it ain't calling you anything. It's only saying, do you know how to talk French?"

"Well, den, why couldn't he say it?"

"Why, he *is* a-saying it. That's a Frenchman's *way* of saying it."

"Well, it's a blame ridicklous way, en I doan' want to hear no mo' 'bout it. Dey ain' no sense in it."

"Looky here, Jim; does a cat talk like we do?"

"No, a cat don't."

"Well, does a cow?"

"No, a cow don't, nuther."

"Does a cat talk like a cow, or a cow talk like a cat?"

"No, dey don't."

"It's natural and right for 'em to talk different from each other, ain't it?"

"Course."

"And ain't it natural and right for a cat and a cow to talk different from *us*?"

"Why, mos' sholy it is."

"Well, then, why ain't it natural and right for a *Frenchman* to talk different from us? You answer me that."

"Is a cat a man, Huck?"

"No."

"Well, den, dey ain't no sense in a cat talkin' like a man. Is a cow a man?—er is a cow a cat?"

"No, she ain't either of them."

"Well, den, she ain't got no business to talk like either one er the yuther of 'em. Is a Frenchman a man?"

"Yes."

"*Well*, den! Dad blame it, why doan' he *talk* like a man? You answer me *dat!*"

I see it warn't no use wasting words—you can't learn a nigger to argue. So I quit.

15 *Huck Loses the Raft—In the Fog— Huck Finds the Raft—Trash*

We judged that three nights more would fetch us to Cairo, at the bottom of Illinois, where the Ohio River comes in, and that was what we was after. We would sell the raft and get on a steamboat and go way up the Ohio amongst the free states, and then be out of trouble.

Well, the second night a fog begun to come on, and we made for a towhead to tie to, for it wouldn't do to try to run in a fog; but when I paddled ahead in the canoe, with the line to make fast, there warn't anything but little saplings to tie to. I passed the line around one of them right on the edge of the cut bank, but there was a stiff current, and the raft come booming down so lively she tore it out by the roots and away she went. I see the fog closing down, and it made me so sick and scared I couldn't budge for most a half a minute it seemed to me—and then there warn't no raft in sight; you couldn't see twenty yards. I jumped into the canoe and run back to the stern, and grabbed the paddle and set him back a stroke. But she didn't come. I was in such a hurry I hadn't untied her. I got up and tried to untie her, but I was so excited my hands shook so I couldn't hardly do anything with them.

As soon as I got started I took out after the raft, hot and heavy, right down the towhead. That was all right as far as it went, but the towhead warn't sixty yards long, and the minute I flew by the foot of it I shot out into the solid white fog, and hadn't no more idea which way I was going than a dead man.

Thinks I, it won't do to paddle; first I know I'll run into the bank or a towhead or something; I got to set still and float, and yet it's mighty fidgety business to have to hold your hands still at such a time. I whooped and listened. Away down there somewheres I hears a small whoop, and up comes my spirits. I went tearing after it, listening sharp to hear it again. The next time it come I see I warn't heading for it, but heading away to the right of it. And the next time I was heading away to the left of it—and not gaining on it much either, for I was flying around, this way and that and t'other, but it was going straight ahead all the time.

I did wish the fool would think to beat a tin pan, and beat it all the time, but he never did, and it was the still places between the whoops that was making the trouble for me. Well, I fought along, and directly I hears the whoop *behind* me. I was tangled good now. That was somebody else's whoop, or else I was turned around.

I throwed the paddle down. I heard the whoop again; it was behind me yet, but in a different place; it kept coming, and kept changing its place, and I kept answering, till by and by it was in front of me again, and I knowed the current had swung the canoe's head down-stream, and I was all right if that was Jim and not some other raftsman hollering. I couldn't tell nothing about voices in a fog, for nothing don't look natural nor sound natural in a fog.

The whooping went on, and in about a minute I come a-booming down on a cut bank with smoky ghosts of big trees on it, and the current throwed me off to the left and shot by, amongst a lot of snags that fairly roared, the current was tearing by them so swift.

In another second or two it was solid white and still again. I set perfectly still then, listening to my heart thump, and I reckon I didn't draw a breath while it thumped a hundred.

I just give up then. I knowed what the matter was. That cut bank was an island, and Jim had gone down t'other side of it. It warn't no towhead that you could float by in ten minutes. It had the big timber of a regular island; it might be five or six miles long and more than half a mile wide.

I kept quiet, with my ears cocked, about fifteen minutes, I reckon. I was floating along, of course, four or five miles an hour; but you don't ever think of that. No, you *feel* like you are laying dead still on the water; and if a little glimpse of a snag slips by you don't think to yourself how fast *you're* going, but you catch your breath and think, my! how that snag's tearing along. If you think it ain't dismal and lonesome out in a fog that way by yourself in the night, you try it once—you'll see.

Next, for about a half an hour, I whoops now and then; at last I hears the answer a long ways off, and tries to follow it, but I couldn't do it, and directly I judged I'd got into a nest of towheads, for I had little dim glimpses of them on both sides of me—sometimes just a narrow channel between, and some that I couldn't see I knowed was there because I'd hear the wash of the current against the old dead brush and trash that hung over the banks. Well, I warn't long loosing the whoops down amongst the tow-heads; and I only tried to chase them a little while, anyway, because it was worse than chasing a Jack-o'-lantern. You never knowed a sound dodge around so, and swap places so quick and so much.

I had to claw away from the bank pretty lively four or five times, to keep from knocking the islands out of the river; and so I judged the raft must be butting into the bank every now and then, or else it would get further ahead and clear out of hearing—it was floating a little faster than what I was.

Well, I seemed to be in the open river again by and by, but I couldn't hear no sign of a whoop nowheres. I reckoned Jim had fetched up on a snag, maybe, and it was all up with him. I was good and tired, so I laid down in the canoe and said I wouldn't bother no more. I didn't want to go sleep, of course; but I was so sleepy I couldn't help it; so I thought I would take just one little cat-nap.

But I reckon it was more than a cat-nap, for when I waked up the stars was shining bright, the fog was all gone, and I was spinning down a big bend stern first. First I didn't know where I was; I thought I was dreaming; and when things began to come back to me they seemed to come up dim out of last week.

It was a monstrous big river here, with the tallest and the thickest kind of timber on both banks; just a solid wall, as well as I could see by the stars. I looked away down-stream, and seen a black speck on the water. I took after it; but when I got to it it warn't nothing but a couple of saw-logs made fast together. Then I see another speck, and chased that; then another, and this time I was right. It was the raft.

When I got to it Jim was setting there with his head down between his knees, asleep, with his right arm hanging over the steering-oar. The other oar was smashed off, and the raft was littered up with leaves and branches and dirt. So she'd had a rough time.

I made fast and laid down under Jim's nose on the raft and began to gap, and stretch my fists out against Jim, and says:

"Hello, Jim, have I been asleep? Why didn't you stir me up?"

"Goodness gracious, is dat you, Huck? En you ain' dead—you ain' drownded—you's back ag'in? It's too good for true, honey, it's too good for true. Lemme look at you chile, lemme feel o' you. No, you ain' dead! you's back ag'in, 'live en soun', jis de same ole Huck—de same ole Huck, thanks to goodness!"

"What's the matter with you, Jim? You been a-drinking?"

"Drinkin'? Has I ben a-drinkin'? Has I had a chance to be a-drinkin'?"

"Well, then, what makes you talk so wild?"

"How does I talk wild?"

"*How?* Why, hain't you been talking about my coming back, and all that stuff, as if I'd been gone away?"

"Huck—Huck Finn, you look me in de eye; look me in de eye. *Hain't* you ben gone away?"

"Gone away? Why, what in the nation do you mean? *I* hain't been gone anywheres. Where would I go to?"

"Well, looky here, boss, dey's sumfn wrong, dey is. Is I *me*, or who *is* I? Is I heah, or whah *is* I? Now dat's what I wants to know."

"Well, I think you're here, plain enough, but I think you're a tangle-headed old fool, Jim."

"I is, is I? Well, you answer me dis: Didn't you tote out de line in de canoe fer to make fas' to de towhead?"

"No, I didn't. What towhead? I hain't seen no towhead."

"You hain't seen no towhead? Looky here, didn't de line pull loose en de raf' go a-hummin' down de river, en leave you en de canoe behine in de fog?"

"What fog?"

"Why, *de* fog!—de fog dat's been aroun' all night. En didn't you whoop, en didn't I whoop, tell we got mix' up in de islands en one un us got los' en t'other one was jis' as good as los', 'kase he didn' know whah he wuz? En didn't I bust up agin a lot er dem islands en have a turrible time en mos' git drownded? Now ain' dat so, boss—ain't it so? You answer me dat."

"Well, this is too many for me, Jim. I hain't seen no fog, nor no islands, nor no troubles, nor nothing. I been setting here talking with you all night till you went to sleep about ten minutes ago, and I reckon I done the same. You couldn't 'a' got drunk in that time, so of course you've been dreaming."

"Dad fetch it, how is I gwyne to dream all dat in ten minutes?"

"Well, hang it all, you did dream it, because there didn't any of it happen."

"But, Huck, it's all jis' as plain to me as—"

"It don't make no difference how plain it is; there ain't nothing in it. I know, because I've been here all the time."

Jim didn't say nothing for about five minutes, but set there studying over it. Then he says:

"Well, den, I reck'n I did dream it, Huck; but dog my cats ef it ain't de powerfulest dream I ever see. En I hain't ever had no dream b'fo' dat's tired me like dis one."

"Oh, well, that's all right, because a dream does tire a body like everything sometimes. But this one was a staving dream; tell me all about it, Jim."

So Jim went to work and told me the whole thing right through, just as it happened, only he painted it up considerable. Then he said he must start in and " 'terpret" it, because it was sent for a warning. He said the first towhead stood for a man that would try to do us some good, but the current was another man that would get us away from him. The whoops was warnings that would come to us every now and then, and if we didn't try hard to make out to understand them they'd just take us into bad luck, 'stead of keeping us out of it. The lot of towheads was troubles we was going to get into with quarrelsome people and all kinds of mean folks, but if we minded our business and didn't talk back and aggravate them, we would pull through and get out of the fog and into the big clear river, which was the free states, and wouldn't have no more trouble.

It had clouded up pretty dark just after I got on to the raft, but it was clearing up again now.

"Oh, well, that's all interpreted well enough as far as it goes, Jim," I says; "but what does *these* things stand for?"

It was the leaves and rubbish on the raft and the smashed oar. You could see them first-rate now.

Jim looked at the trash, and then looked at me, and back at the trash again. He had got the dream fixed so strong in his head that he couldn't seem to shake it loose and get the facts back into its place again right away. But when he did get the thing straightened around he looked at me steady without ever smiling, and says:

"What do dey stan' for? I's gwyne to tell you. When I got all wore out wid work, en wid de callin' for you, en went to sleep, my heart wuz mos' broke bekase you wuz los', en I didn' k'yer no' mo' what become er me en de raf'. En when I wake up en fine you back ag'in, all safe en soun', de tears come, en I could 'a' got down on my knees en kiss yo' foot, I's so thankful. En all you wuz thinkin' 'bout wuz how you could make a fool uv ole Jim wid a lie. Dat truck dah is *trash*; en trash is what people is dat puts dirt on de head er dey fren's en makes 'em ashamed."

Then he got up slow and walked to the wigwam, and went in there without saying anything but that. But that was enough. It made me feel so mean I could almost kissed *his* foot to get him to take it back.

It was fifteen minutes before I could work myself up to go and humble myself to a nigger; but I done it, and I warn't ever sorry for it afterward, neither. I didn't do him no more mean tricks, and I wouldn't done that one if I'd 'a' knowed it would make him feel that way.

16 Expectation—A White Lie—Floating Currency—Running by Cairo—Swimming Ashore

We slept most all day, and started out at night, a little ways behind a monstrous long raft that was as long going by as a procession. She had four long sweeps at each end, so we judged she carried as many as thirty men, likely. She had five big wigwams aboard, wide apart, and an open camp-fire in the middle, and a tall flag-pole at each end. There was a power of style about her. It *amounted* to something being a raftsman on such a craft as that.

We went drifting down into a big bend, and the night clouded up and got hot. The river was very wide, and was walled with solid timber on both sides; you couldn't see a break in it hardly ever, or a light. We talked about Cairo, and wondered whether we would know it when we got to it. I said likely we wouldn't, because I had heard say there warn't but about a dozen houses there, and if they didn't happen to have them lit up, how was we going to know we was passing a town? Jim said if the two big rivers joined together there, that would show. But I said maybe we might think we was passing the foot of an island and coming into the same old river again. That disturbed Jim—and me too. So the question was, what to do? I said, paddle ashore the first time a light showed, and tell them pap was behind, coming along with a trading-scow, and was a green hand at the business, and wanted to know how far it was to Cairo. Jim thought it was a good idea, so we took a smoke on it and waited.

There warn't nothing to do now but to look out sharp for the town, and not pass it without seeing It. He said he'd be mighty sure to see it, because he'd be a free man the minute he seen it, but if he missed it he'd be in a slave country again and no more show for freedom. Every little while he jumps up and says:

"Dah she is?"

But it warn't. It was Jack-o'-lanterns, or lightning-bugs; so he set down again, and went to watching, same as before. Jim said it made him all over trembly and feverish to be so close to freedom. Well, I can tell you it made me all over trembly and feverish, too, to hear him, because I began to get it through my head that he *was* most free—and who was to blame for it? Why, *me*. I couldn't get that out of my conscience, no how nor no way. It got to troubling me so I couldn't rest; I couldn't stay still in one place. It hadn't ever come home to me before, what this thing was that I was doing. But now it did; and it stayed with me, and scorched me more and more. I tried to make out to myself that *I* warn't to blame, because *I* didn't run Jim off from his rightful owner; but it warn't no use, conscience up and says, every time, "But you knowed he was running for his freedom, and you could 'a' paddled ashore and told somebody." That was so—I couldn't get around that no way. That was where it pinched. Conscience says to me, "What had poor Miss Watson done to you that you could see her nigger go off right under your eyes and never say one single word? What did that poor old woman do to you that you could treat her so mean? Why, she tried to learn you your book, she tried to learn you your manners, she tried to be good to you every way she knowed how. *That's* what she done."

I got to feeling so mean and miserable I most wished I was dead. I fidgeted up and down the raft, abusing myself to myself, and Jim was fidgeting up and down past me. We neither of us could keep still. Every time he danced around and says, "Dah's Cairo!" it went through me like a shot, and I thought if it *was* Cairo I reckoned I would die of miserableness.

Jim talked out loud all the time while I was talking to myself. He was saying how the first thing he would do when he got to a free state he would go to saving up money and never spend a single cent, and when he got enough he would buy his wife, which was owned on a farm close to where Miss Watson lived; and then they would both work to buy the two children, and if their master wouldn't sell them, they'd get an Ab'litionist to go and steal them.

It most froze me to hear such talk. He wouldn't ever dared to talk such talk in his life before. Just see what a difference it made in him the minute he judged he was about free. It was according to the old saying "Give a nigger an inch and he'll take an ell." Thinks I, this is what comes of my not thinking. Here was this nigger, which I had as good as helped to run away, coming right out flat-footed and saying he would steal his children—children that belonged to a man I didn't even know; a man that hadn't ever done me no harm.

I was sorry to hear Jim say that, it was such a lowering of him. My conscience got to stirring me up hotter than ever, until at last I says to it, "Let up on me—it ain't too late yet—I'll paddle ashore at the first light and tell." I felt easy and happy and light as a feather right off. All my troubles was gone. I went to looking out sharp for a light, and sort of singing to myself. By and by one showed. Jim sings out:

"We's safe, Huck, we's safe! Jump up and crack yo' heels! Dat's de good ole Cairo at las', I jis knows it!"

I says:

"I'll take the canoe and go and see, Jim. It mightn't be, you know."

He jumped and got the canoe ready, and put his old coat in the bottom for me to set on, and give me the paddle; and as I shoved off, he says:

"Pooty soon I'll be a-shout'n' for joy, en I'll say, it's all on accounts o' Huck; I's a free man, en I couldn't ever ben free ef it hadn' ben for Huck; Huck done it. Jim won't ever forgit you, Huck; you's de bes' fren' Jim's ever had; en you's de *only* fren' ole Jim's got now."

I was paddling off, all in a sweat to tell on him; but when he says this, it seemed to kind of take the tuck all out of me. I went along slow then, and I warn't right down certain whether I was glad I started or whether I warn't. When I was fifty yards off, Jim says:

"Dah you goes, de ole true Huck; de on'y white genlman dat ever kep' his promise to ole Jim."

Well, I just felt sick. But I says, I *got* to do it—I can't get *out* of it. Right then along comes a skiff with two men in it with guns, and they stopped and I stopped. One of them says:

"What's that yonder?"

"A piece of a raft," I says.

"Do you belong on it?"

"Yes, sir."

"Any men on it?"

"Only one, sir."

"Well, there's five niggers run off to-night up yonder, above the head of the bend. Is your man white or black?"

I didn't answer up prompt. I tried to, but the words wouldn't come. I tried for a second or two to brace up and out with it but I warn't man enough—hadn't the spunk of a rabbit. I see I was weakening; so I just give up trying and up and says:

"He's white."

"I reckon we'll go and see for ourselves."

"I wish you would," says I, "because it's pap that's there, and maybe you'd help me tow the raft ashore where the light is. He's sick—and so is mam and Mary Ann."

"Oh, the devil! we're in a hurry, boy. But I s'pose we've got to. Come, buckle to your paddle, and let's get along."

I buckled to my paddle and they laid to their oars. When we had made a stroke or two, I says:

"Pap'll be mighty much obleeged to you, I can tell you. Everybody goes away when I want them to help me tow the raft ashore, and I can't do it by myself."

"Well, that's infernal mean. Odd, too. Say, boy, what's the matter with your father?"

"It's the—a—the—well, it ain't anything much."

They stopped pulling. It warn't but a mighty little ways to the raft now. One says:

"Boy, that's a lie. What *is* the matter with your pap? Answer up square now, and it'll be the better for you."

"I will, sir, I will, honest—but don't leave us, please. It's the—the—Gentlemen, if you'll only pull ahead, and let me heave you the head-line, you won't have to come a-near the raft—please do."

"Set her back, John, set her back!" says one. They backed water. "Keep away, boy—keep to looard. Confound it, I just expect the wind has blowed it to us. Your pap's got the smallpox, and you know it precious well. Why didn't you come out and say so? Do you want to spread it all over?"

"Well," says I, a-blubbering, "I've told everybody before, and they just went away and left us."

"Poor devil, there's something in that. We are right down sorry for you, but we—well, hang it, we don't want the smallpox, you see. Look here, I'll tell you what to do. Don't you try to land by yourself, or you'll smash everything to pieces. You float along down about twenty miles, and you'll come to a town on the left-hand side of the river. It will be long after sun-up then, and when you ask for help you tell them your folks are all down with chills and fever. Don't be a fool again, and let people guess what is the matter. Now we're trying to do you a kindness; so you just put twenty miles between us, that's a good boy. It wouldn't do any good to land yonder where the light is——it's only a wood-yard. Say, I reckon your father's poor, and I'm bound to say he's in pretty hard luck. Here, I'll put a twenty-dollar gold piece on this board, and you get it when it floats by. I feel mighty mean to leave you; but my kingdom! it won't do to fool with smallpox, don't you see?"

"Hold on, Parker," says the man, "here's a twenty to put on the board for me. Good-by, boy; you do as Mr. Parker told you, and you'll be all right."

"That's so, my boy—good-by, good-by. If you see any runaway niggers you get help and nab them, and you can make some money by it."

"Good-by, sir," says I; "I won't let no runaway niggers get by me if I can help it."

They went off and I got aboard the raft, feeling bad and low, because I knowed very well I had done wrong, and I see it warn't no use for me to try to learn to do right; a body that don't get *started* right when he's little ain't got no show—when the pinch comes there ain't nothing to back him up and keep him to his work, and so he gets beat. Then I thought a minute, and says to myself, hold on; s'pose you'd 'a' done right and give Jim up, would you felt better than what you do now? No, says I, I'd feel bad—I'd feel just the same way I do now. Well, then, says I, what's the use you learning to do right when it's troublesome to do right and ain't no trouble to do wrong, and the wages is just the same? I was stuck. I couldn't answer that. So I reckoned I wouldn't bother no more about it, but after this always do whichever come handiest at the time.

I went into the wigwam; Jim warn't there. I looked all around; he warn't anywhere. I says:

"Jim!"

"Here I is, Huck. Is dey out o' sight yit? Don't talk loud."

He was in the river under the stern oar, with just his nose out. I told him they were out of sight, so he come aboard. He says:

"I was a-listenin' to all de talk, en I slips into de river en was gwyne to shove for sho' if dey come aboard. Den I was gwyne to swim to de raf' ag'in when de was gone. But lawsy, how you did fool 'em, Huck! Dat *wuz* de smartes' dodge! I tell you, chile, I 'spec it save' ole Jim —ole Jim ain't going to forgit you for dat, honey."

Then we talked about the money. It was a pretty good raise—twenty dollars apiece. Jim said we could take deck passage on a steamboat now, and the money would last us as far as we wanted to go in the free states. He said twenty mile more warn't far for the raft to go, but he wished we was already there.

Towards daybreak we tied up, and Jim was mighty particular about hiding the raft good. Then he worked all day fixing things in bundles, and getting all ready to quit rafting.

That night about ten we hove in sight of the lights of a town away down in a left-hand bend.

I went off in the canoe to ask about it. Pretty soon I found a man out in the river with a skiff, setting a trotline. I ranged up and says:

"Mister, is that town Cairo?"

"Cairo? no. You must be a blame' fool."

"What town is it, mister?"

"If you want to know, go and find out. If you stay here botherin' around me for about a half a minute longer you'll get something you won't want."

I paddled to the raft. Jim was awful disappointed, but I said never mind, Cairo would be the next place, I reckoned.

We passed another town before daylight, and I was going out again; but it was high ground, so I didn't go. No high ground about Cairo, Jim said. I had forgot it. We laid up for the day on a towhead tolerable close to the left-hand bank. I begun to suspicion something. So did Jim. I says:

"Maybe we went by Cairo in the fog that night."

He says:

"Doan' le's talk about it, Huck. Po' niggers can't have no luck. I awluz 'spected dat rattlesnake-skin warn't done wid its work."

"I wish I'd never seen that snake-skin, Jim—I do wish I'd never laid eyes on it."

"It ain't yo' fault, Huck; you didn't know. Don't you blame yo'self 'bout it."

When it was daylight, here was the clear Ohio water inshore, sure enough, and outside was the old regular Muddy! So it was all up with Cairo.

We talked it all over. It wouldn't do to take to the shore; we couldn't take the raft up stream, of course. There warn't no way but to wait for dark, and start back in the canoe and take the chances. So we slept all day amongst the cotton wood thickets, so as to be fresh for the work, and when we got back to the raft about dark the canoe was gone!

We didn't say a word for a good while. There warn't anything to say. We both knowed well enough it was some more work of the rattlesnake-skin; so what was the use to talk about it? It would only look like we was finding fault, and that would be bound to fetch more bad luck—and keep on fetching it, too, till we knowed enough to keep still.

By and by we talked about what we better do, and found there warn't no way but just to go along down with the raft till we got a chance to buy a canoe to go back in. We warn't going to borrow it when there warn't anybody around, the way pap would do, for that might set people after us.

So we shoved out after dark on the raft.

Anybody that don't believe yet that it's foolishness to handle a snake-skin, after all that that snake-skin done for us, will believe it now if they read on and see what more it done for us.

The place to buy canoes is off of rafts laying up at shore. But we didn't see no rafts laying up; so we went along during three hours and more. Well, the night got gray and ruther thick, which is the next meanest thing to fog. You can't tell the shape of the river, and you can't see no distance. It got to be very late and still, and then along comes a steamboat up the river. We lit the lantern, and judged she would see it. Up-stream boats didn't generly come close to us; they go out and follow the bars and hunt for easy water under the reefs; but nights like this they bull right up the channel against the whole river.

We could hear her pounding along, but we didn't see her good till she was close. She aimed right for us. Often they do that and try to see how close they can come without touching; sometimes the wheel bites off a sweep, and then the pilot sticks his head out and laughs, and thinks he's mighty smart. Well, here she comes, and we said she was going to try and shave us; but she didn't seem to be sheering off a bit. She was a big one, and she was coming in a hurry, too, looking like a black cloud with rows of glow-worms around it; but all of a sudden she bulged out, big and scary, with a long row of wide-open furnace doors shining like red-hot teeth, and her monstrous bows and guards hanging right over us. There was a yell at us, and a jingling of bells to stop the engines, a powwow of cussing, and whistling of steam —and as Jim went overboard on one side and I on the other, she come smashing straight through the raft.

I dived—and I aimed to find the bottom, too, for a thirty-foot wheel had got to go over me, and I wanted it to have plenty of room. I could always stay under water a minute; this time I reckon I stayed under a minute and a half. Then I bounced for the top in a hurry, for I was nearly busting. I popped out to my armpits and blowed the water out of my nose and puffed a bit. Of course there was a booming current; and of course that boat started her engines again ten seconds after she stopped them, for they never care much for raftsmen; so now she was churning along up the river, out of sight in the thick weather, though I could hear her.

I sung out for Jim about a dozen times, but I didn't get any answer; so I grabbed a plank that touched me while I was "treading water," and struck out for shore, shoving it ahead of me. But I made out to see that the drift of the current was towards the left-hand shore, which meant that I was in a crossing; so I changed off and went that way.

It was one of these long, slanting, two-mile crossings; so I was a good long time in getting over. I made a safe landing, and clumb up the bank. I couldn't see but a little ways, but I went poking along over rough ground for a quarter of a mile or more, and then I run across a big old-fashioned double log house before I noticed it. I was going to rush by and get away, but a lot of dogs jumped out and went to howling and barking at me, and I knowed better than to move another peg.

17 *An Evening Call—The Farm in Arkansas —Interior Decorations—Stephen Dowling Bots—Poetical Effusions*

In about a minute somebody spoke out of a window without putting his head out, and says:

"Be done, boys! Who's there?"

I says:

"It's me."

"Who's me?"

"George Jackson, sir?"

"What do you want?"

"I don't want nothing, sir. I only want to go along by, but the dogs won't let me."

"What are you prowling around here this time of night for—hey?"

"I warn't prowling around, sir; I fell overboard off the steamboat."

"Oh, you did, did you? Strike a light there, somebody. What did you say your name was?"

"George Jackson, sir. I'm only a boy."

"Look here, if you're telling the truth you needn't be afraid—nobody'll hurt you. But don't try to budge; stand right where you are. Rouse out Bob and Tom, some of you, and fetch the guns. George Jackson, is there anybody with you?"

"No, sir, nobody."

I heard the people stirring around in the house now, and see a light. The man sung out:

"Snatch that light away, Betsy, you old fool—ain't you got any sense? Put it on the floor behind the front door. Bob, if you and Tom are ready, take your places."

"All ready."

"Now, George Jackson, do you know the Shepherdsons?"

"No, sir; I never heard of them."

"Well, that may be so, and it mayn't. Now, all ready. Step forward, George Jackson. And mind, don't you hurry—come mighty slow. If there's anybody with you, let him keep back—if he shows himself he'll be shot. Come along now. Come slow; push the door open yourself—just enough to squeeze in, d'you hear?"

I didn't hurry; I couldn't if I'd a-wanted to. I took one slow step at a time and there warn't a sound, only I thought I could hear my heart. The dogs were as still as the humans, but they followed a little behind me. When I got to the three log doorsteps I heard them unlocking and unbarring and unbolting. I put my hand on the door and pushed it a little and a little more till somebody said, "There, that's enough—put your head in." I done it, but I judged they would take it off.

The candle was on the floor, and there they all was, looking at me, and me at them, for about a quarter of a minute: Three big men with guns pointed at me, which made me wince, I tell you; the oldest, gray and about sixty, the other two thirty or more—all of them fine and handsome—and the sweetest old gray-headed lady, and back of her two young women which I couldn't see right well. The old gentleman says:

"There; I reckon it's all right. Come in."

As soon as I was in the old gentleman he locked the door and barred it and bolted it, and told the young men to come in with their guns, and they all went in a big parlor that had a new rag carpet on the floor, and got together in a corner that was out of the range of the front windows—there warn't none on the side. They held the candle, and took a good look at me, and all said, "Why, *he* ain't a Shepherdson—no, there ain't any Shepherdson about him." Then the old man said he hoped I wouldn't mind being searched for arms, because he didn't mean no harm by it—it was only to make sure. So he didn't pry into my pockets, but only felt outside with his hands, and said it was all right. He told me to make myself easy and at home, and tell all about myself; but the old lady says:

"Why, bless you, Saul, the poor thing's as wet as he can be; and don't you reckon it may be he's hungry?"

"True for you, Rachel—I forgot."

So the old lady says:

"Betsy" (this was a nigger woman), "you fly around and get him something to eat as quick as you can, poor thing; and one of you girls go and wake up Buck and tell him—or, here he is himself. Buck, take this little stranger and get the wet clothes off from him and dress him up in some of yours that's dry."

Buck looked about as old as me—thirteen or fourteen or along there, though he was a little bigger than me. He hadn't on anything but a shirt, and he was very frowzy-headed. He came in gaping and digging one fist into his eyes, and he was dragging a gun along with the other one. He says:

"Ain't they no Shepherdsons around?"

They said, no, 'twas a false alarm.

"Well," he says, "if they'd 'a' ben some, I reckon I'd 'a' got one."

They all laughed, and Bob says:

"Why, Buck, they might have scalped us all, you've been so slow in coming."

"Well, nobody come after me, and it ain't right. I'm always kept down; I don't get no show."

"Never mind, Buck, my boy," says the old man, "you'll have show enough, all in good time, don't you fret about that. Go 'long with you now, and do as your mother told you."

When we got up-stairs to his room he got me a coarse shirt and a roundabout and pants of his, and I put them on. While I was at it he asked me what my name was, but before I could tell him he started to tell me about a bluejay and a young rabbit he had catched in the woods the day before yesterday, and he asked me where Moses was when the candle went out. I said I didn't know; I hadn't heard about it before, no way.

"Well, guess," he says.

"How'm I going to guess," says I, "when I never heard tell of it before?"

"But you can guess, can't you? It's just as easy."

"*Which* candle?" I says.

"Why, any candle," he says.

"I don't know where he was," says I; "Where was he?"

"Why, he was in the *dark!* That's where he was!"

"Well, if you knowed where he was, what did you ask me for?"

"Why, blame it, it's a riddle, don't you see? Say, how long are you going to stay here? You got to stay always. We can just have booming times—they don't have no school now. Do you own a dog? I've got a dog—and he'll go in the river and bring out chips that you throw in. Do you like to comb up Sundays, and all that kind of foolishness? You bet I don't, but ma she makes me. Confound these ole britches! I reckon I'd better put 'em on, but I'd ruther not, it's so warm. Are you all ready? All right. Come along, old hoss."

Cold corn-pone, cold corn-beef, butter and buttermilk—that is what they had for me down there, and there ain't nothing better that ever I've come across yet. Buck and his ma and all of them smoked cob pipes, except the nigger woman, which was gone, and the two young women. They all smoked and talked, and I eat and talked. The young women had quilts around them, and their hair down their backs. They all asked me questions, and I told them how pap and me and all the family was living on a little farm down at the bottom of Arkansaw, and my sister Mary Ann run off and got married and never was heard of no more, and Bill went to hunt them and he warn't heard of no more, and Tom and Mort died, and then there warn't nobody but just me and pap left, and he was just trimmed down to nothing, on account of his troubles; so when he died I took what there was left, because the farm didn't belong to us, and started up the river, deck passage, and fell overboard; and that was how I come to be here. So they said I could have a home there as long as I wanted it. Then it was most daylight and everybody went to bed, and I went to bed with Buck, and when I waked up in the morning, drat it all, I had forgot what my name was. So I laid there about an hour trying to think, and when Buck waked up I says:

"Can you spell, Buck?"

"Yes," he says.

"I bet you can't spell my name," says I.

"I bet you what you dare I can," says he.

"All right," says I, "go ahead."

"G-e-o-r-g-e J-a-x-o-n—there now," he says.

"Well," says I, "you done it, but I didn't think you could. It ain't no slouch of a name to spell—right off without studying."

I set it down, private, because somebody might want *me* to spell it next, and so I wanted to be handy with it and rattle it off like I was used to it.

It was a mighty nice family, and a mighty nice house, too. I hadn't seen no house out in the country before that was so nice and had so much style. It didn't have an iron latch on the front door, nor a wooden one with a buckskin string, but a brass knob to turn, the same as houses in town. There warn't no bed in the parlor, nor a sign of a bed; but heaps of parlors in towns has beds in them. There was a big fireplace that was bricked on the bottom, and the bricks was kept clean and red by pouring water on them and scrubbing them with another brick; sometimes they wash them over with red water-paint that they call Spanish-brown, same as they do in town. They had big brass dog-irons that could hold up a saw-log. There was a clock on the middle of the mantelpiece, with a picture of a town painted on the bottom half of the glass front, and a round place in the middle of it for the sun, and you could see the pendulum swinging behind it. It was beautiful to hear that clock tick; and sometimes when one of these peddlers had been along and scoured her up and got her in good shape, she would start in and strike a hundred and fifty before she got tuckered out. They wouldn't took any money for her.

Well, there was a big outlandish parrot on each side of the clock, made out of something like chalk, and painted up gaudy. By one of the parrots was a cat made of crockery, and a crockery dog by the other; and when you pressed down on them they squeaked, but didn't open their mouths nor look different nor interested. They squeaked through underneath. There was a couple of big wild-turkey-wing fans spread out behind those things. On the table in the middle of the room was a kind of a lovely crockery basket that had apples and oranges and peaches and grapes piled up in it, which was much redder and yellower and prettier than real ones is, but they warn't real because you could see where pieces had got chipped off and showed the white chalk, or whatever it was, underneath.

This table had a cover made out of a beautiful oilcloth, with a red and blue spread-eagle painted on it, and a painted border all around. It come all the way from Philadelphia, they said. There was some books, too, piled up perfectly exact, on each corner of the table. One was a big family Bible full of pictures. One was *Pilgrim's Progress*, about a man that left his family, it didn't say why. I read considerable in it now and then. The statements was interesting, but tough. Another was *Friendship's Offering*, full of beautiful stuff and poetry; but I didn't read the poetry. Another was Henry Clay's Speeches, and another was Dr. Gunn's *Family Medicine*, which told you all about what to do if a body was sick or dead. There was a hymn-book, and a lot of other books. And there was nice split-bottom chairs, and perfectly sound, too—not bagged down in the middle and busted, like an old basket.

They had pictures hung on the walls—mainly Washingtons and Lafayettes, and battles, and Highland Marys, and one called "Signing the Declaration." There was some that they called crayons, which one of the daughters which was dead made her own self when she was only fifteen years old. They was different from any pictures I ever see before—blacker, mostly, than is common. One was a woman in slim black dress, belted small under the armpits, with bulges like a cabbage in the middle of the sleeves, and a large black scoop-shovel bonnet with a black veil, and white slim ankles crossed about with black tape, and very wee black slippers, like a chisel, and she was leaning pensive on a tombstone on her right elbow, under a weeping willow, and her other hand hanging down her side holding a white handkerchief and a reticule, and underneath the picture it said "Shall I Never See Thee More Alas." Another one was a young lady with her hair all combed up straight to the top of her head, and knotted there in front of a comb like a chair-back, and she was crying into a handkerchief and had a dead bird laying on its back in her other hand with its heels up, and underneath the picture it said "I Shall Never Hear Thy Sweet Chirrup More Alas." There was one where a young lady was at a window looking up at the moon, and tears running down her cheeks; and she had an open letter in one hand with black sealing-wax showing on one edge of it and she was mashing a locket with a chain to it against her mouth, and underneath the picture it said "And Art Thou Gone Yes Thou Art Gone Alas." These was all nice pictures, I reckon, but I didn't somehow seem to take to them, because if ever I was down a little they always give me the fan-tods. Everybody was sorry she died, because she had laid out a lot more of these pictures to do, and a body could see by what she had done what they had lost. But I reckoned that with her disposition she was having a better time in the graveyard. She was at work on what they said was her greatest picture when she took sick, and every day and every night it was her prayer to be allowed to live till she got it done, but she never got the chance. It was a picture of a young woman in a long white gown, standing on the rail of a bridge all ready to jump off, with her hair all down her back, and looking up to the moon, with the tears running down her face, and she had two arms folded across her breast, and two arms stretched out in front, and two more reaching up toward the moon—and the idea was to see which pair would look best and then scratch out all the other arms; but as I was saying, she died before she got her mind made up, and now they kept this picture over the head of the bed in her room, and every time her birthday come they hung flowers on it. Other times it was hid with a little curtain. The young woman in the picture had a kind of nice sweet face, but there was so many arms it made her look too spidery, seemed to me.

This young girl kept a scrap-book when she was alive, and used to paste obituaries and accidents and cases of patient suffering in it out of the *Presbyterian Observer*, and write poetry after them out of her own head. It was very good poetry. This is what she wrote about a boy by the name of Stephen Dowling Bots that fell down a well and was drownded:

ODE TO STEPHEN DOWLING BOTS, DEC'D

And did young Stephen sicken,
  And did young Stephen die?
And did the sad hearts thicken,
  And did the mourners cry?

No; such was not the fate of
  Young Stephen Dowling Bots;
Though sad hearts round him thickened,
  'Twas not from sickness' shots.

No whooping-cough did rack his frame,
  Nor measles drear with spots;
Not these impaired the sacred name
  Of Stephen Dowling Bots.

Despised love struck not with woe
  That head of curly knots,
Nor stomach troubles laid him low,
  Young Stephen Dowling Bots.

O no. Then list with tearful eye,
  Whilst I his fate do tell.
His soul did from this cold world fly
  By falling down a well.

They got him out and emptied him;
  Alas it was too late;
His spirit was gone for to sport aloft
  In the realms of the good and great.

If Emmeline Grangerford could make poetry like that before she was fourteen, there ain't no telling what she could 'a' done by and by. Buck said she could rattle off poetry like nothing. She didn't ever have to stop to think. He said she would slap down a line, and if she couldn't find anything to rhyme with it would just scratch it out and slap down another one, and go ahead. She warn't particular; she could write about anything you choose to give her to write about just so it was sadful. Every time a man died, or a woman died, or a child died, she would be on hand with her "tribute" before he was cold. She called them tributes. The neighbors said it was the doctor first, then Emmeline, then the undertaker—the undertaker never got in ahead of Emmeline but once, and then she hung fire on a rhyme for the dead person's name, which was Whistler. She warn't ever the same after that; she never complained, but she kinder pined away and did not live long. Poor thing, many's the time I made myself go up to the little room that used to be hers and get out her poor old scrap-book and read in it when her pictures had been aggravating me and I had soured on her a little. I liked all that family, dead ones and all, and warn't going to let anything come between us. Poor Emmeline made poetry about all the dead people when she was alive, and it didn't seem right that there warn't nobody to make some about her now she was gone; so I tried to sweat out a verse or two myself, but I couldn't seem to make it go somehow. They kept Emmeline's room trim and nice, and all the things fixed in it just the way she liked to have them when she was alive, and nobody ever slept there. The old lady took care of the room herself, though there was plenty of niggers, and she sewed there a good deal and read her Bible there mostly.

Well, as I was saying about the parlor, there was beautiful curtains on the windows; white, with pictures painted on them of castles with vines all down the walls, and cattle coming down to drink. There was a little old piano, too, that had tin pans in it, I reckon, and nothing was ever so lovely as to hear the young ladies sing "The Last Link is Broken" and play "The Battle of Prague" on it. The walls of all the rooms was plastered, and most had carpets on the floors, and the whole house was whitewashed on the outside.

It was a double house, and the big open place betwixt them was roofed and floored, and sometimes the table was set there in the middle of the day, and it was a cool, comfortable place. Nothing couldn't be better. And warn't the cooking good, and just bushels of it too!

18 *Col. Grangerford—Aristocracy—Feuds—The Testament—Recovering the Raft—The Woodpile—Pork and Cabbage*

Col. Grangerford was a gentleman, you see. He was a gentleman all over; and so was his family. He was well born, as the saying is, and that's worth as much in a man as it is in a horse, so the Widow Douglas said, and nobody ever denied that she was of the first aristocracy in our town; and pap he always said it, too, though he warn't no more quality than a mudcat himself. Col. Grangerford was very tall and very slim, and had a darkish-paly complexion, not a sign of red in it anywheres; he was clean-shaved every morning all over his thin face, and he had the thinnest kind of lips, and the thinnest kind of nostrils, and a high nose, and heavy eyebrows, and the blackest kind of eyes, sunk so deep back that they seemed like they was looking out of caverns at you, as you may say. His forehead was high, and his hair was gray and straight and hung to his shoulders. His hands was long and thin, and every day of his life he put on a clean shirt and a full suit from head to foot made out of linen so white it hurt your eyes to look at it; and on Sundays he wore a blue tail-coat with brass buttons on it. He carried a mahogany cane with a silver head to it. There warn't no frivolishness about him, not a bit, and he warn't ever loud. He was as kind as he could be—you could feel that, you know, and so you had confidence. Sometimes he smiled, and it was good to see; but when he straightened himself up like a liberty-pole, and the lightning begun to flicker out from under his eyebrows, you wanted to climb a tree first, and find out what the matter was afterwards. He didn't ever have to tell anybody to mind their manners—everybody was always good-mannered where he was. Everybody loved to have him around, too; he was sunshine most always—I mean he made it seem like good weather. When he turned into a cloud-bank it was awful dark for half a minute, and that was enough; there wouldn't nothing go wrong again for a week.

When him and the old lady come down in the morning all the family got up out of their chairs and give them good day, and didn't set down again till they had set down. Then Tom and Bob went to the sideboard where the decanter was, and mixed a glass of bitters and handed it to him, and he held it in his hand and waited till Tom's and Bob's was mixed, and then they bowed and said, "Our duty to you, sir, and madam"; and *they* bowed the least bit in the world and said thank you, and so they drank, all three, and Bob and Tom poured a spoonful of water on the sugar and the mite of whisky or apple-brandy in the bottom of their tumblers, and give it to me and Buck, and we drank to the old people too.

Bob was the oldest and Tom next—tall, beautiful men with very broad shoulders and brown faces, and long black hair and black eyes. They dressed in white linen from head to foot, like the old gentleman, and wore broad Panama hats.

Then there was Miss Charlotte; she was twenty-five, and tall and proud and grand, but as good as she could be when she warn't stirred up; but when she was she had a look that would make you wilt in your tracks, like her father. She was beautiful.

So was her sister, Miss Sophia, but it was a different kind. She was gentle and sweet like a dove, and she was only twenty.

Each person had their own nigger to wait on them—Buck too. My nigger had a monstrous easy time, because I warn't used to having anybody to do anything for me, but Buck's was on the jump most of the time.

This was all there was of the family now, but there used to be more —three sons; they got killed; and Emmeline that died.

The old gentleman owned a lot of farms and over a hundred niggers. Sometimes a stack of people would come there, horseback, from ten or fifteen mile around, and stay five or six days, and have such junketings round about and on the river, and dances and picnics in the woods daytimes, and balls at the house nights. These people was mostly kinfolks of the family. The men brought their guns with them. It was a handsome lot of quality, I tell you.

There was another clan of aristocracy around there—five or six families—mostly of the name of Shepherdson. They was as high-toned and well born and rich and grand as the tribe of Grangerfords. The Shepherdsons and Grangerfords used the same steamboat-landing, which was about two mile above our house; so sometimes when I went up there with a lot of our folks I used to see a lot of the Shepherdsons there on their fine horses.

One day Buck and me was away out in the woods hunting, and heard a horse coming. We was crossing the road. Buck says:

"Quick! Jump for the woods!"

We done it, and then peeped down the woods through the leaves. Pretty soon a splendid young man came galloping down the road, setting his horse easy and looking like a soldier. He had his gun across his pommel. I had seen him before. It was young Harney Shepherdson. I heard Buck's gun go off at my ear, and Harney's hat tumbled off from his head. He grabbed his gun and rode straight to the place where we was hid. But we didn't wait. We started through the woods on a run. The woods warn't thick, so I looked over my shoulder to dodge the bullet, and twice I seen Harney cover Buck with his gun; and then he rode away the way he come—to get his hat, I reckon, but I couldn't see. We never stopped running till we got home. The old gentleman's eyes blazed a minute—'twas pleasure, mainly, I judged—then his face sort of smoothed down, and he says, kind of gentle:

"I don't like that shooting from behind a bush. Why didn't you step into the road, my boy?"

"The Shepherdsons don't, father. They always take advantage."

Miss Charlotte she held her head up like a queen while Buck was telling his tale, and her nostrils spread and her eyes snapped. The two young men looked dark, but never said nothing. Miss Sophia she turned pale, but the color came back when she found the man warn't hurt.

Soon as I could get Buck down by the corn-cribs under the trees by ourselves, I says:

"Did you want to kill him, Buck?"

"Well, I bet I did."

"What did he do to you?"

"Him? He never done nothing to me."

"Well, then, what did you want to kill him for?"

"Why, nothing—only it's on account of the feud."

"What's a feud?"

"Why, where was you raised? Don't you know what a feud is?"

"Never heard of it before—tell me about it."

"Well," says Buck, "a feud is this way: A man has a quarrel with another man, and kills him; then that other man's brother kills *him;* then the other brothers, on both sides, goes for one another; then the *cousins* chip in—and by and by everybody's killed off, and there ain't no more feud. But it's kind of slow, and takes a long time."

"Has this one been going on long, Buck?"

"Well, I should *reckon!* It started thirty year ago, or som'ers along there. There was trouble 'bout something, and then a lawsuit to settle it; and the suit went agin one of the men, and so he up and shot the man that won the suit—which he would naturally do, of course. Anybody would."

"What was the trouble about, Buck?—land?"

"I reckon maybe—I don't know."

"Well, who done the shooting? Was it a Grangerford or a Shepherdson?"

"Laws, how do *I* know? It was so long ago."

"Don't anybody know?"

"Oh, yes, pa knows, I reckon, and some of the other older people; but they don't know now what the row was about in the first place."

"Has there been many killed, Buck?"

"Yes; right smart chance of funerals. But they don't always kill. Pa's got a few buckshot in him; but he don't mind it 'cuz he don't weigh much, anyway. Bob's been carved up some with a bowie, and Tom's been hurt once or twice."

"Has anybody been killed this year, Buck?"

"Yes; we got one and they got one. 'Bout three months ago my cousin Bud, fourteen year old, was riding through the woods on t'other side of the river, and didn't have no weapon with him, which was blame' foolishness, and in a lonesome place he hears a horse a-coming behind him, and sees old Baldy Shepherdson a-linkin' after him with his gun in his hand and his white hair a-flying in the wind; and 'stead of jumping off and taking to the brush, Bud 'lowed he could outrun him; so they had it, nip and tuck, for five mile or more, the old man a-gaining all the time; so at last Bud seen it warn't any use, so he stopped and faced around so as to have the bullet-holes in front, you know, and the old man he rode up and shot him down. But he didn't git much chance to enjoy his luck, for inside of a week our folks laid *him* out."

"I reckon that old man was a coward, Buck."

"I reckon he *warn't* a coward. Not by a blame' sight. There ain't a coward amongst them Shepherdsons—not a one. And there ain't no cowards amongst the Grangerfords, either. Why, that old man kep' up his end in a fight one day for half an hour against three Grangerfords, and come out winner. They was all a-horseback; he lit off his horse and got behind a little woodpile, and kep' his horse before him to stop the bullets; but the Grangerfords stayed on their horses and capered around the old man, and peppered away at him, and he peppered away at them. Him and his horse both went home pretty leaky and crippled, but the Grangerfords had to be *fetched* home—and one of 'em was dead, and another died the next day. No, sir; if a body's out hunting for cowards he don't want to fool away any time amongst them Shepherdsons, becuz they don't breed any of that *kind*."

Next Sunday we all went to church, about three mile, everybody a-horseback. The men took their guns along, so did Buck, and kept them between their knees or stood them handy against the wall. The Shepherdsons done the same. It was pretty ornery preaching—all about brotherly love, and such-like tiresomeness; but everybody said it was a good sermon, and they all talked it over going home and had such a powerful lot to say about faith and good works and free grace and preforeordestination, and I don't know what all, that it did seem to me to be one of the roughest Sundays I had run across yet.

About an hour after dinner everybody was dozing around, some in their chairs and some in their rooms, and it got to be pretty dull. Buck and a dog was stretched out on the grass in the sun sound asleep. I went up to our room, and judged I would take a nap myself.

I found that sweet Miss Sophia standing in her door, which was next to ours, and she took me in her room and shut the door very soft, and asked me if I liked her, and I said I did; and she asked me if I would do something for her and not tell anybody, and I said I would. Then she said she'd forgot her Testament, and left it in the seat at church between two other books, and would I slip out quiet and go there and fetch it to her, and not say nothing to nobody. I said I would. So I slid out and slipped off up the road, and there warn't anybody at the church, except maybe a hog or two, for there warn't any lock on the door, and hogs likes a puncheon floor in summer-time because it's cool. If you notice, most folks don't go to church only when they've got to; but a hog is different.

Says I to myself, something's up; it ain't natural for a girl to be in such a sweat about a Testament. So I give it a shake, and out drops a little piece of paper with "*Half past two*" wrote on it with a pencil. I ransacked it, but couldn't find anything else. I couldn't make anything out of that, so I put the paper in the book again, and when I got home and upstairs there was Miss Sophia in her door waiting for me. She pulled me in and shut the door; then she looked in the Testament till she found the paper, and as soon as she read it she looked glad; and before a body could think she grabbed me and give me a squeeze, and said I was the best boy in the world, and not to tell anybody. She was mighty red in the face for a minute, and her eyes lighted up, and it made her powerful pretty. I was a good deal astonished, but when I got my breath I asked her what the paper was about, and she asked me if I had read it, and I said no, and she asked me if I could read writing, and I told her "no, only coarse-hand," and then she said the paper warn't anything but a book-mark to keep her place, and I might go and play now.

I went off down to the river, studying over this thing, and pretty soon I noticed that my nigger was following along behind. When we was out of sight of the house he looked back and around a second, and then comes a-running, and says:

"Mars Jawge, if you'll come down into de swamp I'll show you a whole stack o' water-moccasins."

Thinks I, that's mighty curious; he said that yesterday. He oughter know a body don't love water-moccasins enough to go around hunting for them. What is he up to, anyway? So I says:

"All right; trot ahead."

I followed a half a mile; then he struck out over the swamp, and waded ankle-deep as much as another half-mile. We come to a little flat piece of land which was dry and very thick with trees and bushes, and he says:

"You shove right in dah jist a few steps, Mars Jawge; dah's whah dey is. I's seed 'm befo'; I don't k'yer to see 'em no mo'."

Then he slopped right along and went away, and pretty soon the trees hid him. I poked into the place a ways and come to a little open patch as big as a bedroom all hung around with vines, and found a man laying there asleep—and, by jings, it was my old Jim!

I waked him up, and I reckoned it was going to be a grand surprise to him to see me again, but it warn't. He nearly cried he was so glad, but he warn't surprised. Said he swum along behind me that night, and heard me yell every time, but dasn't answer, because he didn't want nobody to pick *him* up and take him into slavery again. Says he:

"I got hurt a little, en couldn't swim fas', so I wuz a considerable ways behine you towards de las'; when you landed I reck'ned I could ketch up wid you on de lan' 'dout havin' to shout at you, but when I see dat house I begin to go slow. I 'uz off too fur to hear what dey say to you—I wuz 'fraid o' de dogs; but when it 'uz all quiet ag'in I knowed you's in de house, so I struck out for de woods to wait for day. Early in de mawnin' some er de niggers come along, gwyne to de fields, en dey tuk me en showed me dis place, whah de dogs can't track me on account o' de water, en dey brings me truck to eat every night, en tells me how you's a-gittin' along."

"Why didn't you tell my Jack to fetch me sooner."

"Well, 'twarn't no use to 'sturb you, Huck, tell we could do sumfn. I ben a-buyin' pots en pans en vittles, as I got a chanst, en a-patchin' up de raf' nights when—"

"*What* raft, Jim?"

"Our ole raf'."

"You mean to say our old raft warn't smashed all to flinders?"

"No, she warn't. She was tore up a good deal—one en' of her was; but dey warn't no great harm done, on'y our traps was mos' all los'. Ef we hadn' dive' so deep en swum so fur under water, en de night hadn't ben so dark, en we warn't so sk'yerd, en ben sich punkin-heads, as de sayin' is, we'd a seed de raf'. But it jis' as well we didn't, 'kase now she's all fixed up ag'in mos' as good as new, en we's got a new lot o' stuff, in de place o' what 'uz los'."

"Why, how did you get hold of the raft again, Jim—did you catch her?"

"How I gwyne to ketch her en I out in de woods? No; some er de niggers foun' her ketched on a snag along heah in de ben', en dey hid her in a crick 'mongst de willows, en dey wuz so much jawin' 'bout which un 'um she b'long to de mos' dat I come to heah 'bout it pooty soon, so I ups en settles de trouble by tellin' 'um she don't b'long to none uv 'um, but to you en me; en I ast 'm if dey gwyne to grab a young white genlman's propaty, en git a hid'n for it? Den I gin 'm ten cents apiece, en dey 'uz mighty well satisfied, en wisht some mo' raf's 'ud come along en make 'm rich ag'in. Dey's mighty good to me, dese niggers is, en whatever I wants 'm to do fur me I doan' have to ast 'm twice, honey. Dat Jack's a good nigger, en pooty smart."

"Yes, he is. He ain't ever told me you was here; told me to come, and he'd show me a lot of water-moccasins. If anything happens *he* ain't mixed up in it. He can say he never seen us together, and it 'll be the truth."

I don't want to talk much about the next day. I reckon I'll cut it pretty short. I waked up about dawn, and was a-going to turn over and go to sleep again when I noticed how still it was—didn't seem to be anybody stirring. That warn't usual. Next I noticed that Buck was up and gone. Well, I gets up, a-wondering, and goes down-stairs —everything as still as a mouse. Just the same outside. Thinks I, what does it mean? Down by the woodpile I comes across my Jack, and says:

"What's it all about?"

Says he:

"Don't you know, Mars Jawge?"

"No," says I, "I don't."

"Well, den, Miss Sophia's run off! 'deed she has. She run off in de night some time—nobody don't know jis' when; run off to get married to dat young Harney Shepherdson, you know—leastways, so dey 'spec. De fambly foun' it out 'bout half an hour ago—maybe a little mo'—en I *tell* you dey warn't no time los'. Sich another hurryin' up guns en hosses *you* never see! De women folks has gone for to stir up de relations, en ole Mars Saul en de boys tuck dey guns en rode up de river road for to try to ketch dat young man en kill him 'fo' he kin git acrost de river wid Miss Sophia. I reck'n dey's gwyne to be mighty rough times."

"Buck went off 'thout waking me up."

"Well, I reck'n he *did!* Dey warn't gwyne to mix you up in it. Mars Buck he loaded up his gun en 'lowed he's gwyne to fetch home a Shepherdson or bust. Well, dey'll be plenty un 'm dah, I reck'n, en you bet you he'll fetch one ef he gits a chanst."

I took up the river road as hard as I could put. By and by I begin to hear guns a good ways off. When I came in sight of the log store and the woodpile where the steamboats lands I worked along under the trees and brush till I got to a good place, and then I clumb up into the forks of a cottonwood that was out of reach, and watched. There was a wood-rank four foot high a little ways in front of the tree, and first I was going to hide behind that; but maybe it was luckier I didn't.

There was four or five men cavorting around on their horses in the open place before the log store, cussing and yelling, and trying to get at a couple of young chaps that was behind the wood-rank alongside of the steamboat-landing; but they couldn't come in. Every time one of them showed himself on the river side of the woodpile he got shot at. The two boys was squatting back to back behind the pile, so they could watch both ways.

By and by the men stopped cavorting around and yelling. They started riding towards the store; then up gets one of the boys, draws a steady bead over the wood-rank, and drops one of them out of his saddle. All the men jumped off of their horses and grabbed the hurt one and started to carry him to the store; and that minute the two boys started on the run. They got half-way to the tree I was in before the men noticed. Then the men see them, and jumped on their horses and took out after them. They gained on the boys, but it didn't do no good, the boys had too good a start; they got to the woodpile that was in front of my tree, and slipped in behind it, and so they had the bulge on the men again. One of the boys was Buck, and the other was a slim young chap about nineteen years old.

The men ripped around awhile, and then rode away. As soon as they was out of sight I sung out to Buck and told him. He didn't know what to make of my voice coming out of the tree at first. He was awful surprised. He told me to watch out sharp and let him know when the men come in sight again; said they was up to some devilment or other—wouldn't be gone long. I wished I was out of that tree, but I dasn't come down. Buck begun to cry and rip, and 'lowed that him and his cousin Joe (that was the other young chap) would make up for this day yet. He said his father and his two brothers was killed, and two or three of the enemy. Said the Shepherdsons laid for them in ambush. Buck said his father and brothers ought to waited for their relations—the Shepherdsons was too strong for them. I asked him what was become of young Harney and Miss Sophia. He said they'd got across the river and was safe. I was glad of that; but the way Buck did take on because he didn't manage to kill Harney that day he shot at him—I hain't ever heard anything like it.

All of a sudden, bang! bang! bang! goes three or four guns—the men had slipped around through the woods and come in from behind without their horses! The boys jumped for the river—both of them hurt—and as they swum down the current the men run along the bank shooting at them and singing out, "Kill them, kill them!" It made me so sick I most fell out of the tree. I ain't a-going to tell *all* that happened—it would make me sick again if I was to do that. I wished I hadn't ever come ashore that night to see such things. I ain't ever going to get shut of them—lots of times I dream about them.

I stayed in the tree till it begun to get dark, afraid to come down. Sometimes I heard guns away off in the woods; and twice I seen little gangs of men gallop past the log store with guns; so I reckoned the trouble was still a-going on. I was mighty down hearted; so I made up my mind I wouldn't ever go anear that house again, because I reckoned I was to blame, somehow. I judged that that piece of paper meant that Miss Sophia was to meet Harney somewheres at half past two and run off; and I judged I ought to told her father about that paper and the curious way she acted, and then maybe he would 'a' locked her up, and this mess wouldn't happen.

When I got down out of the tree I crept along down the riverbank a piece and found the two bodies laying in the edge of the water, and tugged at them till I got them ashore; then I covered up their faces, and got away as quick as I could. I cried a little when I was covering up Buck's face, for he was mighty good to me.

It was just dark now. I never went near the house, but struck through the woods and made for the swamp. Jim warn't on his island, so I tramped off in a hurry for the crick, and crowded through the willows, red-hot to jump aboard and get out of that awful country. The raft was gone! My souls, but I was scared! I couldn't get my breath for most a minute. Then I raised a yell. A voice not twenty-five foot from me says:

"Good lan'! is dat you, honey? Doan' make no noise."

It was Jim's voice—nothing ever sounded so good before. I run along the bank a piece and got aboard, and Jim he grabbed me and hugged me, he was so glad to see me. He says:

"Laws bless you, chile, I 'uz right down sho' you's dead ag'in. Jack's been heah; he says he reck'n you's ben shot, kase you didn' come home no mo'; so I's jes' dis minute a-startin' de raf' down towards de mouf er de crick, so's to be all ready for to shove out en leave soon as Jack comes ag'in en tells me for certain you *is* dead. Lawsy, I's mighty glad to git you back ag'in, honey."

I says: "All right—that's mighty good; they won't find me, and they'll think I've been killed, and floated down the river—there's something up there that 'll help them think so—so don't you lose no time, Jim, but just shove off for the big water as fast as ever you can."

I never felt easy till the raft was two mile below there and out in the middle of the Mississippi. Then we hung up our signal lantern, and judged that we was free and safe once more. I hadn't had a bite to eat since yesterday, so Jim he got out some corn-dodgers and buttermilk, and pork and cabbage and greens—there ain't nothing in the world so good when it's cooked right—and whilst I eat my supper we talked and had a good time. I was powerful glad to get away from the feuds, and so was Jim to get away from the swamp. We said there warn't no home like a raft, after all. Other places do seem so cramped up and smothery, but a raft don't. You feel mighty free and easy and comfortable on a raft.

19 *Tying Up Daytimes—An Astronomical Theory—Running a Temperance Revival —The Duke of Bridgewater—The Troubles of Royalty*

Two or three days and nights went by; I reckon I might say they swum by, they slid along so quiet and smooth and lovely. Here is the way we put in the time. It was a monstrous big river down there—sometimes a mile and half wide; we run nights, and laid up and hid daytimes; soon as night was most gone we stopped navigating and tied up—nearly always in the dead water under a towhead; and then cut young cottonwoods and willows, and hid the raft with them. Then we set out the lines. Next we slid into the river and had a swim, so as to freshen up and cool off; then we set down on the sandy bottom where the water was about knee-deep, and watched the daylight come. Not a sound anywheres—perfectly still—just like the whole world was asleep, only sometimes the bullfrogs a-cluttering, maybe. The first thing to see, looking away over the water, was a kind of dull line—that was the woods on t'other side; you couldn't make nothing else out; then a pale place in the sky; then more paleness spreading around; then the river softened up away off, and warn't black any more, but gray; you could see little dark spots drifting along ever so far away—trading-scows, and such things; and long black streaks—rafts; sometimes you could hear a sweep screaking; or jumbled-up voices, it was so still, and sounds come so far; and by and by you could see a streak on the water which you know by the look of the streak that there's a snag there in a swift current which breaks on it and makes that streak look that way; and you see the mist curl up off of the water, and the east reddens up, and the river, and you make out a log cabin in the edge of the woods, away on the bank on t'other side of the river, being a wood-yard, likely, and piled by them cheats so you can throw a dog through it anywheres; then the nice breeze springs up, and comes fanning you from over there, so cool and fresh and sweet to smell on account of the woods and the flowers; but sometimes not that way, because they've left dead fish laying around, gars and such, and they do get pretty rank; and next you've got the full day, and everything smiling in the sun, and the song-birds just going it!

A little smoke couldn't be noticed now, so we would take some fish off of the lines and cook up a hot breakfast. And afterwards we would watch the lonesomeness of the river, and kind of lazy along, and by and by lazy off to sleep. Wake up by and by, and look to see what done it, and maybe see a steamboat coughing along upstream, so far off towards the other side you couldn't tell nothing about her only whether she was a stern-wheel or side-wheel; then for about an hour there wouldn't be nothing to hear nor nothing to see—just solid lonesomeness. Next you'd see a raft sliding by, away off yonder, and maybe a galoot on it chopping, because they're most always doing it on a raft; you'd see the ax flash and come down—you don't hear nothing; you see that ax go up again, and by the time it's above the man's head then you hear the *k'chunk!*—it had took all that time to come over the water. So we would put in the day, lazying around, listening to the stillness. Once there was a thick fog, and the rafts and things that went by was beating tin pans so the steamboats wouldn't run over them. A scow or a raft went by so close we could hear them talking and cussing and laughing—heard them plain; but we couldn't see no sign of them; it made you feel crawly; it was like spirits carrying on that way in the air. Jim said he believed it was spirits; but I says:

"No; spirits wouldn't say, 'Dern the dern fog.' "

Soon as it was night out we shoved; when we got her out to about the middle we let her alone, and let her float wherever the current wanted her to; then we lit the pipes, and dangled our legs in the water, and talked about all kinds of things—we was always naked, day and night, whenever the mosquitoes would let us—the new clothes Buck's folks made for me was too good to be comfortable, and besides I didn't go much on clothes, nohow.

Sometimes we'd have that whole river all to ourselves for the longest time. Yonder was the banks and the islands, across the water; and maybe a spark—which was a candle in a cabin window; and sometimes on the water you could see a spark or two—on a raft or a scow,' you know; and maybe you could hear a fiddle or a song coming over from one of them crafts. It's lovely to live on a raft. We had the sky up there, all speckled with stars, and we used to lay on our backs and look up at them, and discuss about whether they was made or only just happened. Jim he allowed they was made, but I allowed they happened; I judged it would have took too long to *make* so many. Jim said the moon could 'a' *laid* them; well, that looked kind of reasonable, so I didn't say nothing against it, because I've seen a frog lay most as many, so of course it could be done. We used to watch the stars that fell, too, and see them streak down. Jim allowed they'd got spoiled and was hove out of the nest.

Once or twice of a night we would see a steamboat slipping along in the dark, and now and then she would belch a whole world of sparks up out of her chimbleys, and they would rain down in the river and look awful pretty; then she would turn a corner and her lights would wink out and her powwow shut off and leave the river still again; and by and by her waves would get to us, a long time after she was gone, and joggle the raft a bit, and after that you wouldn't hear nothing for you couldn't tell how long, except maybe frogs or something.

After midnight the people on shore went to bed, and then for two or three hours the shores was black—no more sparks in the cabin windows. These sparks was our clock—the first one that showed again meant morning was coming, so we hunted a place to hide and tie up right away.

One morning about daybreak I found a canoe and crossed over a chute to the main shore—it was only two hundred yards—and paddled about a mile up a crick amongst the cypress woods, to see if I couldn't get some berries. Just as I was passing a place where a kind of a cowpath crossed the crick, here comes a couple of men tearing up the path as tight as they could foot it. I thought I was a goner, for whenever anybody was after anybody I judged it was *me*—or maybe Jim. I was about to dig out from there in a hurry, but they was pretty close to me then, and sung out and begged me to save their lives—said they hadn't been doing nothing, and was being chashed for it—said there was men and dogs a-coming. They wanted to jump right in, but I says:

"Don't you do it. I don't hear the dogs and horses yet; you've got time to crowd through the brush and get up the crick a little ways; then you take to the water and wade down to me and get in—that'll throw the dogs off the scent."

They done it, and soon as they was aboard I lit out for our towhead, and in about five or ten minutes we heard the dogs and the men away off, shouting. We heard them come along towards the crick, but couldn't see them; they seemed to stop and fool around awhile; then, as we got further and further away all the time, we couldn't hardly hear them at all; by the time we had left a mile of woods behind us and struck the river, everything was quiet, and we paddled over to the towhead and hid in the cottonwoods and was safe.

One of these fellows was about seventy or upwards, and had a bald head and very gray whiskers. He had an old battered-up slouch hat on, and a greasy blue woolen shirt, and ragged old blue jeans britches stuffed into his boot-tops, and home-knit galluses—no, he only had one. He had an old long-tailed blue jeans coat with slick brass buttons flung over his arm, and both of them had big, fat, ratty-looking carpet-bags.

The other fellow was about thirty, and dressed about as ornery. After breakfast we all laid off and talked, and the first thing that come out was that these chaps didn't know one another.

"What got you into trouble?" says the baldhead to t'other chap.

"Well, I'd been selling an article to take the tartar off the teeth—and it does take it off, too, and generly the enamel along with it—but I stayed about one night longer than I ought to, and was just in the act of sliding out when I ran across you on the trail this side of town, and you told me they were coming, and begged me to help you to get off. So I told you I was expecting trouble myself, and would scatter out *with* you. That's the whole yarn—what's yourn?"

"Well, I'd ben a runnin' a little temperance revival thar 'bout a week, and was the pet of the women folks, big and little, for I was makin' it mighty warm for the rummies, I *tell* you, and takin' as much as five or six dollars a night—ten cents a head, children and niggers free—and business a-growin' all the time, when somehow or another a little report got around last night that I had a way of puttin' in my time with a private jug on the sly. A nigger rousted me out this mornin', and told me the people was getherin' on the quiet with their dogs and horses, and they'd be along pretty soon and give me 'bout half an hour's start, and then run me down if they could; and if they got me they'd tar and feather me and ride me on a rail, sure. I didn't wait for no breakfast—I warn't hungry."

"Old man," said the young one, "I reckon we might double-team it together; what do you think?"

"I ain't undisposed. What's your line—mainly?"

"Jour printer by trade; do a little in patent medicines; theater-actor—tragedy, you know; take a turn to mesmerism and phrenology when there's a chance; teach singing-geography school for a change; sling a lecture sometimes—oh, I do lots of things—most anything that comes handy, so it ain't work. What's your lay?"

"I've done considerable in the doctoring way in my time. Layin' on o' hands is my best holt—for cancer and paralysis, and sich things; and I k'n tell a fortune pretty good when I've got somebody along to find out the facts for me. Preachin's my line, too, and workin' camp-meetin's, and missionaryin' around."

Nobody never said anything for a while; then the young man hove a sigh and says:

"Alas!"

"What 're you alassin' about?" says the baldhead.

"To think I should have lived to be leading such a life, and be degraded down into such company." And he begun to wipe the corner of his eye with a rag.

"Dern your skin, ain't the company good enough for you?" says the baldhead pretty pert and uppish.

"Yes it *is* good enough for me; it's as good as I deserve; for who fetched me so low when I was so high? *I* did myself. I don't blame *you*, gentlemen—far from it; I don't blame anybody. I deserve it all. Let the cold world do its worst; one thing I know—there's a grave somewhere for me. The world may go on just as it's always done, and take everything from me—loved ones, property, everything; but it can't take that. Some day I'll lie down in it and forget it all, and my poor broken heart will be at rest." He went on a-wiping.

"Drot your poor broken heart," says the baldhead; "what are you heaving your pore broken heart at *us* f'r? *We* hain't done nothing."

"No, I know you haven't. I ain't blaming you, gentlemen. I brought myself down—yes, I did it myself. It's right I should suffer—perfectly right—I don't make any moan."

"Brought you down from whar? Whar was you brought down from?"

"Ah, you would not believe me; the world never believes—let it pass—'tis no matter. The secret of my birth—"

"The secret of your birth! Do you mean to say—"

"Gentlemen," says the young man, very solemn, "I will reveal it to you, for I feel I may have confidence in you. By rights I am a duke!"

Jim's eyes bugged out when he heard that; and I reckon mine did, too. Then the baldhead says: "No! you can't mean it?"

"Yes. My great-grandfather, eldest son of the Duke of Bridgewater, fled to this country about the end of the last century, to breathe the pure air of freedom; married here, and died, leaving a son, his own father dying about the same time. The second son of the late duke seized the titles and estates—the infant real duke was ignored. I am the lineal descendant of that infant—I am the rightful Duke of Bridgewater; and here am I, forlorn, torn from my high estate, hunted of men, despised by the cold world, ragged, worn, heartbroken, and degraded to the companionship of felons on a raft!"

Jim pitied him ever so much, and so did I. We tried to comfort him, but he said it warn't much use, he couldn't be much comforted; said if we was a mind to acknowledge him, that would do him more good than most anything else; so we said we would, if he would tell us how. He said we ought to bow when we spoke to him, and say "Your Grace," or "My Lord," or "Your Lordship"—and he wouldn't mind it if we called him plain "Bridgewater," which, he said, was a title anyway, and not a name; and one of us ought to wait on him at dinner, and do any little thing for him he wanted done.

Well, that was all easy, so we done it. All through dinner Jim stood around and waited on him, and says, "Will yo' Grace have some o' dis or some o' dat?" and so on, and a body could see it was mighty pleasing to him.

But the old man got pretty silent by and by—didn't have much to say, and didn't look pretty comfortable over all that petting that was going on around that duke. He seemed to have something on his mind. So, along in the afternoon, he says:

"Looky here, Bilgewater," he says, "I'm nation sorry for you, but you ain't the only person that's had troubles like that."

"No?"

"No you ain't. You ain't the only person that's ben snaked down wrongfully out'n a high place."

"Alas!"

"No, you ain't the only person that's had a secret of his birth." And, by jings, *he* begins to cry.

"Hold! What do you mean?"

"Bilgewater, kin I trust you?" says the old man, still sort of sobbing.

"To the bitter death!" He took the old man by the hand and squeezed it, and says, "That secret of your being: speak!"

"Bilgewater, I am the late Dauphin!"

You bet you, Jim and me stared this time. Then the duke says:

"You are what?"

"Yes, my friend, it is too true—your eyes is lookin' at this very moment on the pore disappeared Dauphin, Looy the Seventeen, son of Looy the Sixteen and Marry Antonette."

"You! At your age! No! You mean you're the late Charlemagne; you must be six hundred years old."

"Trouble has done it, Bilgewater, trouble has done it; trouble has brung these gray hairs and this premature balditude. Yes, gentlemen, you see before you, in blue jeans and misery, the wanderin', exiled, trampled-on, and sufferin' rightful King of France."

Well, he cried and took on so that me and Jim didn't know hardly what to do, we was so sorry—and so glad and proud we'd got him with us, too. So we set in, like we done before with the duke, and tried to comfort *him*. But he said it warn't no use, nothing but to be dead and done with it all could do him any good; though he said it often made him feel easier and better for a while if people treated him according to his rights, and got down on one knee to speak to him, and always called him "Your Majesty," and waited on him first at meals, and didn't set down in his presence till he asked them. So Jim and me set to majestying him, and doing this and that and t'other for him, and standing up till he told us we might set down. This done him heaps of good, and so he got cheerful and comfortable. But the duke kind of soured on him, and didn't look a bit satisfied with the way things was going; still, the king acted real friendly towards him, and said the duke's great-grandfather and all the other Dukes of Bilgewater was a good deal thought of by *his* father, and was allowed to come to the palace considerable; but the duke stayed huffy a good while, till by and by the king says:

"Like as not we got to be together a blamed long time on this h-yer raft Bilgewater, and so what's the use o' your bein' sour? It 'll only make things oncomfortable. It ain't my fault I warn't born a duke, it ain't your fault you warn't born a king—so what's the use to worry? Make the best o' things the way you find 'em, says I—that's my motto. This ain't no bad thing that we've struck here—plenty grub and an easy life—come, give us your hand, duke, and le's all be friends."

The duke done it, and Jim and me was pretty glad to see it. It took away all the uncomfortableness and we felt mighty good over it, because it would 'a' been a miserable business to have any unfriendliness on the raft; for what you want, above all things, on a raft, is for everybody to be satisfied, and feel right and kind towards the others.

It didn't take me long to make up my mind that these liars warn't no kings nor dukes at all, but just lowdown humbugs and frauds. But I never said nothing, never let on; kept it to myself; it's the best way; then you don't have no quarrels, and don't get into no trouble. If they wanted us to call them kings and dukes, I hadn't no objections, 'long as it would keep peace in the family; and it warn't no use to tell Jim, so I didn't tell him. If I never learnt nothing else out of pap, I learnt that the best way to get along with his kind of people is to let them have their own way.

20 *Huck Explains—Laying Out a Campaign —Working the Camp-meeting—A Pirate at the Camp-meeting— The Duke as a Printer*

They asked us considerable many questions; wanted to know what we covered up the raft that way for, and laid by in the daytime instead of running—was Jim a runaway nigger? Says I:

"Goodness sakes! would a runaway nigger run *south?*"

No, they allowed he wouldn't. I had to account for things some way, so I says:

"My folks was living in Pike County, in Missouri, where I was born, and they all died off but me and pa and my brother Ike. Pa, he 'lowed he'd break up and go down and live with Uncle Ben, who's got a little one-horse place on the river forty-four mile below Orleans. Pa was pretty poor, and had some debts; so when he'd squared up there warn't nothing left but sixteen dollars and our nigger Jim. That warn't enough to take us fourteen hundred mile, deck passage nor no other way. Well, when the river rose pa had a streak of luck one day; he ketched this piece of a raft; so we reckoned we'd go down to Orleans on it. Pa's luck didn't hold out; a steamboat run over the forrard corner of the raft one night, and we all went overboard and dove under the wheel; Jim and me come up all right, but pa was drunk, and Ike was only four years old, so they never come up no more. Well, for the next day or two we had considerable trouble, because people was always coming out in skiffs and trying to take Jim away from me, saying they believed he was a runaway nigger. We don't run daytimes no more now; nights they don't bother us."

The duke says:

"Leave me alone to cipher out a way so we can run in the daytime if we want to. I'll think the thing over—I'll invent a plan that 'll fix it. We'll let it alone for to-day, because of course we don't want to go by that town yonder in daylight—it mightn't be healthy."

Towards night it begun to darken up and look like rain; the heat-lightning was squirting around low down in the sky, and the leaves was beginning to shiver—it was going to be pretty ugly, it was easy to see that. So the duke and the king went to overhauling our wigwam, to see what the beds was like. My bed was a straw tick—better than Jim's, which was a corn-shuck tick; there's always cobs around about in a shuck tick, and they poke into you and hurt; and when you roll over the dry shucks sound like you was rolling over in a pile of dead leaves; it makes such a rustling that you wake up. Well, the duke allowed he would take my bed; but the king allowed he wouldn't. He says:

"I should 'a' reckoned the difference in rank would a sejested to you that a corn-shuck bed warn't just fitten for me to sleep on. Your Grace 'll take the shuck bed yourself."

Jim and me was in a sweat again for a minute, being afraid there was going to be some more trouble amongst them; so we was pretty glad when the duke says:

" 'Tis my fate to be always ground into the mire under the iron heel of oppression. Misfortune has broken my once haughty spirit; I yield, I submit; 'tis my fate. I am alone in the world—let me suffer; I can bear it."

We got away as soon as it was good and dark. The king told us to stand well out towards the middle of the river, and not show a light till we got a long ways below the town. We come in sight of the little bunch of lights by and by—that was the town, you know—and slid by, about a half a mile out, all right. When we was three-quarters of a mile below we hoisted up our signal lantern; and about ten o'clock it come on to rain and blow and thunder and lighten like everything; so the king told us to both stay on watch till the weather got better; then him and the duke crawled into the wigwam and turned in for the night. It was my watch below till twelve, but I wouldn't 'a' turned in anyway if I'd had a bed, because a body don't see such a storm as that every day in the week, not by a long sight. My souls, how the wind did scream along! And every second or two there'd come a glare that lit up the white-caps for a half a mile around, and you'd see the islands looking dusty through the rain, and the trees thrashing around in the wind; then come a *h-whack!*—bum! bum! bumble-umble-um-bum-bum-bum-bum—and the thunder would go rumbling and grumbling away, and quit—and then *rip* comes another flash and another sock-dolager. The waves most washed me off the raft sometimes, but I hadn't any clothes on, and didn't mind. We didn't have no trouble about snags; the lightning was glaring and flittering around so constant that we could see them plenty soon enough to throw her head this way or that and miss them.

I had the middle watch, you know, but I was pretty sleepy by that time, so Jim he said he would stand the first half of it for me; he was always mighty good that way, Jim was. I crawled into the wigwam, but the king and the duke had their legs sprawled around so there warn't no show for me; so I laid outside—I didn't mind the rain, because it was warm, and the waves warn't running so high now. About two they come up again, though, and Jim was going to call me; but he changed his mind, because he reckoned they warn't high enough yet to do any harm; but he was mistaken about that, for pretty soon all of a sudden along comes a regular ripper and washed me overboard. It most killed Jim a-laughing. He was the easiest nigger to laugh that ever was, anyway.

I took the watch, and Jim he laid down and snored away; and by and by the storm let up for good and all; and the first cabin-light that showed I rousted him out, and we slid the raft into hiding-quarters for the day.

The king got out an old ratty deck of cards after breakfast, and him and the duke played seven-up awhile, five cents a game. Then they got tired of it, and allowed they would "lay out a campaign," as they called it. The duke went down into his carpet-bag, and fetched up a lot of little printed bills and read them out loud. One bill said, "The celebrated Dr. Armand de Montalban, of Paris," would "lecture on the Science of Phrenology" at such and such a place, on the blank day of blank, at ten cents admission, and "furnish charts of character at twenty-five cents apiece." The duke said that was *him*. In another bill he was the "world-renowned Shakespearian tragedian, Garrick the Younger, of Drury Lane, London." In other bills he had a lot of other names and done other wonderful things, like finding water and gold with a "divining-rod," dissipating witch spells," and so on. By and by he says:

"But the histrionic muse is the darling. Have you ever trod the boards, Royalty?"

"No," says the king.

"You shall, then, before you're three days older, Fallen Grandeur," says the duke. "The first good town we come to we'll hire a hall and do the swordfight in 'Richard III.' and the balcony scene in 'Romeo and Juliet.' How does that strike you?"

"I'm in, up to the hub, for anything that will pay, Bilgewater; but, you see, I don't know nothing about play-actin', and hain't ever seen much of it. I was too small when pap used to have 'em at the palace. Do you reckon you can learn me?"

"Easy!"

"All right. I'm jist a-freezin' for something fresh, anyway. Le's commence right away."

So the duke he told him all about who Romeo was and who Juliet was, and said he was used to being Romeo, so the king could be Juliet.

"But if Juliet's such a young gal, duke, my peeled head and my white whiskers is goin' to look oncommon odd on her, maybe."

"No, don't you worry; these country jakes won't ever think of that. Besides, you know, you'll be in costume, and that makes all the difference in the world; Juliet's in a balcony, enjoying the moonlight before she goes to bed, and she's got on her nightgown and her ruffled nightcap. Here are the costumes for the parts."

He got out two or three curtain-calico suits, which he said was meedyevil armor for Richard III. and t'other chap, and a long white cotton nightshirt and a ruffled nightcap to match. The king was satisfied; so the duke got out his book and read the parts over in the most splendid spread-eagle way, prancing around and acting at the same time, to show how it had got to be done; then he give the book to the king and told him to get his part by heart.

There was a little one-horse town about three miles down the bend, and after dinner the duke said he had ciphered out his idea about how to run in daylight without it being dangersome for Jim; so he allowed he would go down to the town and fix that thing. The king allowed he would go, too, and see if he couldn't strike something. We was out of coffee, so Jim said I better go along with them in the canoe and get some.

When we got there there warn't nobody stirring; streets empty, and perfectly dead and still, like Sunday. We found a sick nigger sunning himself in a back yard, and he said everybody that warn't too young or too sick or too old was gone to camp-meeting, about two mile back in the woods. The king got the directions, and allowed he'd go and work that camp-meeting for all it was worth, and I might go, too.

The duke said what he was after was a printing-office. We found it; a little bit of a concern, up over a carpenter-shop—carpenters and printers all gone to the meeting, and no doors locked. It was a dirty, littered-up place, and had ink-marks, and handbills with pictures of horses and runaway niggers on them, all over the walls. The duke shed his coat and said he was all right now. So me and the king lit out for the camp-meeting.

We got there in about a half an hour fairly dripping, for it was a most awful hot day. There was as much as a thousand people there from twenty mile around. The woods was full of teams and wagons, hitched everywheres, feeding out of the wagon-troughs and stomping to keep off the flies. There was sheds made out of poles and roofed over with branches, where they had lemonade and gingerbread to sell, and piles of watermelons and green corn and such-like truck.

The preaching was going on under the same kinds of sheds, only they was bigger and held crowds of people. The benches was made out of outside slabs of logs, with holes bored in the round side to drive sticks into for legs. They didn't have no backs. The preachers had high platforms to stand on at one end of the sheds. The women had on sun-bonnets; and some had linsey-woolsey frocks, some gingham ones, and a few of the young ones had on calico. Some of the young men was barefooted, and some of the children didn't have on any clothes but just a tow-linen shirt. Some of the old women was knitting, and some of the young folks was courting on the sly.

The first shed we come to the preacher was lining out a hymn. He lined out two lines, everybody sung it, and it was kind of grand to hear it, there was so many of them and they done it in such a rousing way; then he lined out two more for them to sing—and so on. The people woke up more and more, and sung louder and louder; and towards the end some begun to groan, and some begun to shout. Then the preacher begun to preach, and begun in earnest, too; and went weaving first to one side of the platform and then the other, and then a-leaning down over the front of it, with his arms and his body going all the time, and shouting his words out with all his might; and every now and then he would hold up his Bible and spread it open, and kind of pass it around this way and that, shouting, "It's the brazen serpent in the wilderness! Look upon it and live!" And people would shout out, "Glory—A-a-*men!*" And so he went on, and the people groaning and crying and saying amen:

"Oh, come to the mourners' bench! come, black with sin! (*amen!*) come, sick and sore! (*amen!*) come, lame and halt and blind! (*amen!*) come, pore and needy, sunk in shame! (*a-a-men!*) come, all that's worn and soiled and suffering!—come with a broken spirit! come with a contrite heart! come in your rags and sin and dirt! the waters that cleanse is free, the door of heaven stands open—oh, enter in and be at rest!" (*a-a-men! glory, glory hallelujah!*)

And so on. You couldn't make out what the preacher said any more, on account of the shouting and crying. Folks got up everywheres in the crowd, and worked their way just by main strength to the mourners' bench, with the tears running down their faces; and when all the mourners had got up there to the front benches in a crowd, they sung and shouted and flung themselves down on the straw, just crazy and wild.

Well, the first I knowed the king got a-going, and you could hear him over everybody; and next he went a-charging up onto the platform, and the preacher he begged him to speak to the people, and he done it. He told them he was a pirate—been a pirate for thirty years out in the Indian Ocean—and his crew was thinned out considerable last spring in a fight, and he was home now to take out some fresh men, and thanks to goodness he'd been robbed last night and put ashore off of a steamboat without a cent, and he was glad of it; it was the blessedest thing that ever happened to him, because he was a changed man now, and happy for the first time in his life; and, poor as he was, he was going to start right off and work his way back to the Indian Ocean, and put in the rest of his life trying to turn the pirates into the true path; for he could do it better than anybody else, being acquainted with all pirate crews in that ocean; and though it would take him a long time to get there without money, he would get there anyway, and every time he convinced a pirate he would say to him, "Don't you thank me, don't you give me no credit; it all belongs to them dear people in Pokeville camp-meeting, natural brothers and benefactors of the race, and that dear preacher there, the truest friend a pirate ever had!"

And then he busted into tears, and so did everybody. Then somebody sings out, "Take up a collection for him, take up a collection!" Well, a half a dozen made a jump to do it, but somebody sings out, "Let *him* pass the hat around!" Then everybody said it, the preacher too.

So the king went all through the crowd with his hat, swabbing his eyes, and blessing the people and praising them and thanking them for being so good to the poor pirates away off there; and every little while the prettiest kind of girls, with the tears running down their cheeks, would up and ask him would he let them kiss him for to remember him by; and he always done it; and some of them he hugged and kissed as many as five or six times—and he was invited to stay a week; and everybody wanted him to live in their houses, and said they'd think it was an honor; but he said as this was the last day of the camp-meeting he couldn't do no good, and besides he was in a sweat to get to the Indian Ocean right off and go to work on the pirates.

When we got back to the raft and he come to count up he found he had collected eighty-seven dollars and seventy-five cents. And then he had fetched away a three-gallon jug of whisky, too, that he found under a wagon when he was starting home through the woods. The king said, take it all around, it laid over any day he'd ever put in in the missionarying line. He said it warn't no use talking, heathens don't amount to shucks alongside of pirates to work a camp-meeting with.

The duke was thinking *he'd* been doing pretty well till the king come to show up, but after that he didn't think so so much. He had set up and printed off two little jobs for farmers in that printing-office—horse bills—and took the money, four dollars. And he had got in ten dollars' worth of advertisements for the paper, which he said he would put in for four dollars if they would pay in advance—so they done it. The price of the paper was two dollars a year, but he took in three subscriptions for half a dollar apiece on condition of them paying him in advance; they were going to pay in cordwood and onions as usual, but he said he had just bought the concern and knocked down the price as low as he could afford it, and was going to run it for cash. He set up a little piece of poetry, which he made, himself, out of his own head—three verses—kind of sweet and saddish—the name of it was, "Yes, crush, cold world, this breaking heart"—and he left that all set up and ready to print in the paper, and didn't charge nothing for it. Well, he took in nine dollars and a half, and said he'd done a pretty square day's work for it.

Then he showed us another little job he'd printed and hadn't charged for, because it was for us. It had a picture of a runaway nigger with a bundle on a stick over his shoulder, and "$200 reward" under it. The reading was all about Jim and just described him to a dot. It said he run away from St. Jacques's plantation, forty mile below New Orleans, last winter, and likely went north, and whoever would catch him and send him back he could have the reward and expenses.

"Now," says the duke, "after to-night we can run in the daytime if we want to. Whenever we see anybody coming we can tie Jim hand and foot with a rope, and lay him in the wigwam and show this handbill and say we captured him up the river, and were too poor to travel on a steamboat, so we got this little raft on credit from our friends and are going down to get the reward. Handcuffs and chains would look still better on Jim, but it wouldn't go well with the story of us being so poor. Too much like jewelry. Ropes are the correct thing—we must preserve the unities, as we say on the boards."

We all said the duke was pretty smart, and there couldn't be no trouble about running daytimes. We judged we could make miles enough that night to get out of the reach of the powwow we reckoned the duke's work in the printing-office was going to make in that little town; then we could boom right along if we wanted to.

We laid low and kept still, and never shoved out till nearly ten o'clock; then we slid by, pretty wide away from the town, and didn't hoist our lantern till we was clear out of sight of it.

When Jim called me to take the watch at four in the morning, he says:

"Huck, does you reck'n we gwyne to run acrost any mo' kings on dis trip?"

"No," I says, "I reckon not."

"Well," says he, "dat's all right, den. I doan' mine one er two kings, but dat's enough. Dis one's powerful drunk, en de duke ain' much better."

I found Jim had been trying to get him to talk French, so he could hear what it was like; but he said he had been in this country so long, and had so much trouble, he'd forgot it.

21 *Sword Exercise—Hamlet's Soliloquy—They Loafed Around Town—A Lazy Town—Old Boggs—Dead*

It was after sun-up now, but we went right on and didn't tie up. The king and the duke turned out by and by looking pretty rusty; but after they'd jumped overboard and took a swim it chippered them up a good deal. After breakfast the king he took a seat on the corner of the raft, and pulled off his boots and rolled up his britches, and let his legs dangle in the water, so as to be comfortable, and lit his pipe, and went to getting his "Romeo and Juliet" by heart. When he had got it pretty good him and the duke began to practise it together. The duke had to learn him over and over again how to say every speech; and he made him sigh, and put his hand on his heart, and after a while he said he done it pretty well; "only," he says, "you mustn't bellow out *Romeo!* that way, like a bull—you must say it soft and sick and languishy, so—*Ro-o-meo!* that is the idea; for Juliet's a dear sweet mere child of a girl, you know, and she doesn't bray like a jackass."

Well, next they got out a couple of long swords that the duke made out of oak laths, and begun to practise the sword-fight—the duke called himself Richard III.; and the way they laid on and pranced around the raft was grand to see. But by and by the king tripped and fell overboard and after that they took a rest, and had a talk about all kinds of adventures they'd had in other times along the river.

After dinner the duke says:

"Well, Capet, we'll want to make this a first-class show, you know, so I guess we'll add a little more to it. We want a little something to answer encores with, anyway."

"What's onkores, Bilgewater?"

The duke told him, and then says:

"I'll answer by doing the Highland fling or the sailor's hornpipe; and you—well, let me see—oh, I've got it—you can do Hamlet's soliloquy."

"Hamlet's which?"

"Hamlet's soliloquy, you know; the most celebrated thing in Shakespeare. Ah, it's sublime, sublime! Always fetches the house. I haven't got it in the book—I've only got one volume—but I reckon I can piece it out from memory. I'll just walk up and down a minute, and see if I can call it back from recollection's vaults."

So he went to marching up and down, thinking, and frowning horrible every now and then; then he would hoist up his eyebrows; next he would squeeze his hand on his forehead and stagger back and kind of moan; next he would sigh, and next he'd let on to drop a tear. It was beautiful to see him. By and by he got it. He told us to give attention. Then he strikes a most noble attitude, with one leg shoved forwards, and his arms stretched away up, and his head tilted back, looking up at the sky; and then he begins to rip and rave and grit his teeth; and after that, all through his speech, he howled, and spread around, and swelled up his chest, and just knocked the spots out of any acting ever *I* see before. This is the speech—I learned it, easy enough, while he was learning it to the king:

To be, or not to be; that is the bare bodkin
That makes calamity of so long life;
For who would fardels bear, till Birnam Wood do come to Dunsinane,
But that the fear of something after death
Murders the innocent sleep,
Great nature's second course,
And makes us rather sling the arrows of outrageous fortune
Than fly to others that we know not of.
There's the respect must give us pause:
Wake Duncan with thy knocking! I would thou couldst;

For who would bear the whips and scorns of time,
The oppressor's wrong, the proud man's contumely,
The law's delay, and the quietus which his pangs might take,
In the dead waste and middle of the night, when churchyards yawn
In customary suits of solemn black,
But that the undiscovered country from whose bourne no traveler
 returns,
Breathes forth contagion on the world,
And thus the native hue of resolution, like the poor cat i' the adage,
Is sicklied o'er with care,
And all the clouds that lowered o'er our housetops,
With this regard their currents turn awry,
And lose the name of action.
'Tis a consummation devoutly to be wished. But soft you, the fair
 Ophelia:
Ope not thy ponderous and marble jaws,
But get thee to a nunnery—go!

Well, the old man he liked that speech, and he mighty soon got it so he could do it first rate. It seemed like he was just born for it; and when he had his hand in and was excited, it was perfectly lovely the way he would rip and tear and rair up behind when he was getting it off.

The first chance we got the duke he had some showbills printed; and after that, for two or three days as we floated along, the raft was a most uncommon lively place, for there warn't nothing but sword-fighting and rehearsing—as the duke called it—going on all the time. One morning, when we was pretty well down the state of Arkansaw, we come in sight of a little one-horse town in a big bend; so we tied up about three-quarters of a mile above it, in the mouth of a crick which was shut in like a tunnel by the cypress trees, and all of us but Jim took the canoe and went down there to see if there was any chance in that place for our show.

We struck it mighty lucky; there was going to be a circus there that afternoon, and the country-people was already beginning to come in, in all kinds of old shackly wagons, and on horses. The circus would leave before night, so our show would have a pretty good chance. The duke he hired the court-house, and we went around and stuck up our bills. They read like this:

Shaksperean Revival ! ! !
Wonderful Attraction!
For One Night Only!
The world renowned tragedians,
David Garrick the younger, of Drury Lane Theatre, London,
and
Edmund Kean the elder, of the Royal Haymarket
Theatre, Whitechapel, Pudding Lane, Piccadilly,
London, and the Royal Continental
Theatres, in their sublime
Shaksperean Spectacle entitled
The Balcony Scene
in
Romeo and Juliet ! ! !

Romeo .... Mr. Garrick
Juliet .... Mr. Kean

Assisted by the whole strength of the company!
New costumes, new scenery, new appointments!
Also:
The thrilling, masterly, and blood-curdling
Broad-sword conflict
In Richard III. ! ! !

Richard III .... Mr. Garrick
Richmond .... Mr. Kean

Also:
(by special request)
Hamlet's Immortal Soliloquy ! !
By the Illustrious Kean!
Done by him 300 consecutive nights in Paris!
For One Night Only,
On account of imperative European engagements!
Admission 25 cents; children and servants, 10 cents.

Then we went loafing around town. The stores and houses was most all old, shackly, dried-up frame concerns that hadn't ever been painted; they was set up three or four feet above ground on stilts, so as to be out of reach of the water when the river was overflowed. The houses had little gardens around them, but they didn't seem to raise hardly anything in them but jimpson-weeds and sunflowers, and ash-piles, and old curled-up boots and shoes, and pieces of bottles, and rags, and played-out tinware. The fences was made of different kinds of boards, nailed on at different times; and they leaned every which way, and had gates that didn't generly have but one hinge—a leather one. Some of the fences had been whitewashed some time or another, but the duke said it was in Columbus's time, like enough. There was generly hogs in the garden, and people driving them out.

All the stores was along one street. They had white domestic awnings in front, and the country-people hitched their horses to the awning-posts. There was empty dry-goods boxes under the awnings, and loafers roosting on them all day long, whittling them with their Barlow knives; and chawing tobacco, and gaping and yawning and stretching—a mighty ornery lot. They generly had on yellow straw hats most as wide as an umbrella, but didn't wear no coats nor waistcoats; they called one another Bill, and Buck, and Hank, and Joe, and Andy, and talked lazy and drawly, and used considerable many cuss-words. There was as many as one loafer leaning up against every awning-post, and he most always had his hands in his britches pockets, except when he fetched them out to lend a chaw of tobacco or scratch. What a body was hearing amongst them all the time was:

"Gimme a chaw 'v tobacker, Hank."

"Cain't; I hain't got but one chaw left. Ask Bill."

Maybe Bill he gives him a chaw; maybe he lies and says he ain't got none. Some of them kinds of loafers never has a cent in the world, nor a chaw of tobacco of their own. They get all their chawing by borrowing; they say to a fellow, "I wisht you'd len' me a chaw, Jack, I jist this minute give Ben Thompson the last chaw I had"—which is a lie pretty much every time; it don't fool nobody but a stranger; but Jack ain't no stranger, so he says:

"*You* give him a chaw, did you? So did your sister's cat's grandmother. You pay me back the chaws you've awready borry'd off'n me, Lafe Buckner, then I'll loan you one or two ton of it, and won't charge you no back intrust, nuther."

"Well, I *did* pay you back some of it wunst."

"Yes, you did—'bout six chaws. You borry'd store tobacker and paid back nigger-head."

Store tobacco is flat black plug, but these fellows mostly chaws the natural leaf twisted. When they borrow a chaw they don't generly cut it off with a knife, but set the plug in between their teeth, and gnaw with their teeth and tug at the plug with their hands till they get it in two; then sometimes the one that owns the tobacco looks mournful at it when it's handed back, and says, sarcastic:

"Here, gimme the *chaw*, and you take the *plug*."

All the streets and lanes was just mud; they warn't nothing else *but* mud—mud as black as tar and nigh about a foot deep in some places, and two or three inches deep in *all* the places. The hogs loafed and grunted around everywheres. You'd see a muddy sow and a litter of pigs come lazying along the street and whollop herself right down in the way, where folks had to walk around her, and she'd stretch out and shut her eyes and wave her ears whilst the pigs was milking her, and look as happy as if she was on salary. And pretty soon you'd hear a loafer sing out, "Hi! *so* boy; sick him, Tige!" and away the sow would go, squealing most horrible, with a dog or two swinging to each ear, and three or four dozen more a-coming; and then you would see all the loafers get up and watch the thing out of sight, and laugh at the fun and look grateful for the noise. Then they'd settle back again till there was a dog-fight. There couldn't anything wake them up all over, and make them happy all over, like a dog-fight—unless it might be putting turpentine on a stray dog and setting fire to him, or tying a tin pan to his tail and see him run himself to death.

On the river-front some of the houses was sticking out over the bank, and they was bowed and bent, and about ready to tumble in. The people had moved out of them. The bank was caved away under one corner of some others, and that corner was hanging over. People lived in them yet, but it was dangersome, because sometimes a strip of land as wide as a house caves in at a time. Sometimes a belt of land a quarter of a mile deep will start in and cave along and cave along till it all caves into the river in one summer. Such a town as that has to be always moving back, and back, and back, because the river's always gnawing at it.

The nearer it got to noon that day the thicker and thicker was the wagons and horses in the streets, and more coming all the time. Families fetched their dinners with them from the country, and eat them in the wagons. There was considerable whisky-drinking going on, and I seen three fights. By and by somebody sings out:

"Here comes old Boggs!—in from the country for his little old monthly drunk; here he comes, boys!"

All the loafers looked glad; I reckoned they was used to having fun out of Boggs. One of them says:

"Wonder who he's a-gwyne to chaw up this time. If he'd a-chawed up all the men he's ben a-gwyne to chaw up in the last twenty year he'd have considerable ruputation now."

Another one says, "I wisht old Boggs 'd threaten me, 'cuz then I'd know I warn't gwyne to die for a thousan' year."

Boggs comes a-tearing along on his horse, whooping and yelling like an Injun, and singing out:

"Cler the track, thar. I'm on the waw-path, and the price uv coffins is a-gwyne to raise."

He was drunk, and weaving about in his saddle; he was over fifty year old, and had a very red face. Everybody yelled at him and laughed at him and sassed him, and he sassed back, and said he'd attend to them and lay them out in their regular turns, but he couldn't wait now because he'd come to town to kill old Colonel Sherburn, and his motto was, "Meat first, and spoon vittles to top off on."

He see me, and rode up and says:

"Whar'd you come f'm, boy? You prepared to die?"

Then he rode on. I was scared, but a man says:

"He don't mean nothing; he's always a-carryin' on like that when he's drunk. He's the best-naturedest old fool in Arkansaw—never hurt nobody, drunk nor sober."

Boggs rode up before the biggest store in town, and bent his head down so he could see under the curtain of the awning and yells:

"Come out here, Sherburn! Come out and meet the man you've swindled. You're the houn' I'm after, and I'm a-gwyne to have you, too!"

And so he went on, calling Sherburn everything he could lay his tongue to, and the whole street packed with people listening and laughing and going on. By and by a proud-looking man about fifty-five—and he was a heap the best-dressed man in that town, too—steps out of the store, and the crowd drops back on each side to let him come. He says to Boggs, mighty ca'm and slow—he says:

"I'm tired of this, but I'll endure it till one o'clock. Till one o'clock, mind—no longer. If you open your mouth against me only once after that time you can't travel so far but I will find you."

Then he turns and goes in. The crowd looked mighty sober; nobody stirred, and there warn't no more laughing. Boggs rode off blackguarding Sherburn as loud as he could yell, all down the street; and pretty soon back he comes and stops before the store, still keeping it up. Some men crowded around him and tried to get him to shut up, but he wouldn't; they told him it would be one o'clock in about fifteen minutes, and so he *must* go home—he must go right away. But it didn't do no good. He cussed away with all his might, and throwed his hat down in the mud and rode over it, and pretty soon away he went a-raging down the street again, with his gray hair a-flying. Everybody that could get a chance at him tried their best to coax him off of his horse so they could lock him up and get him sober; but it warn't no use—up the street he would tear again, and give Sherburn another cussing. By and by somebody says:

"Go for his daughter!—quick, go for his daughter; sometimes he'll listen to her. If anybody can persuade him, she can."

So somebody started on a run. I walked down street a ways and stopped. In about five or ten minutes here comes Boggs again, but not on his horse. He was a-reeling across the street towards me, bareheaded, with a friend on both sides of him a-holt of his arms and hurrying him along. He was quiet, and looked uneasy; and he warn't hanging back any, but was doing some of the hurrying himself. Somebody sings out:

"Boggs!"

I looked over there to see who said it, and it was that Colonel Sherburn. He was standing perfectly still in the street, and had a pistol raised in his right hand—not aiming it, but holding it out with the barrel tilted up towards the sky. The same second I see a young girl coming on the run, and two men with her. Boggs and the men turned round to see who called him, and when they see the pistol the men jumped to one side, and the pistol-barrel come down slow and steady to a level—both barrels cocked. Boggs throws up both of his hands and says, "O Lord, don't shoot!" Bang! goes the first shot, and he staggers back, clawing at the air—bang! goes the second one, and he tumbles backwards onto the ground, heavy and solid, with his arms spread out. That young girl screamed out and comes rushing, and down she throws herself on her father, crying, and saying, "Oh, he's killed him, he's killed him!" The crowd closed up around them, and shouldered and jammed one another, with their necks stretched, trying to see, and people on the inside trying to shove them back and shouting, "Back, back! give him air, give him air!"

Colonel Sherburn he tossed his pistol onto the ground, and turned around on his heels and walked off.

They took Boggs to a little drug store, the crowd pressing around just the same, and the whole town following, and I rushed and got a good place at the window, where I was close to him and could see in. They laid him on the floor and put one large Bible under his head, and opened another one and spread it on his breast; but they tore open his shirt first, and I seen where one of the bullets went in. He made about a dozen long gasps, his breast lifting the Bible up when he drawed in his breath, and letting it down again when he breathed it out—and after that he laid still; he was dead. Then they pulled his daughter away from him, screaming and crying, and took her off. She was about sixteen, and very sweet and gentle looking, but awful pale and scared.

Well, pretty soon the whole town was there, squirming and scrouging and pushing and shoving to get at the window and have a look, but people that had the places wouldn't give them up, and folks behind them was saying all the time, "Say, now, you've looked enough, you fellows; 'tain't right and 'tain't fair for you to stay thar all the time, and never give nobody a chance; other folks has their rights as well as you."

There was considerable jawing back, so I slid out, thinking maybe there was going to be trouble. The streets was full, and everybody was excited. Everybody that seen the shooting was telling how it happened, and there was a big crowd packed around each one of these fellows, stretching their necks and listening. One long, lanky man, with long hair and a big white fur stovepipe hat on the back of his head, and a crooked-handled cane, marked out the places on the ground where Boggs stood and where Sherburn stood, and the people following him around from one place to t'other and watching everything he done, and bobbing their heads to show they understood, and stooping a little and resting their hands on their thighs to watch him mark the places on the ground with his cane; and then he stood up straight and stiff where Sherburn had stood, frowning and having his hat-brim down over his eyes, and sung out, "Boggs!" and then fetched his cane down slow to a level, and says "Bang!" staggered backwards, says "Bang!" again, and fell down flat on his back. The people that had seen the thing said he done it perfect; said it was just exactly the way it all happened. Then as much as a dozen people got out their bottles and treated him.

Well, by and by somebody said Sherburn ought to be lynched. In about a minute everybody was saying it; so away they went, mad and yelling, and snatching down every clothes-line they come to do the hanging with.

22 *Sherburn—Attending the Circus—Intoxication in the Ring—The Thrilling Tragedy*

They swarmed up towards Sherburn's house, a-whooping and raging like Injuns, and everything had to clear the way or get run over and tromped to mush, and it was awful to see. Children was heeling it ahead of the mob, screaming and trying to get out of the way; and every window along the road was full of women's heads, and there was nigger boys in every tree, and bucks and wenches looking over every fence; and as soon as the mob would get nearly to them they would break and skaddle back out of reach. Lots of the women and girls was crying and taking on, scared most to death.

They swarmed up in front of Sherburn's palings as thick as they could jam together, and you couldn't hear yourself think for the noise. It was a little twenty-foot yard. Some sung out "Tear down the fence! tear down the fence!" Then there was a racket of ripping and tearing and smashing, and down she goes, and the front wall of the crowd begins to roll in like a wave.

Just then Sherburn steps out onto the roof of his little front porch, with a double-barrel gun in his hand, and takes his stand, perfectly ca'm and deliberate, not saying a word. The racket stopped, and the wave sucked back.

Sherburn never said a word—just stood there, looking down. The stillness was awful creepy and uncomfortable. Sherburn run his eye slow along the crowd; and wherever it struck the people tried a little to outgaze him, but they couldn't; they dropped their eyes and looked sneaky. Then pretty soon Sherburn sort of laughed; not the pleasant kind, but the kind that makes you feel like you're eating bread with sand in it.

Then he says, slow and scornful:

"The idea of *you* lynching anybody! It's amusing. The idea of you thinking you had pluck enough to lynch a *man!* Because you're brave enough to tar and feather poor friendless cast-out women that come along here, did that make you think you had grit enough to lay your hands on a *man?* Why, a *man's* safe in the hands of ten thousand of your kind—as long as it's daytime and you're not behind him.

"Do I know you? I know you clear through. I was born and raised in the South, and I've lived in the North; so I know the average all around. The average man's a coward. In the North he lets anybody walk over him that wants to, and goes home and prays for a humble spirit to bear it. In the South one man, all by himself, has stopped a stage full of men in the daytime, and robbed the lot. Your newspapers call you a brave people so much that you think you *are* braver than other people—whereas you're just *as* brave, and no braver. Why don't your juries hang murderers? Because they're afraid the man's friends will shoot them in the back, in the dark—and it's just what they *would* do.

"So they always acquit; and then a *man* goes in the night, with a hundred masked cowards at his back, and lynches the rascal. Your mistake is, that you didn't bring a man with you; that's one mistake, and the other is that you didn't come in the dark and fetch your masks. You brought *part* of a man—Buck Harkness, there—and if you hadn't had him to start you, you'd 'a' taken it out in blowing.

"You didn't want to come. The average man don't like trouble and danger. *You* don't like trouble and danger. But if only *half* a man—like Buck Harkness, there—shouts 'Lynch him! lynch him!' you're afraid to back down—afraid you'll be found out to be what you are—*cowards*—and so you raise a yell, and hang yourselves onto that half-a-man's coat-tail, and come raging up here, swearing what big things you're going to do. The pitifulest thing out is a mob; that's what an army is—a mob; they don't fight with courage that's born in them, but with courage that's borrowed from their mass, and from their officers. But a mob without any *man* at the head of it is *beneath* pitifulness. Now the thing for *you* to do is to droop your tails and go home and crawl in a hole. If any real lynching's going to be done it will be done in the dark, Southern fashion; and when they come they'll bring their masks, and fetch a *man* along. Now *leave*—and take your half-a-man with you"—tossing his gun up across his left arm and cocking it when he says this.

The crowd washed back sudden, and then broke all apart, and went tearing off every which way, and Buck Harkness he heeled it after them, looking tolerable cheap. I could 'a' stayed if I wanted to, but I didn't want to.

I went to the circus and loafed around the back side till the watchman went by, and then dived in under the tent. I had my twenty-dollar gold piece and some other money, but I reckoned I better save it, because there ain't no telling how soon you are going to need it, away from home and amongst strangers that way. You can't be too careful. I ain't opposed to spending money on circuses when there ain't no other way, but there ain't no use in *wasting* it on them.

It was a real bully circus. It was the splendidest sight that ever was when they all come riding in, two and two, and gentleman and lady, side by side, the men just in their drawers and undershirts, and no shoes nor stirrups, and resting their hands on their thighs easy and comfortable—there must 'a' been twenty of them—and every lady with a lovely complexion, and perfectly beautiful, and looking just like a gang of real sure-enough queens, and dressed in clothes that cost millions of dollars, and just littered with diamonds. It was a powerful fine sight; I never see anything so lovely. And then one by one they got up and stood, and went a-weaving around the ring so gentle and wavy and graceful, the men looking ever so tall and airy and straight, with their heads bobbing and skimming along, away up there under the tent-roof, and every lady's rose-leafy dress flapping soft and silky around her hips, and she looking like the most loveliest parasol.

And then faster and faster they went, all of them, dancing, first one foot out in the air and then the other, the horses leaning more and more, and the ringmaster going round and round the center pole, cracking his whip and shouting "Hi!—hi!" and the clown cracking jokes behind him; and by and by all hands dropped the reins, and every lady put her knuckles on her hips and every gentleman folded his arms, and then how the horses did lean over and hump themselves! And so one after the other they all skipped off into the ring, and made the sweetest bow I ever see, and then scampered out, and everybody clapped their hands and went just about wild.

Well, all through the circus they done the most astonishing things; and all the time that clown carried on so it most killed the people. The ringmaster couldn't ever say a word to him but he was back at him quick as a wink with the funniest things a body ever said; and how he ever *could* think of so many of them, and so sudden and so pat, was what I couldn't no way understand. Why, I couldn't 'a' thought of them in a year. And by and by a drunken man tried to get into the ring—said he wanted to ride; said he could ride as well as anybody that ever was. They argued and tried to keep him out, but he wouldn't listen, and the whole show come to a standstill. Then the people begun to holler at him and make fun of him, and that made him mad, and he begun to rip and tear; so that stirred up the people, and a lot of men begun to pile down off the benches and swarm toward the ring, saying, "Knock him down! throw him out!" and one or two women begun to scream. So, then, the ringmaster he made a little speech, and said he hoped there wouldn't be no disturbance, and if the man would promise he wouldn't make no more trouble he would let him ride if he thought he could stay on the horse. So everybody laughed and said all right, and the man got on. The minute he was on, the horse begun to rip and tear and jump and cavort around with two circus men hanging on his bridle trying to hold him, and the drunken man hanging on to his neck, and his heels flying in the air every jump, and the whole crowd of people standing up shouting and laughing till tears rolled down. And at last, sure enough, all the circus men could do, the horse broke loose, and away he went like the very nation, round and round the ring, with that sot laying down on him and hanging to his neck, with first one leg hanging most to the ground on one side, and then t'other one on t'other side, and the people just crazy. It warn't funny to me, though; I was all of a tremble to see his danger. But pretty soon he struggled up astraddle and grabbed the bridle, a-reeling this way and that; and the next minute he sprung up and dropped the bridle and stood! and the horse a-going like a house afire, too. He just stood up there, a-sailing around as easy and comfortable as if he warn't ever drunk in his life—and then he begun to pull off his clothes and sling them. He shed them so thick they kind of clogged up the air, and altogether he shed seventeen suits. And, then, there he was, slim and handsome, and dressed the gaudiest and prettiest you ever saw, and he lit into that horse with his whip and made him fairly hum—and finally skipped off, and made his bow and danced off to the dressing-room, and everybody just a-howling with pleasure and astonishment.

Then the ringmaster he see how he had been fooled, and he *was* the slickest ringmaster you ever see, I reckon. Why, it was one of his own men? He had got up that joke all out of his own head, and never let on to nobody. Well, I felt sheepish enough to be took in so, but I wouldn't 'a' been in that ringmaster's place, not for a thousand dollars. I don't know; there may be bullier circuses than what that one was, but I never struck them yet. Anyways, it was plenty good enough for *me;* and wherever I run across it, it can have all of *my* custom every time.

Well, that night we had *our* show; but there warn't only about twelve people there—just enough to pay expenses. And they laughed all the time, and that made the duke mad; and everybody left, anyway, before the show was over, but one boy which was asleep. So the duke said these Arkansaw lunkheads couldn't come up to Shakespeare; what they wanted was low comedy—and maybe something ruther worse than low comedy, he reckoned. He said he could size their style. So next morning he got some big sheets of wrapping-paper and some black paint, and drawed off some handbills, and stuck them up all over the village. The bills said:

AT THE COURT HOUSE!
FOR 3 NIGHTS ONLY!
The World-Renowned Tragedians
DAVID GARRICK THE YOUNGER!
AND
EDMUND KEAN THE ELDER!
Of the London and Continental Theatres
In their Thrilling Tragedy of
THE KING'S CAMELEOPARD
OR
THE ROYAL NONESUCH ! ! !
Admission 50 cents.

Then at the bottom was the biggest line of all:

LADIES AND CHILDREN NOT ADMITTED

"There," says he, "if that line don't fetch them, I don't know Arkansaw!"

23 *Sold—Royal Comparisons— Jim Gets Homesick*

Well, all day him and the king was hard at it, rigging up a stage and a curtain and a row of candles for footlights; and that night the house was jam full of men in no time. When the place couldn't hold no more, the duke he quit tending the door and went around the back way and come onto the stage and stood up before the curtain and made a little speech, and praised up this tragedy, and said it was the most thrillingest one that ever was; and so he went on a-bragging about the tragedy, and about Edmund Kean the Elder, which was to play the main principal part in it; and at last when he'd got everybody's expectations up high enough, he rolled up the curtain, and the next minute the king come a-prancing out on all fours, naked; and he was painted all over, ring-streaked-and-striped, all sorts of colors, as splendid as a rainbow. And—but never mind the rest of his outfit; it was just wild, but it was awful funny. The people most killed themselves laughing; and when the king got done capering and capered off behind the scenes, they roared and clapped and stormed and haw-hawed till he come back and done it over again, and after that they made him do it another time. Well, it would make a cow laugh to see the shines that old idiot cut.

Then the duke he lets the curtain down, and bows to the people, and says the great tragedy will be performed only two nights more, on accounts of pressing London engagements, where the seats is all sold already for it in Drury Lane; and then he makes them another bow, and says if he has succeeded in pleasing them and instructing them, he will be deeply obleeged if they will mention it to their friends and get them to come and see it.

Twenty people sings out:

"What, is it over? Is that *all?*"

The duke says yes. Then there was a fine time. Everybody sings out, "Sold!" and rose up mad, and was a-going for that stage and them tragedians. But a big, fine-looking man jumps up on a bench and shouts:

"Hold on! Just a word, gentlemen." They stopped to listen. "We are sold—mighty badly sold. But we don't want to be the laughing-stock of this whole town, I reckon, and never hear the last of this thing as long as we live. *No*. What we want is to go out of here quiet, and talk this show up, and sell the *rest* of the town! Then we'll all be in the same boat. Ain't that sensible?" ("You bet it is!—the jedge is right!" everybody sings out.) "All right, then—not a word about any sell. Go along home, and advise everybody to come and see the tragedy."

Next day you couldn't hear nothing around that town but how splendid that show was. House was jammed again that night, and we sold this crowd the same way. When me and the king and the duke got home to the raft we all had a supper; and by and by, about midnight, they made Jim and me back her out and float her down the middle of the river, and fetch her in and hide her about two mile below town.

The third night the house was crammed again—and they warn't new-comers this time, but people that was at the show the other two nights. I stood by the duke at the door, and I see that every man that went in had his pockets bulging, or something muffled up under his coat—and I see it warn't no perfumery, neither, not by a long sight. I smelt sickly eggs by the barrel, and rotten cabbages, and such things; and if I know the signs of a dead cat being around, and I bet I do, there was sixty-four of them went in. I shoved in there for a minute, but it was too various for me; I couldn't stand it. Well, when the place couldn't hold no more people the duke he give a fellow a quarter and told him to tend door for him a minute, and then he started around for the stage door, I after him; but the minute we turned the corner and was in the dark he says:

"Walk fast now till you get away from the houses, and then shin for the raft like the dickens was after you!"

I done it, and he done the same. We struck the raft at the same time, and in less than two seconds we was gliding down-stream, all dark and still, and edging towards the middle of the river, nobody saying a word. I reckoned the poor king was in for a gaudy time of it with the audience, but nothing of the sort; pretty soon he crawls out from under the wigwam, and says:

"Well, how'd the old thing pan out this time, duke?" He hadn't been up-town at all.

We never showed a light till we was about ten mile below the village. Then we lit up and had a supper, and the king and the duke fairly laughed their bones loose over the way they'd served them people. The duke says:

"Greenhorns, flatheads! *I* knew the first house would keep mum and let the rest of the town get roped in; and I knew they'd lay for us the third night, and consider it was *their* turn now. Well, it *is* their turn, and I'd give something to know how much they'd take for it. I *would* just like to know how they're putting in their opportunity. They can turn it into a picnic if they want to—they brought plenty provisions."

Them rapscallions took in four hundred and sixty-five dollars in that three nights. I never see money hauled in by the wagon-load like that before.

By and by, when they was asleep and snoring, Jim says:

"Don't it s'prise you de way dem kings carries on, Huck?"

"No," I says, "it don't."

"Why don't it, Huck?"

"Well, it don't, because it's in the breed. I reckon they're all alike."

"But, Huck, dese kings o' ourn is rapscallions dat's jist what dey is; dey's reglar rapscallions."

"Well, that's what I'm a-saying; all kings is mostly rapscallions, as fur as I can make out."

"Is dat so?"

"You read about them once—you'll see. Look at Henry the Eight; this 'n' 's a Sunday-school Superintendent to *him*. And look at Charles Second, and Louis Fourteen, and Louis Fifteen, and James Second, and Edward Second and Richard Third, and forty more; besides all them Saxon heptarchies that used to rip around so in old times and raise Cain. My, you ought to seen old Henry the Eight when he was in bloom. He *was* a blossom. He used to marry a new wife every day, and chop off her head next morning. And he would do it just as indifferent as if he was ordering up eggs. 'Fetch up Nell Gwynn,' he says. They fetch her up. Next morning, 'Chop off her head!' And they chop it off. 'Fetch up Jane Shore,' he says; and up she comes. Next morning, 'Chop off her head'—and they chop it off. 'Ring up Fair Rosamun.' Fair Rosamun answers the bell. Next morning, 'Chop off her head.' And he made every one of them tell him a tale every night; and he kept that up till he had hogged a thousand and one tales that way and then he put them all in a book, and called it Domesday Book—which was a good name and stated the case. You don't know kings, Jim, but I know them; and this old rip of ourn is one of the cleanest I've struck in history. Well, Henry he takes a notion he wants to get up some trouble with his country. How does he go at it—give notice?—give the country a show? No. All of a sudden he heaves all the tea in Boston Harbor overboard, and whacks out a declaration of independence, and dares them to come on. That was *his* style—he never give anybody a chance. He had suspicions of his father, the Duke of Wellington. Well, what did he do? Ask him to show up? No—drownded him in a butt of mamsey, like a cat. S'pose people left money laying around where he was—what did he do? He collared it. S'pose he contracted to do a thing, and you paid him, and didn't set down there and see that he done it—what did he do? He always done the other thing. S'pose he opened his mouth—what then? If he didn't shut it up powerful quick he'd lose a lie every time. That's the kind of a bug Henry was; and if we'd 'a' had him along 'stead of our king he'd 'a' fooled that town a heap worse than ourn done. I don't say that ourn is lambs, because they ain't, when you come right down to the cold facts; but they ain't nothing to *that* old ram, anyway. All I say is, kings is kings, and you got to make allowances. Take them all around, they're a mighty ornery lot. It's the way they're raised."

"But dis one do *smell* so like de nation, Huck."

"Well, they all do, Jim. *We* can't help the way a king smells; history don't tell no way."

"Now de duke, he's a tolerble likely man in some ways."

"Yes, a duke's different. But not very different. This one's a middling hard lot for a duke. When he's drunk there ain't no near-sighted man could tell him from a king."

"Well, anyways, I doan' hanker for no mo' un um, Huck. Dese is all I kin stan'."

"It's the way I feel, too, Jim. But we've got them on our hands, and we got to remember what they are, and make allowances. Sometimes I wish we could hear of a country that's out of kings."

What was the use to tell Jim these warn't real kings and dukes? It wouldn't 'a' done no good; and, besides, you couldn't tell them from the real kind.

I went to sleep, and Jim didn't call me when it was my turn. He often done that. When I waked up just at daybreak, he was sitting there with his head down betwixt his knees, moaning and mourning to himself. I didn't take notice nor let on. I knowed what it was about. He was thinking about his wife and his children, away up yonder, and he was low and homesick; because he hadn't ever been away from home before in his life; and I do believe he cared just as much for his people as white folks does for their'n. It don't seem natural, but I reckon it's so. He was often moaning and mourning that way nights, when he judged I was asleep, and saying, 'Po' little Lizabeth! po' little Johnny! it's mighty hard; I spec' I ain't ever gwyne to see you no mo', no mo'!" He was a mighty good nigger, Jim was.

But this time I somehow got to talking to him about his wife and young ones; and by and by he says:

"What makes me feel so bad dis time 'uz bekase I hear sumpn over yonder on de bank like a whack, er a slam, while ago, en it mine me er de time I treat my little 'Lizabeth so ornery. She warn't on'y 'bout fo' year ole, en she tuck de sk'yarlet fever, en had a powerful rough spell; but she got well, en one day she was a-stannin' aroun', en I says to her, I says:

" 'Shet de do'.'

"She never done it; jis' stood dah, kiner smilin' up at me. It make me mad; en I says ag'in, mighty loud, I says:

" 'Doan' you hear me? Shet de do'!'

"She jis' stood de same way, kiner smilin' up. I was a-bilin'! I says:

" 'I lay I *make* you mine!'

"En wid dat I fetch' her a slap side de head dat sont her a-sprawlin'. Den I went into de yuther room, en 'uz gone 'bout ten minutes; en when I come back dah was dat do' a-stannin' open *yit*, en dat chile stannin' mos' right in it, a-lookin' down and mournin', en de tears runnin' down. My, but I *wuz* mad! I was a-gwyne for de chile, but jis' den—it was a do' dat open inners—jis' den, 'long come de wind en slam it to, behine de chile, ker-*blam!*—en my lan', de chile never move'! My breff mos' hop outer me; en I feel so—so—I doan' know *how* I feel. I crope out, all a-tremblin', en crope aroun' en open de do' easy en slow, en poke my head in behine de chile, sof' en still, en all uv a sudden I says *pow!* jis' as loud as I could yell. *She never budge!* Oh, Huck, I bust out a-cryin' en grab her up in my arms, en say, 'Oh, de po' little thing! De Lord God Amighty fogive po' ole Jim, kaze he never gwyne to fogive hisself as long's he live!' Oh, she was plumb deef en dumb, Huck, plumb deef en dumb—en I'd ben a-treat'n her so!"

24 *Jim in Royal Robes—They Take a Passenger—Getting Information—Family Grief*

Next day, towards night, we laid up under a little willow towhead out in the middle, where there was a village on each side of the river, and the duke and the king begun to lay out a plan for working them towns. Jim he spoke to the duke, and said he hoped it wouldn't take but a few hours, because it got mighty heavy and tiresome to him when he had to lay all day in the wigwam tied with the rope. You see, when we left him all alone we had to tie him, because if anybody happened on to him all by himself and not tied it wouldn't look much like he was a runaway nigger, you know. So the duke said it *was* kind of hard to have to lay roped all day, and he'd cipher out some way to get around it.

He was uncommon bright, the duke was, and he soon struck it. He dressed Jim up in King Lear's outfit—it was a long curtain-calico gown, and a white horse-hair wig and whiskers; and then he took his theater paint and painted Jim's face and hands and ears and neck all over a dead, dull solid blue, like a man that's been drownded nine days. Blamed if he warn't the horriblest-looking outrage I ever see. Then the duke took and wrote out a sign on a shingle so:

Sick Arab—but harmless when not out of his head.

And he nailed that shingle to a lath, and stood the lath up four or five foot in front of the wigwam. Jim was satisfied. He said it was a sight better than lying tied a couple of years every day, and trembling all over every time there was a sound. The duke told him to make himself free and easy, and if anybody ever come meddling around, he must hop out of the wigwam, and carry on a little, and fetch a howl or two like a wild beast, and he reckoned they would light out and leave him alone. Which was sound enough judgment; but you take the average man, and he wouldn't wait for him to howl. Why, he didn't only look like he was dead, he looked considerable more than that.

These rapscallions wanted to try the Nonesuch again, because there was so much money in it, but they judged it wouldn't be safe, because maybe the news might 'a' worked along down by this time. They couldn't hit no project that suited exactly; so at last the duke said he reckoned he'd lay off and work his brains an hour or two and see if he couldn't put up something on the Arkansaw village; and the king he allowed he would drop over to t'other village without any plan, but just trust in Providence to lead him the profitable way—meaning the devil, I reckon. We had all bought store clothes where we stopped last; and now the king put his'n on, and he told me to put mine on. I done it, of course. The king's duds was all black, and he did look real swell and starchy. I never knowed how clothes could change a body before. Why, before, he looked like the orneriest old rip that ever was; but now, when he'd take off his new white beaver and make a bow and do a smile, he looked that grand and good and pious that you'd say he had walked right out of the ark, and maybe was old Leviticus himself. Jim cleaned up the canoe, and I got my paddle ready. There was a big steamboat laying at the shore away up under the point, about three mile above the town—been there a couple of hours, taking on freight. Says the king:

"Seein' how I'm dressed, I reckon maybe I better arrive down from St. Louis or Cincinnati, or some other big place. Go for the steamboat, Huckleberry; we'll come down to the village on her."

I didn't have to be ordered twice to go and take a steamboat ride. I fetched the shore a half a mile above the village, and then went scooting along the bluff bank in the easy water. Pretty soon we come to a nice innocent-looking young country jake setting on a log swabbing the sweat off of his face, for it was powerful warm weather; and he had a couple of big carpet-bags by him.

"Run her nose inshore," says the king. I done it. "Wher' you bound for, young man?"

"For the steamboat; going to Orleans."

"Git aboard," says the king. "Hold on a minute, my servant'll he'p you with them bags. Jump out and he'p the gentleman, Adolphus"—meaning me, I see.

I done so, and then we all three started on again. The young chap was mighty thankful; said it was tough work toting his baggage such weather. He asked the king where he was going, and the king told him he'd come down the river and landed at the other village this morning, and now he was going up a few mile to see an old friend on a farm up there. The young fellow says:

"When I first see you I says to myself, 'It's Mr. Wilks, sure, and he come mighty near getting here in time.' But then I says again, 'No, I reckon it ain't him, or else he wouldn't be paddling up the river.' You *ain't* him, are you?"

"No, my name's Blodgett—Elexander Blodgett—*Reverend* Elexander Blodgett, I s'pose I must say, as I'm one o' the Lord's poor servants. But still I'm jist as able to be sorry for Mr. Wilks for not arriving in time, all the same, if he's missed anything by it—which I hope he hasn't."

"Well, he don't miss any property by it, because he'll get that all right; but he's missed seeing his brother Peter die—which he mayn't mind, nobody can tell as to that—but his brother would 'a' give anything in this world to see *him* before he died; never talked about nothing else all these three weeks; hadn't seen him since they was boys together—and hadn't ever seen brother William at all—that's the deef and dumb one—William ain't more than thirty or thirty-five. Peter and George were the only ones that come out here; George was the married brother; him and his wife both died last year. Harvey and William's the only ones that's left now; and, as I was saying, they haven't got here in time."

"Did anybody send 'em word?"

"Oh, yes; a month or two ago, when Peter was first took; because Peter said then that he sorter felt like he warn't going to get well this time. You see, he was pretty old, and George's g'yirls was too young to be much company for him, except Mary Jane, the red-headed one;

and so he was kinder lonesome after George and his wife died, and didn't seem to care much to live. He most desperately wanted to see Harvey—and William, too, for that matter—because he was one of them kind that can't bear to make a will. He left a letter behind for Harvey, and said he'd told in it where his money was hid, and how he wanted the rest of the property divided up so George's g'yirls would be all right—for George didn't leave nothing. And that letter was all they could get him to put a pen to."

"Why do you reckon Harvey don't come? Wher' does he live?"

"Oh, he lives in England—Sheffield—preaches there—hasn't ever been in this country. He hasn't had any too much time—and besides he mightn't 'a' got the letter at all, you know."

"Too bad, too bad he couldn't 'a' lived to see his brothers, poor soul. You going to Orleans, you say?"

"Yes, but that ain't only a part of it. I'm going in a ship, next Wednesday, for Ryo Janeero, where my uncle lives."

"It's a pretty long journey. But it'll be lovely; I wisht I was a-going. Is Mary Jane the oldest? How old is the others?"

"Mary Jane's nineteen. Susan's fifteen, and Joanna's about fourteen—that's the one that gives herself to good works and has a hare-lip."

"Poor things! to be left alone in the cold world so."

"Well, they could be worse off. Old Peter had friends, and they ain't going to let them come to no harm. There's Hobson, the Babtis' preacher; and Deacon Lot Hovey, and Ben Rucker, and Abner Shackleford, and Levi Bell, the lawyer; and Dr. Robinson, and their wives, and the widow Bartley, and—well, there's a lot of them; but these are the ones that Peter was thickest with, and used to write about sometimes, when he wrote home; so Harvey'll know where to look for friends when he gets here."

Well, the old man went on asking questions till he just fairly emptied that young fellow. Blamed if he didn't inquire about everybody and everything in that blessed town, and all about the Wilkses; and about Peter's business—which was a tanner; and about George's, which was a carpenter; and about Harvey's—which was a dissentering minister; and so on, and so on. Then he says:

"What did you want to walk all the way up to the steamboat for?"

"Because she's a big Orleans boat, and I was afeared she mightn't stop there. When they're deep they won't stop for a hail. A Cincinnati boat will, but this is a St. Louis one."

"Was Peter Wilks well off?"

"Oh, yes, pretty well off. He had houses and land, and it's reckoned he left three or four thousand in cash hid up som'ers."

"When did you say he died?"

"I didn't say, but it was last night."

"Funeral to-morrow, likely?"

"Yes, 'bout the middle of the day."

"Well, it's terrible sad; but we've all got to go, one time or another. So what we want to do is to be prepared; then we're all right."

"Yes, sir, it's the best way. Ma used to always say that."

When we struck the boat she was about done loading, and pretty soon she got off. The king never said nothing about going aboard, so I lost my ride, after all. When the boat was gone the king made me paddle up another mile to a lonesome place, and then he got ashore and says:

"Now, hustle back, right off, and fetch the duke up here, and the new carpet-bags. And if he's gone over to t'other side, go over there and git him. And tell him to git himself up regardless. Shove along, now."

I see what *he* was up to; but I never said nothing, of course. When I got back with the duke we hid the canoe, and then they set down on a log, and the king told him everything, just like the young fellow had said it—every last word of it. And all the time he was a-doing it he tried to talk like an Englishman; and he done it pretty well, too, for a slouch. I can't imitate him, and so I ain't a-going to try to; but he really done it pretty good. Then he says:

"How are you on the deef and dumb, Bilgewater?"

The duke said, leave him alone for that; said he had played a deef and dumb person on the histrionic boards. So then they waited for a steamboat.

About the middle of the afternoon a couple of little boats come along, but they didn't come from high enough up the river; but at last there was a big one, and they hailed her. She sent out her yawl, and we went aboard, and she was from Cincinnati; and when they found we only wanted to go four or five mile they was booming mad, and gave us a cussing, and said they wouldn't land us. But the king was ca'm. He says:

"If gentlemen kin afford to pay a dollar a mile apiece to be took on and put off in a yawl, a steamboat kin afford to carry 'em, can't it?"

So they softened down and said it was all right; and when we got to the village they yawled us ashore. About two dozen men flocked down when they see the yawl a-coming, and when the kings says:

"Kin any of you gentlemen tell me wher' Mr. Peter Wilks lives?" they give a glance at one another, and nodded their heads, as much as to say, "What 'd I tell you?" Then one of them says, kind of soft and gentle:

"I'm sorry, sir, but the best we can do is to tell you where he *did* live yesterday evening."

Sudden as winking the ornery old cretur went all to smash, and fell up against the man, and put his chin on his shoulder, and cried down his back, and says:

"Alas, alas, our poor brother—gone, and we never got to see him; oh, it's too, *too* hard!"

Then he turns around, blubbering, and makes a lot of idiotic signs to the duke on his hands, and blamed if *he* didn't drop a carpet-bag and bust out a-crying. If they warn't the beatenest lot, them two frauds, that ever I struck.

Well, the men gathered around and sympathized with them, and said all sorts of kind things to them, and carried their carpet-bags up the hill for them, and let them lean on them and cry, and told the king all about his brother's last moments, and the king he told it all over again on his hands to the duke, and both of them took on about that dead tanner like they'd lost the twelve disciples. Well, if ever I struck anything like it, I'm a nigger. It was enough to make a body ashamed of the human race.

25 *Is It Them?—Singing the "Doxologer"—Awful Square—Funeral Orgies—A Bad Investment*

The news was all over town in two minutes, and you could see the people tearing down on the run from every which way, some of them putting on their coats as they come. Pretty soon we was in the middle of a crowd, and the noise of the tramping was like a soldier march. The windows and dooryards was full; and every minute somebody would say, over a fence:

"Is it *them?*"

And somebody would answer back and say:

"You bet it is."

When we got to the house the street in front of it was packed, and the three girls was standing in the door. Mary Jane *was* red-headed, but that don't make no difference, she was most awful beautiful, and her face and her eyes was all lit up like glory, she was so glad her uncles was come. The king he spread his arms, and Mary Jane she jumped for them, and the hare-lip jumped for the duke, and there they *had* it! Everybody most, leastways women, cried for joy to see them meet again at last and have such good times.

Then the king he hunched the duke private—I see him do it—and then he looked around and see the coffin, over in the corner on two chairs; so then him and the duke, with a hand across each other's shoulder, and t'other hand to their eyes, walked slow and solemn over there, everybody dropping back to give them room, and all the talk and noise stopping, people saying "Sh!" and all the men taking their hats off and drooping their heads, so you could 'a' heard a pin fall. And when they got there they bent over and looked in the coffin, and took one sight, and then they bust out a-crying so you could 'a' heard them to Orleans, most; and then they put their arms around each other's necks, and hung their chins over each other's shoulders; and then for three minutes, or maybe four, I never see two men leak the way they done. And, mind you, everybody was doing the same;

and the place was that damp I never see anything like it. Then one of them got on one side of the coffin, and t'other on t'other side, and they kneeled down and rested their foreheads on the coffin, and let on to pray all to themselves. Well, when it come to that it worked the crowd like you never see anything like it, and everybody broke down and went to sobbing right out loud—the poor girls, too; and every woman, nearly, went up to the girls, without saying a word, and kissed them, solemn, on the forehead, and then put their hand on their head, and looked up towards the sky, with the tears running down, and then busted out and went off sobbing and swabbing, and give the next woman a show. I never see anything so disgusting.

Well, by and by the king he gets up and comes forward a little, and works himself up and slobbers out a speech, all full of tears and flap-doodle, about its being a sore trial for him and his poor brother to lose the diseased, and to miss seeing diseased alive after the long journey of four thousand mile, but it's a trial that's sweetened and sanctified to us by this dear sympathy and these holy tears, and so he thanks them out of his heart and out of his brother's heart, because out of their mouths they can't, words being too weak and cold, and all that kind of rot and slush, till it was just sickening; and then he blubbers out a pious goody-goody Amen, and turns himself loose and goes to crying fit to bust.

And the minute the words were out of his mouth somebody over in the crowd struck up the doxologer, and everybody joined in with all their might, and it just warmed you up and made you feel as good as church letting out. Music *is* a good thing; and after all that soul-butter and hogwash I never see it freshen up things so, and sound so honest and bully.

Then the king begins to work his jaw again, and say how him and his nieces would be glad if a few of the main principal friends of the family would take supper here with them this evening, and help set up with the ashes of the diseased; and says if his poor brother laying yonder could speak he knows who he would name, for they was names that was very dear to him, and mentioned often in his letters; and so he will name the same, to wit, as follows, viz.:—Rev. Mr. Hobson, and Deacon Lot Hovey, and Mr. Ben Rucker, and Abner Shackleford, and Levi Bell, and Dr. Robinson, and their wives, and the widow Bartley.

Rev. Hobson and Dr. Robinson was down to the end of the town a-hunting together—that is, I mean the doctor was shipping a sick man to t'other world, and the preacher was pinting him right. Lawyer Bell was away up to Louisville on business. But the rest was on hand, and so they all come and shook hands with the king and thanked him and talked to him; and then they shook hands with the duke and didn't say nothing, but just kept a-smiling and bobbing their heads like a passel of sapheads whilst he made all sorts of signs with his hands and said "Goo-goo—goo-goo-goo" all the time.

So the king he blattered along, and managed to inquire about pretty much everybody and dog in town, by his name, and mentioned all sorts of little things that happened one time or another in the town, or to George's family, or to Peter. And he always let on that Peter wrote him the things; but that was a lie: he got every blessed one of them out of that young flathead that we canoed up to the steamboat.

Then Mary Jane she fetched the letter her father left behind, and the king he read it out loud and cried over it. It give the dwelling-house and three thousand dollars, gold, to the girls; and it give the tanyard (which was doing a good business), along with some other houses and land (worth about seven thousand), and three thousand dollars in gold to Harvey and William, and told where the six thousand cash was hid down cellar. So these two frauds said they'd go and fetch it up, and have everything square and above-board; and told me to come with a candle. We shut the cellar door behind us, and when they found the bag they spilt it out on the floor, and it was a lovely sight, all them yaller-boys. My, the way the king's eyes did shine!

"Oh, *this* ain't bully nor noth'n! Oh, no, I reckon not! Why, Biljy, it beats the Nonesuch, *don't* it?"

The duke allowed it did. They pawed the yaller-boys, and sifted them through their fingers and let them jingle down on the floor; and the king says:

"It ain't no use talkin'; bein' brothers to a rich dead man and representatives of furrin heirs that's got left is the line for you and me, Bilge. Thish yer comes of trust'n to Providence. It's the best way, in the long run. I've tried 'em all, and ther' ain't no better way."

Most everybody would 'a' been satisfied with the pile, and took it on trust; but no, they must count it, and it comes out four hundred and fifteen dollars short. Says the king:

"Dern him, I wonder what he done with that four hundred and fifteen dollars?"

They worried over that awhile, and ransacked all around for it. Then the duke says:

"Well, he was a pretty sick man, and likely he made a mistake—I reckon that's the way of it. The best way's to let it go, and keep still about it. We can spare it."

"Oh, shucks, yes, we can *spare* it. I don't k'yer nothin' 'bout that —it's the *count* I'm thinkin' about. We want to be awful square and open and above-board here, you know. We want to lug this h'yer money upstairs and count it before everybody—then ther' ain't noth'n suspicious. But when the dead man says ther's six thous'n dollars, you know, we don't want to—"

"Hold on," says the duke. "Let's make up the deffisit," and he begun to haul out yaller-boys out of his pocket.

"It's a most amaz'n' good idea, duke—you *have* got a rattlin' clever head on you," says the king. "Blest if the old Nonesuch ain't a heppin' us out ag'in," and *he* begun to haul out yaller-jackets and stack them up.

"Say," says the duke, "I got another idea. Le's go upstairs and count this money, and then *give it to the girls*."

"Good land, duke, lemme hug you! It's the most dazzling idea 'at ever a man struck. You have cert'nly got the most astonishin' head I ever see. Oh, this is the boss dodge, ther' ain't no mistake 'bout it. Let 'em fetch along their suspicions now if they want to—this'll lay 'em out."

When we got up-stairs everybody gethered around the table, and the king he counted it and stacked it up, three hundred dollars in a pile—twenty elegant little piles. Everybody looked hungry at it, and licked their chops. Then they raked it into the bag again, and I see the king begin to swell himself up for another speech:

"Friends all, my poor brother that lays yonder has done generous by them that's left behind in the vale of sorrers. He has done generous by these yer poor little lambs that he loved and sheltered, and that's left fatherless and motherless. Yes, and we that knowed him knows that he would 'a' done *more* generous by 'em if he hadn't ben afeared o' woundin' his dear William and me. Now, *wouldn't* he?

Ther' ain't no question 'bout it in *my* mind. Well, then, what kind o' brothers would it be that 'd stand in his way at sech a time? And what kind o' uncles would it be that 'd rob—yes, *rob*—sech poor sweet lambs as these 'at he loved so at sech a time? If I know William—and I *think* I do—he—well, I'll jest ask him." He turns around and begins to make a lot of signs to the duke with his hands, and the duke he looks at him stupid and leather-headed awhile; then all of a sudden he seems to catch his meaning, and jumps for the king, goo-gooing with all his might for joy, and hugs him about fifteen times before he lets up. Then the king says, "I knowed it; I reckon *that* 'll convince anybody the way *he* feels about it. Here, Mary Jane, Susan, Joanner, take the money—take it *all*. It's the gift of him that lays yonder, cold but joyful."

Mary Jane she went for him, Susan and the hare-lip went for the duke, and then such another hugging and kissing I never see yet. And everybody crowded up with the tears in their eyes, and most shook the hands off of them frauds, saying all the time:

"You *dear* good souls!—how *lovely!*—how *could* you!"

Well, then, pretty soon all hands got to talking about the diseased again, and how good he was, and what a loss he was, and all that; and before long a big iron-jawed man worked himself in there from outside, and stood a-listening and looking, and not saying anything; and nobody saying anything to him either, because the king was talking and they was all busy listening. The king was saying—

"—they bein' partickler friends o' the diseased. That's why they're invited here this evenin'; but to-morrow we want *all* to come—everybody; for he respected everybody, he liked everybody, and so it's fitten that his funeral orgies sh'd be public."

And so he went a-mooning on and on, liking to hear himself talk, and every little while he fetched in his funeral orgies again, till the duke he couldn't stand it no more; so he writes on a little scrap of paper, "*Obsequies*, you old fool," and folds it up, and goes to goo-gooing and reaching it over people's heads to him. The king he reads it and puts it in his pocket, and says:

"Poor William, afflicted as he is, his *heart's* aluz right. Asks me to invite everybody to come to the funeral—wants me to make 'em all welcome. But he needn't 'a' worried—it was jest what I was at."

Then he weaves along again, perfectly ca'm, and goes to dropping in his funeral orgies again every now and then, just like he done before. And when he done it the third time he says:

"I say orgies, not because it's the common term, because it ain't—obsequies bein' the common term—but because orgies is the right term. Obsequies ain't used in England no more now—it's gone out. We say orgies in England. Orgies is better, because it means the thing you're after more exact. It's a word that's made up out'n the Greek *orgo*, outside, open, abroad; and the Hebrew *jeesum*, to plant, cover up; hence in*ter*. So, you see, funeral orgies is an open er public funeral."

He was the *worst* I ever struck. Well, the iron-jawed man he laughed right in his face. Everybody was shocked. Everybody says, "Why, *doctor!*" and Abner Shackleford says:

"Why, Robinson, hain't you heard the news? This is Harvey Wilks."

The king he smiled eager, and shoved out his flapper, and says:

"*Is* it my poor brother's dear good friend and physician? I—"

"Keep your hands off me!" says the doctor. "*You* talk like an Englishman, *don't* you. It's the worst imitation I ever heard. *You* Peter Wilks's brother! You're a fraud, that's what you are!"

Well, how they all took on! They crowded around the doctor and tried to quiet him down, and tried to explain to him and tell him how Harvey'd showed in forty ways that he *was* Harvey, and knowed everybody by name, and the names of the very dogs, and begged and *begged* him not to hurt Harvey's feelings and the poor girls' feelings, and all that. But it warn't no use; he stormed right along, and said any man that pretended to be an Englishman and couldn't imitate the lingo no better than what he did was a fraud and a liar. The poor girls was hanging to the king and crying; and all of a sudden the doctor ups and turns on *them*. He says:

"I was your father's friend, and I'm your friend; and I warn you *as* a friend, and an honest one that wants to protect you and keep you out of harm and trouble, to turn your backs on that scoundrel and have nothing to do with him, the ignorant tramp, with his idiotic Greek and Hebrew, as he calls it. He is the thinnest kind of an impostor—has come here with a lot of empty names and facts which he picked up somewheres; and you take them for *proofs*, and are helped to fool yourselves by these foolish friends here, who ought to know better. Mary Jane Wilks, you know me for your friend, and for your unselfish friend, too. Now listen to me; turn this pitiful rascal out—I *beg* you to do it. Will you?"

Mary Jane straightened herself up, and my, but she was handsome! She says:

"*Here* is my answer." She hove the bag of money and put it in the king's hands, and says, "Take this six thousand dollars and invest for me and my sisters any way you want to, and don't give us no receipt for it."

Then she put her arm around the king on one side, and Susan and the hare-lip done the same on the other. Everybody clapped their hands and stomped on the floor like a perfect storm, whilst the king held up his head and smiled proud. The doctor says:

"All right; I wash *my* hands of the matter. But I warn you all that a time's coming when you're going to feel sick whenever you think of this day." And away he went.

"All right, doctor," says the king, kinder mocking him; "we'll try and get 'em to send for you"; which made them all laugh, and they said it was a good hit.

26 *A Pious King—The King's Clergy—She Asked His Pardon—Hiding in the Room—Huck Takes the Money*

Well, when they was all gone the king he asks Mary Jane how they was off for spare rooms, and she said she had one spare room, which would do for Uncle William, and she'd give her own room to Uncle Harvey, which was a little bigger, and she would turn into the room with her sisters and sleep on a cot; and up garret there was a little cubby, with a pallet in it. The king said the cubby would do for his valley*—meaning me.

So Mary Jane took us up, and she showed them their rooms, which

valley (valet): personal manservant

was plain but nice. She said she'd have her frocks and a lot of other traps took out of her room if they was in Uncle Harvey's way, but he said they warn't. The frocks was hung along the wall, and before them was a curtain made out of calico that hung down to the floor. There was an old hair trunk in one corner, and a guitar-box in another, and all sorts of little knickknacks and jimcracks around, like girls brisken up a room with. The king said it was all the more homely and more pleasanter for these fixings, and so don't disturb them. The duke's room was pretty small, but plenty good enough, and so was my cubby.

That night they had a big supper, and all them men and women was there, and I stood behind the king and the duke's chairs and waited on them, and the niggers waited on the rest. Mary Jane she set at the head of the table, with Susan alongside of her, and said how bad the biscuits was, and how mean the preserves was, and how ornery and tough the fried chicken was—and all that kind of rot, the way women always do for to force out compliments; and the people all knowed everything was tiptop, and said so—said "How *do* you get biscuits to brown so nice?" and "Where, for the land's sake, *did* you get these amaz'n pickles?" and all that kind of humbug talky-talk, just the way people always does.

And when it was all done me and the hare-lip had supper in the kitchen off of the leavings, whilst the others was helping the niggers clean up the things. The hare-lip she got to pumping me about England, and blest if I didn't think the ice was getting mighty thin sometimes. She says:

"Did you ever see the king?"

"Who? William Fourth? Well, I bet I have—he goes to our church." I knowed he was dead years ago, but I never let on. So when I says he goes to our church, she says:

"What—regular?"

"Yes—regular. His pew's right over opposite ourn—on t'other side the pulpit."

"I thought he lived in London?"

"Well, he does. Where *would* he live?"

"But I though *you* lived in Sheffield?"

I see I was up a stump. I had to let on to get choked with a chicken-bone, so as to get time to think how to get down again. Then I says:

"I mean he goes to our church regular when he's in Sheffield.

That's only in the summer-time when he comes there to take the sea baths."

"Why, how you talk—Sheffield ain't on the sea."

"Well, who said it was?"

"Why, you did."

"I *didn't*, nuther."

"You did!"

"I didn't."

"You did."

"I never said nothing of the kind."

"Well, what *did* you say, then?"

"Said he come to take the sea *baths*."

"Well, then, how's he going to take the sea baths if it ain't on the sea?"

"Looky here," I says: "did you ever see any Congresswater?"

"Yes."

"Well, did you have to go to Congress to get it?"

"Why, no."

"Well, neither does William Fourth have to go to the sea to get a sea bath."

"How does he get it, then?"

"Gets it the way people down here gets Congresswater—in barrels. There in the palace at Sheffield they've got furnaces, and he wants his water hot. They can't bile that amount of water away off there at the sea. They haven't got no conveniences for it."

"Oh, I see, now. You might 'a' said that in the first place and saved time."

When she said that I see I was out of the woods again, and so I was comfortable and glad. Next, she says:

"Do you go to church, too?"

"Yes—regular."

"Where do you set?"

"Why, in our pew."

"*Whose* pew?"

"Why, *ourn*—your Uncle Harvey's."

"His'n? What does *he* want with a pew?"

"Wants it to set in. What did you *reckon* he wanted with it?"

"Why, I thought he'd be in the pulpit."

Rot him, I forgot he was a preacher. I see I was up a stump again, so I played another chicken-bone and got another think. Then I says:

"Blame it, do you suppose there ain't but one preacher to a church?"

"Why, what do they want with more?"

"What!—to preach before a king? I never did see such a girl. They don't have no less than seventeen."

"Seventeen! My land! Why, I wouldn't set out such a string as that, not if I *never* got to glory. It must take 'em a week."

"Shucks, they don't *all* of 'em preach the same day—only *one* of 'em."

"Well, then, what does the rest of 'em do?"

"Oh, nothing much. Loll around, pass the plate—and one thing or another. But mainly they don't do nothing."

"Well, then, what are they *for?*"

"Why, they're for *style*. Don't you know nothing?"

"Well, I don't *want* to know no such foolishness as that. How is servants treated in England? Do they treat 'em better 'n we treat our niggers?"

"*No!* A servant ain't nobody there. They treat them worse than dogs."

"Don't they give 'em holidays, the way we do, Christmas and New Year's week, the Fourth of July?"

"Oh, just listen! A body could tell *you* hain't ever been to England by that. Why, Hare-l—why, Joanna, they never see a holiday from year's end to year's end; never go to the circus, nor theater, nor nigger shows, nor nowheres."

"Nor church?"

"Nor church."

"But *you* always went to church."

Well, I was gone up again. I forgot I was the old man's servant. But next minute I whirled in on a kind of an explanation how a valley was different from a common servant, and *had* to go to church whether he wanted to or not, and set with the family, on account of its being the law. But I didn't do it pretty good, and when I got done I see she warn't satisfied. She says:

"Honest injun, now, hain't you been telling me a lot of lies?"

"Honest injun," says I.

"None of it at all?"

"None of it at all. Not a lie in it," says I.

"Lay your hand on this book and say it."

I see it warn't nothing but a dictionary, so I laid my hand on it and said it. So then she looked a little better satisfied, and says:

"Well, then, I'll believe some of it; but I hope to gracious if I'll believe the rest."

"What is it you won't believe, Jo?" says Mary Jane, stepping in with Susan behind her. "It ain't right nor kind for you to talk so to him, and him a stranger and so far from his people. How would you like to be treated so?"

"That's always your way, Maim—always sailing in to help somebody before they're hurt. I hain't done nothing to him. He's told some stretchers, I reckon, and I said I wouldn't swallow it all; and that's every bit and grain I *did* say. I reckon he can stand a little thing like that."

"I don't care whether 'twas little or whether 'twas big; he's here in our house and a stranger, and it wasn't good of you to say it. If you was in his place it would make you feel ashamed; and so you oughn't to say a thing to another person that will make *them* feel ashamed."

"Why, Maim, he said—"

"It don't make no difference what he *said*—that ain't the thing. The thing is for you to treat him *kind*, and not be saying things to make him remember he ain't in his own country and amongst his own folks."

I says to myself, *this* is a girl that I'm letting that old reptile rob her of her money!

Then Susan *she* waltzed in; and if you'll believe me, she did give Hare-lip hark from the tomb!

Says I to myself, and this is *another* one that I'm letting him rob her of her money!

Then Mary Jane she took another inning, and went in sweet and lovely again—which was her way; but when she got done there warn't hardly anything left o' poor Hare-lip. So she hollered.

"All right, then," says the other girls; "you just ask his pardon."

She done it, too; and she done it beautiful. She done it so beautiful it was good to hear; and I wished I could tell her a thousand lies, so she could do it again.

I says to myself, this is *another* one that I'm letting him rob her of her money. And when she got through they all jest laid theirselves out to make me feel at home and know I was amongst friends. I felt so ornery and low down and mean that I says to myself, my mind's made up; I'll hive that money for them or bust.

So then I lit out—for bed, I said, meaning some time or another. When I got by myself I went to thinking the thing over. I says to myself, shall I go to that doctor, private, and blow on these frauds? No—that won't do. He might tell who told him; then the king and the duke would make it warm for me. Shall I go, private, and tell Mary Jane? No—I dasn't do it. Her face would give them a hint, sure; they've got the money, and they'd slide right out and get away with it. If she was to fetch in help I'd get mixed up in the business before it was done with, I judge. No; there ain't no good way but one. I got to steal that money, somehow; and I got to steal it some way that they won't suspicion that I done it. They've got a good thing here, and they ain't a-going to leave till they've played this family and this town for all they're worth, so I'll find a chance time enough. I'll steal it and hide it; and by and by, when I'm away down the river, I'll write a letter and tell Mary Jane where it's hid. But I better hide it to-night if I can, because the doctor maybe hasn't let up as much as he lets on he has; he might scare them out of here yet.

So, thinks I, I'll go up and search them rooms. Upstairs the hall was dark, but I found the duke's room, and started to paw around it with my hands; but I recollected it wouldn't be much like the king to let anybody else take care of that money but his own self; so then I went to his room and begun to paw around there. But I see I couldn't do nothing without a candle, and I dasn't light one, of course. So I judged I'd got to do the other thing—lay for them and eavesdrop. About that time I hears their footsteps coming, and was going to skip under the bed; I reached for it, but it wasn't where I thought it would be; but I touched the curtain that hid Mary Jane's frocks, so I jumped in behind that and snuggled in amongst the gowns, and stood there perfectly still.

They come in and shut the door; and the first thing the duke done was to get down and look under the bed. Then I was glad I hadn't found the bed when I wanted it. And yet, you know, it's kind of natural to hide under the bed when you are up to anything private. They sets down then, and the king says:

"Well, what is it? And cut it middlin' short, because it's better for us to be down there a-whoopin' up the mournin' than up here givin' 'em a chance to talk us over."

"Well, this is it, Capet. I ain't easy; I ain't comfortable. That doctor lays on my mind. I wanted to know your plans. I've got a notion, and I think it's sound."

"What is it, duke?"

"That we better glide out of this before three in the morning, and clip it down the river with what we've got. Specially, seeing we got it so easy—*given* back to us, flung at our heads, as you may say, when of course we allowed to have to steal it back. I'm for knocking off and lighting out."

That made me feel pretty bad. About an hour or two ago it would 'a' been a little different, but now it made me feel bad and disappointed. The king rips out and says:

"What! And not sell out the rest o' the property? March off like a passel of fools and leave eight or nine thous'n dollars' worth o' property layin' around jest sufferin' to be scooped in?—and all good, salable stuff."

The duke he grumbled; said the bag of gold was enough, and he didn't want to go no deeper—didn't want to rob a lot of orphans of *everything* they had.

"Why, how you talk!" says the king. "We sha'n't rob 'em of nothing at all but jest this money. The people that *buys* the property is the suff'rers; because as soon 's it's found out 'at we didn't own it—which won't be long after we've slid—the sale won't be valid, and it 'll all go back to the estate. These yer orphans 'll git their house back ag'in, and that's enough for *them*; they're young and spry, and k'n easy earn a livin'. *They* ain't a-goin' to suffer. Why, jest think—there's thous'n's and thous'n's that ain't nigh so well off. Bless you, *they* ain't got noth'n' to complain of."

Well, the king he talked him blind; so at last he give in, and said all right, but said he believed it was blamed foolishness to stay, and that doctor hanging over them. But the king says:

"Cuss the doctor! What do we k'yer for *him?* Hain't we got all the fools in town on our side? And ain't that a big enough majority in any town?"

So they got ready to go down-stairs again. The duke says:

"I don't think we put that money in a good place."

That cheered me up. I'd begun to think I warn't going to get a hint of no kind to help me. The king says:

"Why?"

"Because Mary Jane 'll be in mourning from this out; and first you know the nigger that does up the rooms will get an order to box these duds up and put 'em away; and do you reckon a nigger can run across money and not borrow some of it?"

"Your head's level ag'in, duke," says the king; and he comes a-fumbling under the curtain two or three foot from where I was. I stuck tight to the wall and kept mighty still, though quivery; and I wondered what them fellows would say to me if they catched me; and I tried to think what I'd better do if they did catch me. But the king he got the bag before I could think more than about half a thought, and he never suspicioned I was around. They took and shoved the bag through a rip in the straw tick that was under the feather-bed, and crammed it in a foot or two amongst the straw and said it was all right now, because a nigger only makes up the feather-bed, and don't turn over the straw tick only about twice a year, and so it warn't in no danger of getting stole now.

But I knowed better. I had it out of there before they was half-way down-stairs. I groped along up to my cubby, and hid it there till I could get a chance to do better. I judged I better hide it outside of the house somewheres, because if they missed it they would give the house a good ransacking: I knowed that very well. Then I turned in, with my clothes all on; but I couldn't 'a' gone to sleep if I'd 'a' wanted to, I was in such a sweat to get through with the business. By and by I heard the king and the duke come up; so I rolled off my pallet and laid with my chin at the top of my ladder, and waited to see if anything was going to happen. But nothing did.

So I held on till all the late sounds had quit and the early ones hadn't begun yet; and then I slipped down the ladder.

27 *The Funeral—Satisfying Curiosity—Suspicious of Huck—Quick Sales and Small Profits*

I crept to their doors and listened; they was snoring. So I tiptoed along, and got downstairs all right. There warn't a sound anywheres. I peeped through a crack of the dining-room door, and see the men that was watching the corpse all sound asleep on their chairs. The door was open into the parlor, where the corpse was laying, and there was a candle in both rooms. I passed along, and the parlor door was open; but I see there warn't nobody in there but the remainders of Peter; so I shoved on by; but the front door was locked, and the key wasn't there. Just then I heard somebody coming down the stairs, back behind me. I run in the parlor and took a swift look around, and the only place I see to hide the bag was in the coffin. The lid was shoved along about a foot, showing the dead man's face down in there, with a wet cloth over it, and his shroud on. I tucked the money-bag in under the lid, just down beyond where his hands was crossed, which made me creep, they was so cold, and then I run back across the room and in behind the door.

The person coming was Mary Jane. She went to the coffin, very soft, and kneeled down and looked in; then she put up her handkerchief, and I see she begun to cry, though I couldn't hear her, and her back was to me. I slid out, and as I passed the dining-room I thought I'd make sure them watchers hadn't seen me; so I looked through the crack, and everything was all right. They hadn't stirred.

I slipped up to bed, feeling ruther blue, on accounts of the thing playing out that way after I had took so much trouble and run so much resk about it. Says I, if it could stay where it is, all right; because when we get down the river a hundred mile or two I could write back to Mary Jane, and she could dig him up again and get it; but that ain't the thing that's going to happen; the thing that's going to happen is, the money'll be found when they come to screw on the lid. Then the king 'll get it again, and it 'll be a long day before he gives anybody another chance to smouch it from him. Of course I *wanted* to slide down and get it out of there, but I dasn't try it. Every minute it was getting earlier now, and pretty soon some of them watchers would begin to stir, and I might get catched—catched with six thousand dollars in my hands that nobody hadn't hired me to take care of. I don't wish to be mixed up in no such business as that, I says to myself.

When I got down-stairs in the morning the parlor was shut up, and the watchers was gone. There warn't nobody around but the family and the widow Bartley and our tribe. I watched their faces to see if anything had been happening, but I couldn't tell.

Towards the middle of the day the undertaker come with his man, and they set the coffin in the middle of the room on a couple of chairs and then set all our chairs in rows, and borrowed more from the neighbors till the hall and the parlor and the dining-room was full. I see the coffin lid was the way it was before, but I dasn't go to look in under it, with folks around.

Then the people begun to flock in, and the beats and the girls took seats in the front row at the head of the coffin, and for a half an hour the people filed around slow, in single rank, and looked down at the dead man's face a minute, and some dropped in a tear, and it was all very still and solemn, only the girls and the beats holding handkerchiefs to their eyes and keeping their heads bent, and sobbing a little. There warn't no other sound but the scraping of the feet on the floor and blowing noses—because people always blows them more at a funeral than they do at other places except church.

When the place was packed full the undertaker he slid around in his black gloves with his softy soothering ways, putting on the last touches, and getting people and things all ship-shape and comfortable, and making no more sound than a cat. He never spoke; he moved people around, he squeezed in late ones, he opened up passageways, and done it with nods, and signs with his hands. Then he took his place over against the wall. He was the softest, glidingest, stealthiest man I ever see; and there warn't no more smile to him than there is to a ham.

They had borrowed a melodeum—a sick one; and when everything was ready a young woman set down and worked it, and it was pretty skreeky and colicky, and everybody joined in and sung, and Peter was the only one that had a good thing, according to my notion. Then the Reverend Hobson opened up, slowly and solemn, and begun to talk; and straight off the most outrageous row busted out in the cellar a body ever heard; it was only one dog, but he made a most powerful racket, and he kept it up right along; the parson he had to stand there, over the coffin, and wait—you couldn't hear yourself think. It was right down awkward, and nobody didn't seem to know what to do. But pretty soon they see that long-legged undertaker make a sign to the preacher as much as to say, "Don't you worry—just depend on me." Then he stooped down and begun to glide along the wall, just his shoulders showing over the people's heads. So he glided along, and the powwow and racket getting more and more outrageous all the time; and at last, when he had gone around two sides of the room, he disappears down cellar. Then in about two seconds we heard a whack, and the dog he finished up with a most amazing howl or two, and then everything was dead still, and the parson begun his solemn talk where he left off. In a minute or two here comes this undertaker's back and shoulders gliding along the wall again; and so he glided and glided around three sides of the room, and then rose up, and shaded his mouth with his hands, and stretched his neck out towards the preacher, over the people's heads, and says, in a kind of a coarse whisper, "*He had a rat!*" Then he drooped down and glided along the wall again to his place. You could see it was a great satisfaction to the people, because naturally they wanted to know. A little thing like that don't cost nothing, and it's just the little things that makes a man to be looked up to and liked. There warn't no more popular man in town than what that undertaker was.

Well, the funeral sermon was very good, but pison long and tiresome; and then the king he shoved in and got off some of his usual rubbage, and at last the job was through, and the undertaker begun to sneak up on the coffin with his screw-driver. I was in a sweat then, and watched him pretty keen. But he never meddled at all; just slid the lid along as soft as mush, and screwed it down tight and fast. So there I was! I didn't know whether the money was in there or not. So, says I, s'pose somebody has hogged that bag on the sly?—now how do *I* know whether to write to Mary Jane or not? S'pose she dug him up and didn't find nothing, what would she think of me? Blame it, I says, I might get hunted up and jailed; I'd better lay low and keep dark, and not write at all; the thing's awful mixed; trying to better it, I've worsened it a hundred times, and I wish to goodness I'd just let it alone, dad fetch the whole business!

They buried him, and we come back home, and I went to watching faces again—I couldn't help it, and I couldn't rest easy. But nothing come of it; the faces didn't tell me nothing.

The king he visited around in the evening, and sweetened everybody up, and made himself ever so friendly; and he give out the idea that his congregation over in England would be in a sweat about him, so he must hurry and settle up the estate right away and leave for home. He was very sorry he was so pushed, and so was everybody; they wished he could stay longer, but they said they could see it couldn't be done. And he said of course him and William would take the girls home with them; and that pleased everybody too, because then the girls would be well fixed and amongst their own relations; and it pleased the girls, too—tickled them so they clean forgot they ever had a trouble in the world; and told him to sell out as quick as he wanted to, they would be ready. Them poor things was that glad and happy it made my heart ache to see them getting fooled and lied to so, but I didn't see no safe way for me to chip in and change the general tune.

Well, blamed if the king didn't bill the house and the niggers and all the property for auction straight off—sale two days after the funeral; but anybody could buy private beforehand if they wanted to.

So the next day after the funeral, along about noontime, the girls' joy got the first jolt. A couple of nigger-traders come along, and the king sold them the niggers reasonable, for three-day drafts as they called it, and away they went, the two sons up the river to Memphis, and their mother down the river to Orleans. I thought them poor girls and them niggers would break their hearts for grief; they cried around each other, and took on so it most made me down sick to see it. The girls said they hadn't ever dreamed of seeing the family separated or sold away from the town. I can't ever get it out of my memory, the sight of them poor miserable girls and niggers hanging around each other's necks and crying; and I reckon I couldn't 'a' stood it all, but would 'a' had to bust out and tell on our gang if I hadn't knowed the sale warn't no account and the niggers would be back home in a week or two.

The thing made a big stir in the town, too, and a good many come out flatfooted and said it was scandalous to separate the mother and the children that way. It injured the frauds some; but the old fool he bulled right along, spite of all the duke could say or do, and I tell you the duke was powerful uneasy.

Next day was auction day. About broad day in the morning the king and the duke come up in the garret and woke me up, and I see by their look that there was trouble. The king says:

"Was you in my room night before last?"

"No, your majesty"—which was the way I always called him when nobody but our gang warn't around.

"Was you in there yisterday er last night?"

"No, your majesty."

"Honor bright, now—no lies."

"Honor bright, your majesty, I'm telling you the truth. I hain't been a-near your room since Miss Mary Jane took you and the duke and showed it to you."

The duke says:

"Have you seen anybody else go in there?"

"No, your grace, not as I remember, I believe."

"Stop and think."

I studied awhile and see my chance; then I says:

"Well, I see the niggers go in there several times."

Both of them gave a little jump, and looked like they hadn't ever expected it, and then like they *had*. Then the duke says:

"What, *all* of them?"

"No—leastways, not all at once—that is, I don't think I ever seen them all come *out* at once but just one time."

"Hello! When was that?"

"It was the day we had the funeral. In the morning. It warn't early, because I overslept. I was just starting down the ladder, and I see them."

"Well, go on, *go* on! What did they do? How'd they act?"

"They didn't do nothing. And they didn't act anyway much, as fur as I see. They tiptoed away; so I seen, easy enough, that they'd shoved in there to do up your majesty's room, or something, s'posing you was up; and found you *warn't* up, and so they was hoping to slide out of the way of trouble without waking you up, if they hadn't already waked you up."

"Great guns, *this* is a go!" says the king; and both of them looked pretty sick and tolerable silly. They stood there a-thinking and scratching their heads a minute, and the duke he bust into a kind of a little raspy chuckle, and says:

"It does beat all how neat the niggers played their hand. They let on to be *sorry* they was going out of this region! And I believed they *was* sorry, and so did you, and so did everybody. Don't ever tell *me* any more that a nigger ain't got any histrionic talent. Why, the way they played that thing it would fool *anybody*. In my opinion, there's a fortune in 'em. If I had capital and a theater, I wouldn't want a better lay-out than that—and here we've gone and sold 'em for a song. Yes, and ain't privileged to sing the song yet. Say, where *is* that song—that draft?"

"In the bank for to be collected. Where *would* it be?"

"Well, *that's* all right then, thank goodness."

Says I, kind of timid-like:

"Is something gone wrong?"

The king whirls on me and rips out:

"None o' your business! You keep your head shet, and mind y'r own affairs—if you got any. Long as you're in this town don't you forgit *that*—you hear?" Then he says to the duke, "We got to jest swaller it and say noth'n'; mum's the word for *us*."

As they was starting down the ladder the duke he chuckles again, and says:

"Quick sales *and* small profits! It's a good business—yes."

The king snarls around on him and says:

"I was trying to do for the best in sellin' 'em out so quick. If the profits has turned out to be none, lackin' considable, and none to carry, is it my fault any more'n it's yourn?"

"Well, *they'd* be in this house yet and we *wouldn't* if I could 'a' got my advice listened to."

The king sassed back as much as was safe for him, and then swapped around and lit into *me* again. He give me down the banks for not coming and *telling* him I see the niggers come out of his room acting that way—said any fool would 'a' *knowed* something was up. And then waltzed in and cussed *himself* awhile, and said it all come of him not laying late and taking his natural rest that morning, and he'd be blamed if he'd ever do it again. So they went off a-jawing; and I felt dreadful glad I'd worked it all off onto the niggers, and yet hadn't done the niggers no harm by it.

28 *The Trip to England—"The Brute!"—Mary Jane Decides to Leave—Huck Parting with Mary Jane—Mumps—The Opposition Line*

By and by it was getting-up time. So I come down the ladder and started for down-stairs; but as I come to the girls' room the door was open, and I see Mary Jane setting by her old hair trunk, which was open and she'd been packing things in it—getting ready to go to England. But she had stopped now with a folded gown in her lap, and had her face in her hands, crying. I felt awful bad to see it; of course anybody would. I went in there and says:

"Miss Mary Jane, you can't a-bear to see people in trouble, and *I* can't—most always. Tell me about it."

So she done it. And it was the niggers—I just expected it. She said the beautiful trip to England was most about spoiled for her; she didn't know *how* she was ever going to be happy there, knowing the mother and the children warn't ever going to see each other no more—and then busted out bitterer than ever, and flung up her hands, and says:

"Oh, dear, dear, to think they ain't *ever* going to see each other any more!"

"But they *will*—and inside of two weeks—and I *know* it!" says I.

Laws, it was out before I could think! And before I could budge she throws her arms around my neck and told me to say it *again*, say it *again*, say it *again!*

I see I had spoken too sudden and said too much, and was in a close place. I asked her to let me think a minute; and she set there, very impatient and excited and handsome, but looking kind of happy and eased-up, like a person that's had a tooth pulled out. So I went to studying it out. I says to myself, I reckon a body that ups and tells the truth when he is in a tight place is taking considerable many resks, though I ain't had no experience, and can't say for certain; but it looks so to me, anyway; and yet here's a case where I'm blest if it don't look to me like the truth is better and actuly *safer* than a lie. I must lay it by in my mind, and think it over some time or other, it's so kind of strange and unregular. I never see nothing like it. Well, I says to myself at last, I'm a-going to chance it; I'll up and tell the truth this time, though it does seem most like setting down on a kag of powder and touching it off just to see where you'll go to. Then I says:

"Miss Mary Jane, is there any place out of town a little ways where you could go and stay three or four days?"

"Yes; Mr. Lothrop's. Why?"

"Never mind why yet. If I'll tell you how I know the niggers will see each other again—inside of two weeks—here in this house—and *prove* how I know it—will you go to Mr. Lothrop's and stay four days?"

"Four days!" she says; "I'll stay a year!"

"All right," I says, "I don't want nothing more out of *you* than just your word—I druther have it than another man's kiss-the-Bible." She smiled and reddened up very sweet, and I says, "If you don't mind it, I'll shut the door—and bolt it."

Then I come back and set down again, and says:

"Don't you holler. Just set still and take it like a man. I got to tell the truth, and you want to brace up, Miss Mary, because it's a bad kind, and going to be hard to take, but there ain't no help for it. These uncles of yourn ain't no uncles at all; they're a couple of frauds—regular dead-beats. There, now we're over the worst of it, you can stand the rest middling easy."

It jolted her up like everything, of course; but I was over the shoal water now, so I went right along, her eyes a-blazing higher and higher all the time, and told her every blame thing, from where we first struck that young fool going up to the steamboat, clear through to where she flung herself onto the king's breast at the front door and he kissed her sixteen or seventeen times—and then up she jumps with her face afire like sunset, and says:

"The brute! Come, don't waste a minute—not a *second*—we'll have them tarred and feathered, and flung in the river!"

Says I:

"Cert'nly. But do you mean *before* you go to Mr. Lothrop's, or—"

"Oh," she says, "what am I *thinking* about!" she says, and set right down again. "Don't mind what I said—please—don't—you *won't*, now, *will* you?" Laying her silky hand on mine in that kind of a way that I said I would die first. "I never thought, I was so stirred up," she says; "now go on, and I won't do so any more. You tell me what to do, and whatever you say I'll do it."

"Well," I says, "it's a rough gang, them two frauds, and I'm fixed so I got to travel with them a while longer, whether I want to or not—I druther not tell you why; and if you was to blow on them this town would get me out of their claws, and *I'd* be all right; but there'd be another person that you don't know about who'd be in big trouble. Well, we got to save *him*, hain't we? Of course. Well, then, we won't blow on them."

Saying them words put a good idea in my head. I see how maybe I could get me and Jim rid of the frauds; get them jailed here, and then leave. But I didn't want to run the raft in the daytime without anybody aboard to answer questions but me; so I didn't want the plan to begin working till pretty late to-night. I says:

"Miss Mary Jane, I'll tell you what we'll do, and you won't have to stay at Mr. Lothrop's so long, nuther. How fur is it?"

"A little short of four miles—right out in the country, back here."

"Well, that 'll answer. Now you go along out there, and lay low till nine or half past to-night, and then get them to fetch you home again—tell them you've thought of something. If you get here before eleven put a candle in this window, and if I don't turn up wait *till* eleven, and *then* if I don't turn up it means I'm gone, and out of the way, and safe. Then you come out and spread the news around, and get these beats jailed."

"Good," she says, "I'll do it."

"And if it just happens so that I don't get away, but get took up along with them, you must up and say I told you the whole thing beforehand, and you must stand by me all you can."

"Stand by you! indeed I will. They sha'n't touch a hair of your head!" she says, and I see her nostrils spread and her eyes snap when she said it, too.

"If I get away I sha'n't be here," I says, "to prove these rapscallions ain't your uncles, and I couldn't do it if I *was* here. I could swear they was beats and bummers, that's all, though that's worth something. Well, there's others can do that better than what I can, and they're people that ain't going to be doubted as quick as I'd be. I'll tell you how to find them. Gimme a pencil and a piece of paper. There—'*Royal Nonesuch, Bricksville.*' Put it away, and don't lose it. When the court wants to find out something about these two, let them send up to Bricksville and say they've got the men that played the 'Royal Nonesuch,' and ask for some witnesses—why, you'll have that entire town down here before you can hardly wink, Miss Mary. And they'll come a-biling, too."

I judged we had got everything fixed about right now. So I says:

"Just let the auction go right along, and don't worry. Nobody don't have to pay for the things they buy till a whole day after the auction on accounts of the short notice, and they ain't going out of this till they get that money; and the way we've fixed it the sale ain't going to count, and they ain't going to *get* no money. It's just like the way it was with the niggers—it warn't no sale, and the niggers will be back before long. Why, they can't collect the money for the *niggers* yet—they're in the worst kind of a fix, Miss Mary."

"Well," she says, "I'll run down to breakfast now, and then I'll start straight for Mr. Lothrop's."

" 'Deed, *that* ain't the ticket, Miss Mary Jane," I says, "by no manner of means; go *before* breakfast."

"Why?"

"What did you reckon I wanted you to go at all for, Miss Mary?"

"Well, I never thought—and come to think, I don't know. What was it?"

"Why, it's because you ain't one of these leather-face people. I don't want no better book than what your face is. A body can set down and read it off like coarse print. Do you reckon you can go and face your uncles when they come to kiss you good-morning, and never—"

"There, there, don't! Yes, I'll go before breakfast—I'll be glad to. And leave my sisters with them?"

"Yes; never mind about them. They've got to stand it yet awhile. They might suspicion something if all of you was to go. I don't want you to see them, nor your sisters, nor nobody in this town; if a neighbor was to ask how is your uncles this morning your face would tell something. No, you go right along, Miss Mary Jane, and I'll fix it with all of them. I'll tell Miss Susan to give your love to your uncles and say you've went away for a few hours for to get a little rest and change, or to see a friend, and you'll be back to-night."

"Gone to see a friend is all right, but I won't have my love given to them."

"Well, then, it sha'n't be." It was well enough to tell *her* so—no harm in it. It was only a little thing to do, and no trouble; and it's the little things that smooths people's roads the most, down here below; it would make Mary Jane comfortable, and it wouldn't cost nothing. Then I says: "There's one more thing—that bag of money."

"Well, they've got that; and it makes me feel pretty silly to think *how* they got it."

"No, you're out, there. They hain't got it."

"Why, who's got it?"

"I wish I knowed, but I don't. I *had* it, because I stole it from them; and I stole it to give to you; and I know where I hid it, but I'm afraid it ain't there no more. I'm awful sorry, Miss Mary Jane, I'm just as sorry as I can be; but I done the best I could; I did honest. I come nigh getting caught, and I had to shove it into the first place I come to, and run—and it warn't a good place."

"Oh, stop blaming yourself—it's too bad to do it, and I won't allow it—you couldn't help it; it wasn't your fault. Where did you hide it?"

I didn't want to set her to thinking about her troubles again; and I couldn't seem to get my mouth to tell her what would make her see that corpse laying in the coffin with that bag of money on his stomach. So for a minute I didn't say nothing; then I says:

"I'd ruther not *tell* you where I put it, Miss Mary Jane, if you don't mind letting me off; but I'll write it for you on a piece of paper, and you can read it along the road to Mr. Lothrop's, if you want to. Do you reckon that 'll do?"

"Oh, yes."

So I wrote: "I put it in the coffin. It was in there when you was crying there, away in the night. I was behind the door, and I was mighty sorry for you."

It made my eyes water a little to remember her crying there all by herself in the night, and them devils laying there right under her own roof, shaming her and robbing her; and when I folded it up and give it to her I see the water come into her eyes, too; and she shook me by the hand, hard, and says:

"*Good-by*. I'm going to do everything just as you've told me; and if I don't ever see you again, I sha'n't ever forget you, and I'll think of you a many and a many a time, and I'll *pray* for you, too!"—and she was gone.

Pray for me! I reckoned if she knowed me she'd take a job that was more nearer her size. But I bet she done it, just the same—she was just that kind. She had the grit to pray for Judus if she took the notion—there warn't no back-down to her, I judge. You may say what you want to, but in my opinion she had more sand in her than any girl I ever see; in my opinion she was just full of sand. It sounds like flattery, but it ain't no flattery. And when it comes to beauty—and goodness, too—she lays over them all. I hain't ever seen her since that time that I see her go out of that door; no, I hain't ever seen her since, but I reckon I've thought of her a many and a many a million times, and of her saying she would pray for me; and if ever I'd 'a' thought it would do any good for me to pray for *her*, blamed if I wouldn't 'a' done it or bust.

Well, Mary Jane she lit out the back way, I reckon; because nobody see her go. When I struck Susan and the hare-lip, I says:

"What's the name of them people over on t'other side of the river that you all goes to see sometimes?"

They says:

"There's several; but it's the Proctors, mainly."

"That's the name," I says; "I most forgot it. Well, Miss Mary Jane she told me to tell you she's gone over there in a dreadful hurry—one of them's sick."

"Which one?"

"I don't know; leastways, I kinder forgot; but I thinks it's—"

"Sakes alive, I hope it ain't *Hanner?*"

"I'm sorry to say it," I says, "but Hanner's the very one."

"My goodness, and she so well only last week! Is she took bad?"

"It ain't no name for it. They set up with her all night, Miss Mary Jane said, and they don't think she'll last many hours."

"Only think of that, now! What's the matter with her?"

I couldn't think of anything reasonable, right off that way, so I says:

"Mumps."

"Mumps your granny! They don't set up with people that's got the mumps."

"They don't, don't they? You better bet they do with *these* mumps. These mumps is different. It's a new kind, Miss Mary Jane said."

"How's it a new kind?"

"Because it's mixed up with other things."

"What other things?"

"Well, measles, and whooping-cough, and erysiplas, and consumption, and yaller janders, and brain-fever, and I don't know what all."

"My land! And they call it the *mumps?*"

"That's what Miss Mary Jane said."

"Well, what in the nation do they call it the *mumps* for?"

"Why, because it *is* the mumps. That's what it starts with."

"Well, ther' ain't no sense in it. A body might stump his toe, and take pison, and fall down the well, and break his neck, and bust his brains out, and somebody come along and ask what killed him, and some numbskull up and say, 'Why, he stumped his *toe.*' Would ther' be any sense in that? *No.* And ther' ain't no sense in *this,* nuther. Is it ketching?"

"Is it *ketching?* Why, how you talk. Is a *harrow* catching—in the dark? If you don't hitch on to one tooth, you're bound to on another, ain't you? And you can't get away with that tooth without fetching the whole harrow along, can you? Well, these kind of mumps is a kind of a harrow, as you may say—and it ain't no slouch of a harrow, nuther, you come to get it hitched on good."

"Well, it's awful, *I* think," says the hare-lip. "I'll go to Uncle Harvey and—"

"Oh, yes," I says, "I *would.* Of *course* I would. I wouldn't lose no time."

"Well, why wouldn't you?"

"Just look at it a minute, and maybe you can see. Hain't your uncles obleeged to get along home to England as fast as they can? And do you reckon they'd be mean enough to go off and leave you to go all that journey by yourselves? *You* know they'll wait for you. So fur, so good. Your uncle Harvey's a preacher, ain't he? Very well, then; is a *preacher* going to deceive a *ship clerk?*—so as to get them to let Miss Mary Jane go aboard? Now *you* know he ain't. What *will* he do, then? Why, he'll say, 'It's a great pity, but my church matters has got to get along the best way they can; for my niece has been exposed to the dreadful pluribus-unum mumps, and so it's my bounden duty to set down here and wait the three months it takes to show on her if she's got it.' But never mind, if you think it's best to tell your uncle Harvey—"

"Shucks, and stay fooling around here when we could all be having good times in England whilst we was waiting to find out whether Mary Jane's got it or not?"

"Well, anyway, maybe you'd better tell some of the neighbors."

"Listen at that, now. You do beat all for natural stupidness. Can't you *see* that *they'd* go and tell? Ther' ain't no way but just to not tell anybody at *all*."

"Well, maybe you're right—yes, I judge you *are* right."

"But I reckon we ought to tell Uncle Harvey she's gone out awhile, anyway, so he won't be uneasy?"

"Yes, Miss Mary Jane she wanted you to do that. She says, 'Tell them to give Uncle Harvey and William my love and a kiss, and say I've run over the river to see Mr.—Mr.—what *is* the name of that rich family your uncle Peter used to think so much of?—I mean the one that—"

"Why, you must mean the Apthorps, ain't it?"

"Of course; bother them kind of names, a body can't ever seem to remember them, half the time, somehow. Yes, she said, say she has run over for to ask the Apthorps to be sure and come to the auction and buy this house, because she allowed her uncle Peter would ruther they had it than anybody else; and she's going to stick to them till they say they'll come, and then, if she ain't too tired, she's coming home; and if she is, she'll be home in the morning anyway. She said, don't say nothing about the Proctors, but only about the Apthorps—which 'll be perfectly true, because she *is* going there to speak about their buying the house; I know it, because she told me so herself."

"All right," they said, and cleared out to lay for their uncles, and give them the love and the kisses, and tell them the message.

Everything was all right now. The girls wouldn't say nothing because they wanted to go to England; and the king and the duke would ruther Mary Jane was off working for the auction than around in reach of Doctor Robinson. I felt very good; I judged I had done it pretty neat—I reckoned Tom Sawyer couldn't 'a' done it no neater himself. Of course he would 'a' throwed more style into it, but I can't do that very handy, not being brung up to it.

Well, they held the auction in the public square, along towards the end of the afternoon, and it strung along, and strung along, and the old man he was on hand and looking his level pisonest, up there longside of the auctioneer, and chipping in a little Scripture now and then, or a little goody-goody saying of some kind, and the duke he was around goo-gooing for sympathy all he knowed how, and just spreading himself generly.

But by and by the thing dragged through, and everything was sold —everything but a little old trifling lot in the graveyard. So they'd got to work *that* off—I never see such a girafft as the king was for wanting to swallow *everything*. Well, whilst they was at it a steamboat landed, and in about two minutes up comes a crowd a-whooping and yelling and laughing and carrying on, and singing out:

"*Here's* your opposition line! here's your two sets o' heirs to old Peter Wilks—and you pays your money and you takes your choice!"

29 *Contested Relationship—The King Explains the Loss—A Question of Handwriting—Digging up the Corpse—Huck Escapes*

They was fetching a very nice-looking old gentleman along, and a nice-looking younger one, with his right arm in a sling. And, my soul, how the people yelled and laughed, and kept it up. But I didn't see no joke about it, and I judged it would strain the duke and king some to see any. I reckoned they'd turn pale. But no, nary a pale did *they* turn. The duke he never let on he suspicioned what was up, but just went a goo-gooing around, happy and satisfied, like a jug that's googling out buttermilk; and as for the king, he just gazed and gazed down sorrowful on them new-comers like it give him the stomach-ache in his very heart to think there could be such frauds and rascals in the world. Oh, he done it admirable. Lots of the principal people gethered around the king, to let him see they was on his side. That old gentleman that had just come looked all puzzled to death. Pretty soon he begun to speak, and I see straight off he pronounced *like* an Englishman—not the king's way, though the king's *was* pretty good for an imitation. I can't give the old gent's words, nor I can't imitate him; but he turned around to the crowd, and says, about like this:

"This is a surprise to me which I wasn't looking for; and I'll acknowledge, candid and frank, I ain't very well fixed to meet it and answer it; for my brother and me has had misfortunes; he's broke his arm, and our baggage got put off at a town above here last night in the night by a mistake. I am Peter Wilks's brother Harvey, and this is his brother William, which can't hear nor speak—and can't even make signs to amount to much, now't he's only got one hand to work them with. We are who we say we are; and in a day or two, when I get the baggage, I can prove it. But up till then I won't say nothing more, but go to the hotel and wait."

So him and the new dummy started off; and the king he laughs, and blethers out:

"Broke his arm—*very* likely, *ain't* it?—and very convenient, too, for a fraud that's got to make signs, and ain't learn't how. Lost their baggage! That's *mighty* good!—and mighty ingenious—under the *circumstances!*"

So he laughed again; and so did everybody else, except three or four, or maybe half a dozen. One of these was that doctor; another one was a sharp-looking gentleman, with a carpet-bag of the old-fashioned kind made out of carpet-stuff, that had just come off of the steamboat and was talking to him in a low voice, and glancing towards the king now and then and nodding their heads—it was Levi Bell, the lawyer that was gone up to Louisville; and another one was a big rough husky that come along and listened to all the old gentlemen said, and was listening to the king now. And when the king got done this husky up and says:

"Say, looky here; if you are Harvey Wilks, when'd you come to this town?"

"The day before the funeral, friend," says the king.

"But what time o' day?"

"In the evenin'—'bout an hour er two before sundown."

"How'd you come?"

"I come down on the *Susan Powell* from Cincinnati."

"Well, then, how'd you come to be up at the Pint in the *mornin'* —in a canoe?"

"I warn't up at the Pint in the mornin'."

"It's a lie."

Several of them jumped for him and begged him not to talk that way to an old man and a preacher.

"Preacher be hanged, he's a fraud and a liar. He was up at the Pint that mornin'. I live up there, don't I? Well, I was up there, and he was up there. I *see* him there. He come in a canoe, along with Tom Collins and a boy."

The doctor he up and says:

"Would you know the boy again if you was to see him, Hines?"

"I reckon I would, but I don't know. Why, yonder he is, now. I know him perfectly easy."

It was me he pointed at. The doctor says:

"Neighbors, I don't know whether the new couple is frauds or not; but if *these* two ain't frauds, I am an idiot, that's all. I think it's our duty to see that they don't get away from here till we've looked into this thing. Come along, Hines; come along, the rest of you. We'll take these fellows to the tavern and affront them with t'other couple, and I reckon we'll find out *something* before we get through."

It was nuts for the crowd, though maybe not for the king's friends; so we all started. It was about sundown. The doctor he led me along by the hand, and was plenty kind enough, but he never let *go* my hand.

We all got in a big room in the hotel, and lit up some candles, and fetched in the new couple. First, the doctor says:

"I don't wish to be too hard on these two men, but *I* think they're frauds, and they may have complices that we don't know nothing about. If they have, won't the complices get away with the bag of gold Peter Wilks left? It ain't unlikely. If these men ain't frauds, they won't object to sending for that money and letting us keep it till they prove they're all right—ain't that so?"

Everybody agreed to that. So I judged they had our gang in a pretty tight place right at the outstart. But the king he only looked sorrowful, and says:

"Gentlemen, I wish the money was there, for I ain't got no disposition to throw anything in the way of a fair, open, out-and-out investigation o' this misable business; but, alas, the money ain't there; you k'n send and see, if you want to."

"Where is it, then?"

"Well, when my niece give it to me to keep for her I took and hid it inside o' the straw tick o' my bed, not wishin' to bank it for the few days we'd be here, and considerin' the bed a safe place, we not bein' used to niggers, and suppos'n' 'em honest, like servants in England. The niggers stole it the very next mornin' after I had went down-stairs; and when I sold 'em I hadn't missed the money yit, so they got clean away with it. My servant here k'n tell you 'bout it, gentlemen."

The doctor and several said "Shucks!" and I see nobody didn't altogether believe him. One man asked me if I see the niggers steal it. I said no, but I see them sneaking out of the room and hustling away, and I never thought nothing, only I reckoned they was afraid they had waked up my master and was trying to get away before he made trouble with them. That was all they asked me. Then the doctor whirls on me and says:

"Are *you* English, too?"

I says yes; and him and some others laughed, and said, "Stuff!"

Well, then they sailed in on the general investigation, and there we had it, up and down, hour in, hour out, and nobody never said a word about supper, nor ever seemed to think about it—and so they kept it up, and kept it up; and it *was* the worst mixed-up thing you ever see. They made the king tell his yarn, and they made the old gentleman tell his'n; and anybody but a lot of predjudiced chuckleheads would 'a' *seen* that the old gentleman was spinning truth and t'other one lies. And by and by they had me up to tell what I knowed. The king he give me a left-handed look out of the corner of his eye, and so I knowed enough to talk on the right side. I begun to tell about Sheffield, and how we lived there, and all about the English Wilkses, and so on; but I didn't get pretty fur till the doctor begun to laugh; and Levi Bell, the lawyer, says:

"Set down, my boy; I wouldn't strain myself if I was you. I reckon you ain't used to lying, it don't seem to come handy; what you want is practice. You do it pretty awkward."

I didn't care nothing for the compliment, but I was glad to be let off, anyway.

The doctor he turns and says:

"If you'd been in town at first, Levi Bell—"

The king broke in and reached out his hand, and says:

"Why, is this my poor dead brother's old friend that he's wrote so often about?"

The lawyer and him shook hands, and the lawyer smiled and looked pleased, and they talked right along awhile, and then got to one side and talked low; and at last the lawyer speaks up and says:

"That 'll fix it. I'll take the order and send it, along with your brother's, and then they'll know it's all right."

So they got some paper and a pen, and the king he set down and twisted his head to one side, and chawed his tongue, and scrawled off something; and then they give the pen to the duke—and then for the first time the duke looked sick. But he took the pen and wrote. So the lawyer turns to the new old gentleman and says:

"You and your brother please write a line or two and sign your names."

The old gentleman wrote, but nobody couldn't read it. The lawyer looked powerful astonished, and says:

"Well, it beats *me*"—and snaked a lot of old letters out of his pocket, and examined them and then examined the old man's writing, and then *them* again; and then says: "These old letters is from Harvey Wilks; and here's *these* two handwritings, and anybody can see *they* didn't write them" (the king and the duke looked sold and foolish, I tell you, to see how the lawyer had took them in), "and here's *this* old gentleman's handwriting, and anybody can tell, easy enough, *he* didn't write them—fact is, the scratches he makes ain't properly *writing* at all. Now, here's some letters from—"

The new old gentleman says:

"If you please, let me explain. Nobody can read my hand but my brother there—so he copies for me. It's *his* hand you've got there, not mine."

"*Well!*" says the lawyer, "this *is* a state of things. I've got some of William's letters, too; so if you'll get him to write a line or so we can com—"

"He *can't* write with his left hand," says the old gentleman. "If he could use his right hand, you would see that he wrote his own letters and mine too. Look at both, please—they're by the same hand."

The lawyer done it, and says:

"I believe it's so—and if it ain't so, there's a heap stronger resemblance than I'd noticed before, anyway. Well, well, well! I thought we was right on the track of a slution, but it's gone to grass, partly. But anyway, *one* thing is proved—*these* two ain't either of 'em Wilkses"—and he wagged his head towards the king and the duke.

Well, what do you think? That mule-headed old fool wouldn't give in *then!* Indeed he wouldn't. Said it warn't no fair test. Said his brother William was the cussedest joker in the world, and hadn't *tried* to write—*he* see William was going to play one of his jokes the minute he put the pen to paper. And so he warmed up and went warbling right along till he was actuly beginning to believe what he was saying *himself;* but pretty soon the new gentleman broke in, and says:

"I've thought of something. Is there anybody here that helped to lay out my br—helped to lay out the late Peter Wilks for burying?"

"Yes," says somebody, "me and Ab Turner done it. We're both here."

Then the old man turns toward the king, and says:

"Peraps this gentleman can tell me what was tattooed on his breast?"

Blamed if the king didn't have to brace up mighty quick, or he'd 'a' squshed down like a bluff bank that the river has cut under, it took him so sudden; and, mind you, it was a thing that was calculated to make most *anybody* sqush to get fetched such a solid one as that without any notice, because how was *he* going to know what was tattooed on the man? He whitened a little; he couldn't help it; and it was mighty still in there, and everybody bending a little forwards and gazing at him. Says I to myself, *Now* he'll throw up the sponge—there ain't no more use. Well, did he? A body can't hardly believe it, but he didn't. I reckon he thought he'd keep the thing up till he tired them people out, so they'd thin out, and him and the duke could break loose and get away. Anyway, he set there, and pretty soon he begun to smile, and says:

"Mf! It's a *very* tough question, *ain't* it! *Yes,* sir, I k'n tell you what's tattooed on his breast. It's jest a small, thin, blue arrow—that's what it is; and if you don't look clost, you can't see it. *Now* what do you say—hey?"

Well, *I* never see anything like that old blister for clean out-and-out cheek.

The new old gentleman turns brisk towards Ab Turner and his

pard, and his eye lights up like he judged he'd got the king *this* time, and says:

"There—you've heard what he said! Was there any such mark on Peter Wilks's breast?"

Both of them spoke up and says:

"We didn't see no such mark."

"Good!" says the old gentleman. "Now, what you *did* see on his breast was a small dim P, and a B (which is an initial he dropped when he was young), and a W, and dashes between them, so: P—B—W"—and he marked them that way on a piece of paper. "Come, ain't that what you saw?"

Both of them spoke up again, and says:

"No, we *didn't*. We never seen any marks at all."

Well, everybody *was* in a state of mind now, and they sings out:

"The whole *bilin'* of 'm 's frauds! Le's duck 'em! le's drown 'em! le's ride 'em on a rail!" and everybody was whooping at once, and there was a rattling powwow. But the lawyer he jumps on the table and yells:

"Gentlemen—gentle*men!* Hear me just a word—just a *single* word—if you PLEASE! There's one way yet—let's go and dig up the corpse and look."

That took them.

"Hooray!" they all shouted, and was starting right off; but the lawyer and the doctor sung out:

"Hold on, hold on! Collar all these four men and the boy, and fetch *them* along, too!"

"We'll do it!" they all shouted; "and if we don't find them marks we'll lynch the whole gang!"

I *was* scared, now, I tell you. But there warn't no getting away, you know. They gripped us all, and marched us right along, straight for the graveyard, which was a mile and a half down the river, and the whole town at our heels, for we made noise enough, and it was only nine in the evening.

As we went by our house I wished I hadn't sent Mary Jane out of town; because now if I could tip her the wink she'd light out and save me.

Well, we swarmed along down the river road, just carrying on like wildcats; and to make it more scary the sky was darking up, and the lightning beginning to wink and flitter, and the wind to shiver amongst the leaves. This was the most awful trouble and most dangersome I ever was in; and I was kinder stunned; everything was going so different from what I had allowed for; stead of being fixed so I could take my own time if I wanted to, and see all the fun, and have Mary Jane at my back to save me and set me free when the close-fit come, here was nothing in the world betwixt me and sudden death but just them tattoo-marks. If they didn't find them—

I couldn't bear to think about it; and yet, somehow, I couldn't think about nothing else. It got darker and darker, and it was a beautiful time to give the crowd the slip; but that big husky had me by the wrists—Hines—and a body might as well try to give Goliar the slip. He dragged me right along, he was so excited, and I had to run to keep up.

When they got there they swarmed into the graveyard and washed over it like an overflow. And when they got to the grave they found they had about a hundred times as many shovels as they wanted, but nobody hadn't thought to fetch a lantern. But they sailed into digging anyway by the flicker of the lightning, and sent a man to the nearest house to borrow one.

So they dug and dug like everything; and it got awful dark, and the rain started, and the wind swished and swushed along, and the lightning come brisker and brisker, and the thunder boomed; but them people never took notice of it, they was so full of this business; and one minute you could see everything and every face in that big crowd, and the shovelfuls of dirt sailing up out of the grave, and the next second the dark wiped it all out, and you couldn't see nothing at all.

At last they got out the coffin and begun to unscrew the lid, and then such another crowding and shouldering and shoving as there was, to scrouge in and get a sight, you never see; and in the dark, that way, it was awful. Hines he hurt my wrist dreadful pulling and tugging so, and I reckon he clean forgot I was in the world, he was so excited and panting.

All of a sudden the lightning let go a perfect sluice of white glare, and somebody sings out:

"By the living jingo, here's the bag of gold on his breast!"

Hines let out a whoop, like everybody else, and dropped my wrist and give a big surge to bust his way in and get a look, and the way

I lit out and shinned for the road in the dark there ain't nobody can tell.

I had the road all to myself, and I fairly flew—leastways, I had it all to myself except the solid dark, and the now-and-then glares, and the buzzing of the rain, and the thrashing of the wind, and the splitting of the thunder; and sure as you are born I did clip it along!

When I struck the town I see there warn't nobody out in the storm, so I never hunted for no back streets, but humped it straight through the main one; and when I begun to get towards our house I aimed my eye and set it. No light there; the house all dark—which made me feel sorry and disappointed, I didn't know why. But at last, just as I was sailing by, *flash* comes the light in Mary Jane's window! and my heart swelled up sudden, like to bust; and the same second the house and all was behind me in the dark, and wasn't ever going to be before me no more in this world. She *was* the best girl I ever see, and had the most sand.

The minute I was far enough above the town to see I could make the towhead, I begun to look sharp for a boat to borrow, and the first time the lightning showed me one that wasn't chained I snatched it and shoved. It was a canoe, and warn't fastened with nothing but a rope. The towhead was a rattling big distance off, away out there in the middle of the river, but I didn't lose no time; and when I struck the raft at last I was so fagged I would 'a' just laid down to blow and gasp if I could afforded it. But I didn't. As I sprung aboard I sung out:

"Out with you, Jim, and set her loose! Glory be to goodness, we're shut of them!"

Jim lit out, and was a-coming for me with both arms spread, he was so full of joy; but when I glimpsed him in the lightning my heart shot up in my mouth and I went overboard backwards; for I forgot he was old King Lear and a drownded A-rab all in one, and it most scared the livers and lights out of me. But Jim fished me out, and was going to hug me and bless me, and so on, he was so glad I was back and we was shut of the king and the duke, but I says:

"Not now; have it for breakfast, have it for breakfast! Cut loose and let her slide!"

So in two seconds away we went a-sliding down the river, and it *did* seem so good to be free again and all by ourselves on the big river, and nobody to bother us. I had to skip around a bit, and jump up and crack my heels a few times—I couldn't help it; but about the third crack I noticed a sound that I knowed mighty well, and held my breath and listened and waited; and sure enough, when the next flash busted out over the water, here they come!—and just a-laying to their oars and making their skiff hum! It was the king and the duke.

So I wilted right down onto the planks then, and give up; and it was all I could do to keep from crying.

30 *The King Went for Him—A Royal Row—Powerful Mellow*

When they got aboard the king went for me, and shook me by the collar, and says:

"Tryin' to give us the slip, was ye, you pup! Tired of our company, hey?"

I says:

"No, your majesty, we warn't—*please* don't, your majesty!"

"Quick, then, and tell us what *was* your idea, or I'll shake the insides out o' you!"

"Honest, I'll tell you everything just as it happened, your majesty. The man that had a-holt of me was very good to me, and kept saying he had a boy about as big as me that died last year, and he was sorry to see a boy in such a dangerous fix; and when they was all took by surprise by finding the gold, and made a rush for the coffin, he lets go of me and whispers, 'Heel it now, or they'll hang ye, sure!' and I lit out. It didn't seem no good for *me* to stay—*I* couldn't do nothing, and I didn't want to be hung if I could get away. So I never stopped running till I found the canoe; and when I got here I told Jim to hurry, or they'd catch me and hang me yet, and said I was afeared you and the duke wasn't alive now, and I was awful sorry, and so was Jim, and was awful glad when we see you coming; you may ask Jim if I didn't."

Jim said it was so; and the king told him to shut up, and said,

"Oh, yes, it's *mighty* likely!" and shook me up again, and said he reckoned he'd drownd me. But the duke says:

"Leggo the boy, you old idiot! Would *you* 'a' done any different? Did you inquire around for *him* when you got loose? *I* don't remember it."

So the king let go of me, and began to cuss that town and everybody in it. But the duke says:

"You better a blame' sight give *yourself* a good cussing, for you're the one that's entitled to it most. You hain't done a thing from the start that had any sense in it; except coming out so cool and cheeky with that imaginary blue-arrow mark. That *was* bright—it was right down bully; and it was the thing that saved us. For if it hadn't been for that they'd 'a' jailed us till them Englishmen's baggage come—and then—the penitentiary, you bet! But the trick took 'em to the graveyard, and the gold done us a still bigger kindness; for if the excited fools hadn't let go all holts and made that rush to get a look we'd 'a' slept in our cravats to-night—cravats warranted to *wear*, too—longer than *we'd* need 'em."

They was still a minute—thinking; then the king says, kind of absent-minded like:

"Mf! And we reckoned the *niggers* stole it!"

That made me squirm!

"Yes," says the duke, kinder slow and deliberate and sarcastic, "*we* did."

After about a half a minute the king drawls out:

"Leastways, *I* did."

The duke says, the same way:

"On the contrary, *I* did."

The king kind of ruffles up, and says:

"Looky here, Bilgewater, what'r you referrin' to?" The duke says, pretty brisk:

"When it comes to that, maybe you'll let me ask what was *you* referring to?"

"Shucks!" says the king, very sarcastic: "but *I* don't know—maybe you was asleep, and didn't know what you was about."

The duke bristles up now, and says:

"Oh, let *up* on this cussed nonsense; do you take me for a blame' fool? Don't you reckon *I* know who hid that money in that coffin?"

"*Yes*, sir! I know you *do* know, because you done it yourself!"

"It's a lie!"—and the duke went for him. The king sings out:

"Take y'r hands off!—leggo my throat—I take it all back!"

The duke says:

"Well, you just own up, first, that you *did* hide that money there, intending to give me the slip one of these days, and come back and dig it up, and have it all to yourself."

"Wait jest a minute, duke—answer me this one question, honest and fair; if you didn't put the money there, say it, and I'll b'lieve you, and take back everything I said."

"You old scoundrel, I didn't, and you know I didn't. There, now!"

"Well, then, I b'lieve you. But answer me only jest this one more —now *don't* git mad; didn't you have it in your *mind* to hook the money and hide it?"

The duke never said nothing for a little bit; then he says:

"Well, I don't care if I *did*, I didn't *do* it, anyway. But you not only had it in mind to do it, but you *done* it."

"I wisht I never die if I done it, duke, and that's honest. I won't say I warn't *goin'* to do it, because I *was*; but you—I mean somebody—got in ahead o' me."

"It's a lie! You done it, and you got to *say* you done it, or—"

The king began to gurgle, and then he gasps out:

" 'Nough!—*I own up!*"

I was very glad to hear him say that; it made me feel much more easier than what I was feeling before. So the duke took his hands off and says:

"If you ever deny it again I'll drown you. It's *well* for you to set there and blubber like a baby—it's fitten for you, after the way you've acted. I never see such an old ostrich for wanting to gobble everything—and I a-trusting you all the time, like you was my own father. You ought to been ashamed of yourself to stand by and hear it saddled on to a lot of poor niggers, and you never say a word for 'em. It makes me feel ridiculous to think I was soft enough to *believe* that rubbage. Cuss you, I can see now why you was so anxious to make up the deffisit—you wanted to get what money I'd got out of the 'Nonesuch' and one thing or another, and scoop it *all!*"

The king says, timid, and still a-snuffling:

"Why, duke, it was you that said make up the deffersit; it warn't me."

"Dry up! I don't want to hear no more *out* of you!" says the duke.

"And *now* you see what you *got* by it. They've got all their own money back, and all of *ourn* but a shekel or two *besides*. G'long to bed, and don't you deffersit *me* no more deffersits, long's *you* live!"

So the king sneaked into the wigwam and took to his bottle for comfort, and before long the duke tackled *his* bottle; and so in about a half an hour they was as thick as thieves again, and the tighter they got the lovinger they got, and went off a-snoring in each other's arms. They both got powerful mellow, but I noticed the king didn't get mellow enough to forget to remember to not deny about hiding the money-bag again. That made me feel easy and satisfied. Of course when they got to snoring we had a long gabble, and I told Jim everything.

31 *Ominous Plans—News from Jim—Old Recollections—A Sheep Story—Valuable Information*

We dasn't stop again at any town for days and days; kept right along down the river. We was down south in the warm weather now, and a mighty long ways from home. We begun to come to trees with Spanish moss on them, hanging down from the limbs like long, gray beards. It was the first I ever see it growing, and it made the woods look solemn and dismal. So now the frauds reckoned they was out of danger, and they begun to work the villages again.

First they done a lecture on temperance; but they didn't make enough for them both to get drunk on. Then in another village they started a dancing-school; but they didn't know no more how to dance than a kangaroo does; so the first prance they made the general public jumped in and pranced them out of town. Another time they tried to go at yellocution; but they didn't yellocute long till the audience got up and give them a solid good cussing, and made them skip out. They tackled missionarying, and mesmerizing, and doctoring, and telling fortunes, and a little of everything; but they couldn't seem to have no luck. So at last they got just about dead broke, and laid around the raft as she floated along, thinking and thinking, and never saying nothing, by the half a day at a time, and dreadful blue and desperate.

And at last they took a change and begun to lay their heads together in the wigwam and talk low and confidential two or three hours at a time. Jim and me got uneasy. We didn't like the look of it. We judged they was studying up some kind of worse deviltry than ever. We turned it over and over, and at last we made up our minds they was going to break into somebody's house or store, or was going into the counterfeit-money business, or something. So then we was pretty scared, and made up an agreement that we wouldn't have nothing in the world to do with such actions, and if we ever got the least show we would give them the cold shake and clear out and leave them behind. Well, early one morning we hid the raft in a good, safe place about two mile below a little bit of a shabby village named Pikesville, and the king he went ashore and told us all to stay hid whilst he went up to town and smelt around to see if anybody had got any wind of the "Royal Nonesuch" there yet. ("House to rob, you *mean*," says I to myself; "and when you get through robbing it you'll come back here and wonder what has become of me and Jim and the raft—and you'll have to take it out in wondering.") And he said if he warn't back by midday the duke and me would know it was all right, and we was to come along.

So we stayed where we was. The duke he fretted and sweated around, and was in a mighty sour way. He scolded us for everything, and we couldn't seem to do nothing right; he found fault with every little thing. Something was a-brewing, sure. I was good and glad when midday come and no king; we could have a change, anyway—and maybe a chance for *the* chance on top of it. So me and the duke went up to the village, and hunted around there for the king, and by and by we found him in the back room of a little low doggery, very tight, and a lot of loafers bullyragging him for sport, and he a-cussing and a-threatening with all his might, and so tight he couldn't walk, and couldn't do nothing to them. The duke he begun to abuse him for an old fool, and the king begun to sass back, and the minute they was fairly at it I lit out and shook the reefs out of my hind legs, and spun down the river road like a deer, for I see our chance; and I made up my mind that it would be a long day before they ever see me and Jim again. I got down there all out of breath but loaded up with joy, and sung out:

"Set her loose, Jim; we're all right now!"

But there warn't no answer, and nobody come out of the wigwam. Jim was gone! I set up a shout—and then another—and then another one; and run this way and that in the woods, whooping and screeching; but it warn't no use—old Jim was gone. Then I set down and cried; I couldn't help it. But I couldn't set still long. Pretty soon I went out on the road, trying to think what I better do, and I run across a boy walking, and asked him if he'd seen a strange nigger dressed so and so, and he says:

"Yes."

"Whereabouts?" says I.

"Down to Silas Phelps's place, two mile below here. He's a runaway nigger, and they've got him. Was you looking for him?"

"You bet I ain't! I run across him in the woods about an hour or two ago, and he said if I hollered he'd cut my livers out—and told me to lay down and stay where I was; and I done it. Been there ever since; afeared to come out."

"Well," he says, "you needn't be afeared no more, becuz they've got him. He run off f'm down South, som'ers."

"It's a good job they got him."

"Well, I *reckon!* There's two hundred dollars' reward on him. It's like picking up money out'n the road."

"Yes, it is—and *I* could 'a' had it if I'd been big enough; I see him first. Who nailed him?

"It was an old fellow—a stranger—and he sold out his chance in him for forty dollars, becuz he's got to go up the river and can't wait. Think o' that, now! You bet *I'd* wait, if it was seven year."

"That's me, every time," says I. "But maybe his chance ain't worth no more than that, if he'll sell it so cheap. Maybe, there's something ain't straight about it."

"But it *is*, though—straight as a string. I see the handbill myself. It tells all about him, to a dot—paints him like a picture, and tells the plantation he's frum, below New*rleans*. No-sirree-*bob*, they ain't no trouble 'bout *that* speculation, you bet you. Say, gimme a chaw tobacker, won't ye?"

I didn't have none, so he left. I went to the raft, and set down in the wigwam to think. But I couldn't come to nothing. I thought till I wore my head sore, but I couldn't see no way out of the trouble. After all this long journey, and after all we'd done for them scoundrels, here it was all come to nothing, everything all busted up and ruined, because they could have the heart to serve Jim such a trick as that, and make him a slave again all his life, and amongst strangers, too, for forty dirty dollars.

Once I said to myself it would be a thousand times better for Jim to be a slave at home where his family was, as long as he'd *got* to be a slave, and so I'd better write a letter to Tom Sawyer and tell him to tell Miss Watson where he was. But I soon give up that notion for two things: she'd be mad and disgusted at his rascality and ungratefulness for leaving her, and so she'd sell him straight down the river again; and if she didn't, everybody naturally despises an ungrateful nigger, and they'd make Jim feel it all the time, and so he'd feel ornery and disgraced. And then think of *me!* It would get all around that Huck Finn helped a nigger to get his freedom; and if I was ever to see anybody from that town again I'd be ready to get down and lick his boots for shame. That's just the way: a person does a low-down thing, and then he don't want to take no consequences of it. Thinks as long as he can hide, it ain't no disgrace. That was my fix exactly. The more I studied about this the more my conscience went to grinding me, and the more wicked and low-down and ornery I got to feeling. And at last, when it hit me all of a sudden that here was the plain hand of Providence slapping me in the face and letting me know my wickedness was being watched all the time from up there in heaven, whilst I was stealing a poor old woman's nigger, that hadn't ever done me no harm, and now was showing me there's One that's always on the lookout, and ain't a-going to allow no such miserable doings to go only just so fur and no further, I most dropped in my tracks I was so scared. Well, I tried the best I could to kinder soften it up somehow for myself by saying I was brung up wicked, and so I warn't so much to blame; but something inside of me kept saying, "There was the Sunday-school, you could 'a' gone to it; and if you'd 'a' done it they'd 'a' learnt you there that people that acts as I'd been acting about that nigger goes to everlasting fire."

It made me shiver. And I about made up my mind to pray, and see if I couldn't try to quit being the kind of a boy I was and be better. So I kneeled down. But the words wouldn't come. Why wouldn't they? It warn't no use to try and hide it from Him. Nor from *me*, neither. I knowed very well why they wouldn't come. It was because my heart warn't right; it was because I warn't square; it was because I was playing double. I was letting *on* to give up sin, but away inside of me I was holding on to the biggest one of all. I was trying to make my mouth *say* I would do the right thing and the clean thing, and go and write to that nigger's owner and tell where he was; but deep down in me I knowed it was a lie, and He knowed it. You can't pray a lie—I found that out.

So I was full of trouble, full as I could be; and didn't know what to do. At last I had an idea; and I says, I'll go and write the letter—and *then* see if I can pray. Why, it was astonishing, the way I felt as light as a feather right straight off, and my troubles all gone. So I got a piece of paper and a pencil, all glad and excited, and set down and wrote:

Miss Watson, your runaway nigger Jim is down here two mile below Pikesville, and Mr. Phelps has got him and he will give him up for the reward if you send.

HUCK FINN.

I felt good and all washed clean of sin for the first time I had ever felt so in my life, and I knowed I could pray now. But I didn't do it straight off, but laid the paper down and set there thinking—thinking how good it was all this happened so, and how near I come to being lost and going to hell. And went on thinking. And got to thinking over our trip down the river; and I see Jim before me all the time: in the day and in the night-time, sometimes moonlight, sometimes storms, and we a-floating along, talking and singing and laughing. But somehow I couldn't seem to strike no places to harden me against him, but only the other kind. I'd see him standing my watch on top of his'n, 'stead of calling me, so I could go on sleeping; and see him how glad he was when I come back out of the fog; and when I come to him again in the swamp, up there where the feud was; and such-like times; and would always call me honey, and pet me, and do everything he could think of for me, and how good he always was; and at last I struck the time I saved him by telling the men we had smallpox aboard, and he was so grateful, and said I was the best friend old Jim ever had in the world, and the *only* one he's got now; and then I happened to look around and see that paper.

It was a close place. I took it up, and held it in my hand. I was a-trembling, because I'd got to decide, forever, betwixt two things, and I knowed it. I studied a minute, sort of holding my breath, and then says to myself:

"All right, then, I'll *go* to hell"—and tore it up.

It was awful thoughts and awful words, but they was said. And I let them stay said; and never thought no more about reforming. I shoved the whole thing out of my head, and said I would take up wickedness again, which was in my line, being brung up to it, and the other warn't. And for a starter I would go to work and steal Jim out of slavery again; and if I could think up anything worse, I would do that, too; because as long as I was in, and in for good, I might as well go the whole hog.

Then I set to thinking over how to get at it, and turned over some considerable many ways in my mind; and at last fixed up a plan that suited me. So then I took the bearings of a woody island that was down the river a piece, and as soon as it was fairly dark I crept out with my raft and went for it, and hid it there, and then turned in. I slept the night through, and got up before it was light, and had my breakfast, and put on my store clothes, and tied up some others and one thing or another in a bundle, and took the canoe and cleared for shore. I landed below where I judged was Phelps's place, and hid my bundle in the woods, and then filled up the canoe with water, and loaded rocks into her and sunk her where I could find her again when I wanted her, about a quarter of a mile below a little steam-sawmill that was on the bank.

Then I struck up the road, and when I passed the mill I see a sign on it, "Phelps's Sawmill," and when I come to the farm-houses, two or three hundred yards further along, I kept my eyes peeled, but didn't see nobody around, though it was good daylight now. But I didn't mind, because I didn't want to see nobody just yet—I only wanted to get the lay of the land. According to my plan, I was going to turn up there from the village, not from below. So I just took a look, and shoved along, straight for town. Well, the very first man I see when I got there was the duke. He was sticking up a bill for the "Royal Nonesuch"—three-night performance—like that other time. *They* had the cheek, them frauds! I was right on him before I could shirk. He looked astonished, and says:

"Hel-*lo!* Where'd *you* come from?" Then he says, kind of glad and eager, "Where's the raft?—got her in a good place?"

I says:

"Why, that's just what I was going to ask your grace."

Then he didn't look so joyful, and says:

"What was your idea for asking *me?*" he says.

"Well," I says, "when I see the king in that doggery yesterday I says to myself, we can't get him alone for hours, till he's soberer; so I went a-loafing around town to put in the time and wait. A man up and offered me ten cents to help him pull a skiff over the river and back to fetch a sheep, and so I went along; but when we was dragging him to the boat, and the man left me a-holt of the rope and went behind him to shove him along, he was too strong for me and jerked loose and run, and we after him. We didn't have no dog, and so we had to chase him all over the country till we tired him out. We never got him till dark; then we fetched him over, and I started down for the raft. When I got there and see it was gone, I says to myself, 'They've got into trouble and had to leave; and they've took my nigger, which is the only nigger I've got in the world, and now I'm in a strange country, and ain't got no property no more, nor nothing, and no way to make my living'; so I set down and cried. I slept in the woods all night. But what *did* become of the raft, then?—and Jim—poor Jim!"

"Blamed if *I* know—that is, what's become of the raft. That old fool had made a trade and got forty dollars, and when we found him in the doggery the loafers had matched half-dollars with him and got every cent but what he'd spent for whisky; and when I got him home late last night and found the raft gone, we said, 'That little rascal has stole our raft and shook us, and run off down the river.'"

"I wouldn't shake my *nigger*, would I?—the only nigger I had in the world, and the only property."

"We never thought of that. Fact is, I reckon we'd come to consider him *our* nigger; yes, we did consider him so—goodness knows we had trouble enough for him. So when we see the raft was gone and we flat broke, there warn't anything for it but to try the 'Royal Nonesuch' another shake. And I've pegged along ever since, dry as a powder-horn. Where's that ten cents? Give it here."

I had considerable money, so I give him ten cents, but begged him to spend it for something to eat, and give me some, because it was all the money I had, and I hadn't had nothing to eat since yesterday. He never said nothing. The next minute he whirls on me and says:

"Do you reckon that nigger would blow on us? We'd skin him if he done that!"

"How can he blow? Hain't he run off?"

"No! That old fool sold him, and never divided with me, and the money's gone."

"*Sold* him?" I says, and begun to cry; "why, he was *my* nigger, and that was my money. Where is he?—I want my nigger."

"Well, you can't *get* your nigger, that's all—so dry up your blubbering. Looky here—do you think *you'd* venture to blow on us? Blamed if I think I'd trust you—"

He stopped, but I never see the duke look so ugly out of his eyes before. I went on a-whimpering, and says:

"I don't want to blow on nobody; and I ain't got no time to blow, nohow; I got to turn out and find my nigger."

He looked kinder bothered, and stood there with his bills fluttering on his arm, thinking, and wrinkling up his forehead. At last he says:

"I'll tell you something. We got to be here three days. If you'll promise you won't blow, and won't let the nigger blow, I'll tell you where to find him."

So I promised, and he says:

"A farmer by the name of Silas Ph—" and then he stopped. You see, he started to tell me the truth; but when he stopped that way, and begun to study and think again, I reckoned he was changing his mind. And so he was. He wouldn't trust me; he wanted to make sure of having me out of the way the whole three days. So pretty soon he says:

"The man that bought him is named Abram Foster—Abram G. Foster—and he lives forty mile back here in the country, on the road to Lafayette."

"All right," I says, "I can walk it in three days. And I'll start this very afternoon."

"No you won't, you'll start *now;* and don't you lose any time about it, neither, nor do any gabbling by the way. Just keep a tight tongue in your head and move right along, and then you won't get into trouble with *us,* d'ye hear?"

That was the order I wanted, and that was the one I played for. I wanted to be left free to work my plans.

"So clear out," he says; "and you can tell Mr. Foster whatever you want to. Maybe you can get him to believe that Jim *is* your nigger—some idiots don't require documents—leastways I've heard there's such down South here. And when you tell him the handbill and the reward's bogus, maybe he'll believe you when you explain to him what the idea was for getting 'em out. Go 'long now, and tell him anything you want to; but mind you don't work your jaw *between* here and there."

So I left, and struck for the back country. I didn't look around, but I kinder felt like he was watching me. But I knowed I could tire him out at that. I went straight out in the country as much as a mile before I stopped; then I doubled back through the woods towards Phelps's. I reckoned I better start in on my plan straight off without fooling around, because I wanted to stop Jim's mouth till these fellows could get away. I didn't want no trouble with their kind. I'd seen all I wanted to of them, and wanted to get entirely shut of them.

32 *Still and Sunday-like—Mistaken Identity—Up a Stump—In a Dilemma*

When I got there it was all still and Sunday-like, and hot and sunshiny; the hands was gone to the fields; and there was them kind of faint dronings of bugs and flies in the air that makes it seem so lonesome and like everybody's dead and gone; and if a breeze fans along and quivers the leaves it makes you feel mournful, because you feel like its spirits whispering—spirits that's been dead ever so many years—and you always think they're talking about *you*. As a general thing it makes a body wish *he* was dead, too, and done with it all.

Phelps's was one of these little one-horse cotton plantations, and they all look alike. A rail fence round a two-acre yard; a stile made out of logs sawed off and up-ended in steps, like barrels of a different length, to climb over the fence with, and for the women to stand on when they are going to jump onto a horse; some sickly grass-patches in the big yard, but mostly it was bare and smooth, like an old hat with the nap rubbed off; big double log house for the white folks—hewed logs, with the chinks stopped up with mud or mortar, and these mud-stripes been whitewashed some time or another; round-log kitchen, with a big broad, open but roofed passage joining it to the house; log smokehouse back of the kitchen; three little log nigger cabins in a row t'other side the smokehouse; one little hut all by itself away down against the back fence, and some out-buildings down a piece the other side; ash-hopper and big kettle to bile soap in by the little hut; bench by the kitchen door, with bucket of water and a gourd; hound asleep there in the sun; more hounds alseep round about; about three shade trees away off in a corner; some currant bushes and gooseberry bushes in one place by the fence; outside of the fence a garden and a watermelon patch; then the cottonfields begins, and after the fields the woods.

I went around and clumb over the back stile by the ash-hopper, and started for the kitchen. When I got a little ways I heard the dim hum on a spinning-wheel wailing along up and sinking along down again; and then I knowed for certain I wished I was dead—for that *is* the lonesomest sound in the whole world.

I went right along, not fixing up any particular plan, but just trusting to Providence to put the right words in my mouth when the time come; for I'd noticed that Providence always did put the right words in my mouth if I left it alone.

When I got half-way, first one hound and then another got up and went for me, and of course I stopped and faced them, and kept still. And such another pow-wow as they made! In a quarter of a minute I was a kind of a hub of a wheel, as you may say—spokes made out of dogs—circle of fifteen of them packed together around me, with their necks and noses stretched up towards me, a-barking and howling; and more a-coming; you could see them sailing over fences and around corners from everywheres.

A nigger woman come tearing out of the kitchen with a rolling-pin in her hand, singing out, "Begone! *you* Tige! you Spot! begone sah!" and she fetched first one and then another of them a clip and sent them howling, and then the rest followed; and the next second half of them come back, wagging their tails around me, and making friends with me. There ain't no harm in a hound, nohow.

And behind the woman comes a little nigger girl and two little nigger boys without anything on but tow-linen shirts, and they hung on to their mother's gown, and peeped out from behind her at me, bashful, the way they always do. And here comes the white woman running from the house, about forty-five or fifty year old, bareheaded, and her spinning-stick in her hand; and behind her comes her little white children, acting the same way the little niggers was going. She was smiling all over so she could hardly stand—and says:

"It's *you*, at last!—*ain't* it?"

I out with a "Yes'm" before I thought.

She grabbed me and hugged me tight; and then gripped me by both hands and shook and shook; and the tears come in her eyes, and run down over; and she couldn't seem to hug and shake enough, and kept saying, "You don't look as much like your mother as I reckoned you would; but law sakes, I don't care for that, I'm *so* glad to see you! Dear, dear, it does seem like I could eat you up! Children, it's your cousin Tom!—tell him howdy."

But they ducked their heads, and put their fingers in their mouths, and hid behind her. So she run on:

"Lize, hurry up and get him a hot breakfast right away—or did you get your breakfast on the boat?"

I said I had got it on the boat. So then she started for the house, leading me by the hand, and the children tagging after. When we got there she set me down in a split-bottomed chair, and set herself down on a little low stool in front of me, holding both of my hands, and says:

"Now I can have a *good* look at you; and, laws-a-me, I've been hungry for it a many and a many a time, all these long years, and it's come at last! We been expecting you a couple of days and more. What kep' you?—boat get aground?"

"Yes'm—she—"

"Don't say yes'm—say Aunt Sally. Where'd she get aground?"

I didn't rightly know what to say, because I didn't know whether the boat would be coming up the river or down. But I go a good deal on instinct; and my instinct said she would be coming up—from down towards Orleans. That didn't help me much, though; for I didn't know the names of bars down that way. I see I'd got to invent a bar, or forget the name of the one we got aground on—or— Now I struck an idea, and fetched it out:

"It warn't the grounding—that didn't keep us back but a little. We blowed out a cylinder-head."

"Good gracious! anybody hurt?"

"No'm. Killed a nigger."

"Well, it's lucky! because sometimes people do get hurt. Two years ago last Christmas your uncle Silas was coming up from Newrleans on the old *Lally Rook*, and she blowed out a cylinder-head and crippled a man. And I think he died afterwards. He was a Baptist. Your uncle Silas knowed a family in Baton Rouge that knowed his people very well. Yes, I remember now, he *did* die. Mortification set in, and they had to amputate him. But it didn't save him. Yes, it was mortification—that was it. He turned blue all over, and died in the hope of a glorious resurrection. They say he was a sight to look at. Your uncle's been up to the town every day to fetch you. And he's gone again, not more'n an hour ago; he'll be back any minute now. You must 'a' met him on the road, didn't you?—oldish man, with a—"

"No, I didn't see nobody, Aunt Sally. The boat landed just at daylight, and I left my baggage on the wharf-boat and went looking around the town and out a piece in the country, to put in the time and not get here too soon; and so I come down the back way."

"Who'd you give the baggage to?"

"Nobody."

"Why, child, it'll be stole!"

"Not where *I* hid it I reckon it won't," I says.

"How'd you get your breakfast so early on the boat?"

It was kinder thin ice, but I says:

"The captain see me standing around, and told me I better have something to eat before I went ashore; so he took me in the texas to the officers' lunch, and give me all I wanted."

I was getting so uneasy I couldn't listen good. I had my mind on the children all the time; I wanted to get them out to one side and pump them a little, and find out who I was. But I couldn't get no show, Mrs. Phelps kept it up and run on so. Pretty soon she made the cold chills streak all down my back, because she says:

"But here we're a-running on this way, and you hain't told me a word about Sis, nor any of them. Now I'll rest my works a little, and you start up yourn; just tell me *everything*—tell me all about'm all—every one of'm; and how they are, and what they're doing, and what they told you to tell me; and every last thing you can think of."

Well, I see I was up a stump—and up it good. Providence had stood by me this fur all right, but I was hard and tight aground now. I see it warn't a bit of use to try to go ahead—I'd *got* to throw up my hand. So I says to myself, here's another place where I got to resk the truth. I opened my mouth to begin; but she grabbed me and hustled me in behind the bed, and says:

"Here he comes! Stick your head down lower—there, that 'll do; you can't be seen now. Don't you let on you're here. I'll play a joke on him. Children, don't you say a word."

I see I was in a fix now. But it warn't no use to worry; there warn't nothing to do but just hold still, and try and be ready to stand from under when the lightning struck.

I had just one little glimpse of the old gentleman when he come in; then the bed hid him. Mrs. Phelps she jumps for him, and says:

"Has he come?"

"No," says her husband.

"Good-*ness* gracious!" she says, "what in the world *can* have become of him?"

"I can't imagine," says the old gentleman; "and I must say it makes me dreadful uneasy."

"Uneasy!" she says; "I'm ready to go distracted! He *must* 'a' come; and you've missed him along the road. I *know* it's so— something *tells* me so."

"Why, Sally, I *couldn't* miss him along the road—*you* know that."

"But oh, dear, dear, what *will* Sis say! He must 'a' come! You must 'a' missed him. He—"

"Oh, don't distress me any more'n I'm already distressed. I don't know what in the world to make of it. I'm at my wit's end, and I don't mind acknowledging 't I'm right down scared. But there's no hope that he's come; for he *couldn't* come and me miss him. Sally, it's terrible—just terrible—something's happened to the boat, sure!"

"Why, Silas! Look yonder!—up the road!—ain't that somebody coming?"

He sprung to the window at the head of the bed, and that give Mrs. Phelps the chance she wanted. She stooped down quick at the foot of the bed and give me a pull, and out I come; and when he turned back from the window there she stood, a-beaming and a-smiling like a house afire, and I standing pretty meek and sweaty alongside. The old gentleman stared, and says:

"Why, who's that?"

"Who do you reckon 'tis?"

"I hain't no idea. Who *is* it?"

"It's *Tom Sawyer!*"

By jings, I most slumped through the floor! But there warn't no time to swap knives; the old man grabbed me by the hand and shook, and kept on shaking; and all the time how the woman did dance around and laugh and cry; and then how they both did fire off questions about Sid, and Mary, and the rest of the tribe.

But if they was joyful, it warn't nothing to what I was; for it was like being born again, I was so glad to find out who I was. Well, they froze to me for two hours; and at last, when my chin was so tired it couldn't hardly go any more, I had told them more about my family—I mean the Sawyer family—than ever happened to any six Sawyer families. And I explained all about how we blowed out a cylinder-head at the mouth of White River, and it took us three days to fix it. Which was all right, and worked first-rate; because *they* didn't know but what it would take three days to fix it. If I'd 'a' called it a bolt-head it would 'a' done just as well.

Now I was feeling pretty comfortable all down one side, and pretty uncomfortable all up the other. Being Tom Sawyer was easy and comfortable, and it stayed easy and comfortable till by and by I hear a steamboat coughing along down the river. Then I says to myself, s'pose Tom Sawyer comes down on that boat? And s'pose he steps in here any minute, and sings out my name before I can throw him a wink to keep quiet?

Well, I couldn't *have* it that way; it wouldn't do at all. I must go up the road and waylay him. So I told the folks I reckoned I would go up to the town and fetch down my baggage. The old gentleman was for going along with me, but I said no, I could drive the horse myself, and I druther he wouldn't take no trouble about me.

33 *A Nigger Stealer—Southern Hospitality—A Pretty Long Blessing—Tar and Feathers*

So I started for town in the wagon, and when I was half-way I see a wagon coming, and sure enough it was Tom Sawyer, and I stopped and waited till he come along. I says "Hold on!" and it stopped alongside, and his mouth opened up like a trunk, and stayed so; and he swallowed two or three times like a person that's got a dry throat, and then says:

"I hain't ever done you no harm. You know that. So, then, what you want to come back and ha'nt *me* for?"

I says:

"I hain't come back—I hain't been *gone*."

When he heard my voice it righted him up some, but he warn't quite satisfied yet. He says:

"Don't you play nothing on me, because I wouldn't on you. Honest injun, you ain't a ghost?"

"Honest injun, I ain't," I says.

"Well—I—I—well, that ought to settle it, of course; but I can't somehow seem to understand it no way. Looky here, warn't you ever murdered *at all?*

"No. I warn't ever murdered at all—I played it on them. You come in here and feel of me if you don't believe me."

So he done it; and it satisfied him; and he was that glad to see me again he didn't know what to do. And he wanted to know all about it right off, because it was a grand adventure, and mysterious, and so it hit him where he lived. But I said, leave it alone till by and by; and told his driver to wait, and we drove off a little piece, and I told him the kind of a fix I was in, and what did he reckon we better do? He said, let him alone a minute, and don't disturb him. So he thought and thought, and pretty soon he says:

"It's all right; I've got it. Take my trunk in your wagon, and let on it's yourn; and you turn back and fool along slow, so as to get to the house about the time you ought to; and I'll go towards town a piece, and take a fresh start, and get there a quarter or a half an hour after you; and you needn't let on to know me at first."

I says:

"All right; but wait a minute. There's one more thing—a thing that *nobody* don't know but me. And that is, there's a nigger here that I'm a-trying to steal out of slavery, and his name is *Jim*—old Miss Watson's Jim."

He says:

"What! Why, Jim is—"

He stopped and went to studying. I says:

"*I* know what you'll say. You'll say it's dirty, low-down business; but what if it is? I'm low down; and I'm a-going to steal him, and I want you keep mum and not let on. Will you?"

His eye lit up, and he says:

"I'll *help* you steal him!"

Well, I let go all holts then, like I was shot. It was the most astonishing speech I ever heard—and I'm bound to say Tom Sawyer fell considerable in my estimation. Only I couldn't believe it. Tom Sawyer a *nigger-stealer!*

"Oh, shucks!" I says; "you're joking."

"I ain't joking, either."

"Well, then," I says, "joking or no joking, if you hear anything said about a runaway nigger, don't forget to remember that *you* don't know nothing about him, and *I* don't know nothing about him."

Then we took the trunk and put it in my wagon, and he drove off his way and I drove mine. But of course I forgot all about driving slow on accounts of being glad and full of thinking; so I got home a heap too quick for that length of a trip. The old gentleman was at the door, and he says:

"Why, this is wonderful! Whoever would 'a' thought it was in that mare to do it? I wish we'd 'a' timed her. And she hain't sweated a hair—not a hair. It's wonderful. Why, I wouldn't take a hundred dollars for that horse now—I wouldn't, honest; and yet I'd 'a' sold her for fifteen before, and thought 'twas all she was worth."

That's all he said. He was the innocentest, best old soul I ever see. But it warn't surprising; because he warn't only just a farmer, he was a preacher, too, and had a little one-horse log church down back of the plantation, which he built it himself at his own expense, for a church and schoolhouse, and never charged nothing for his preaching, and it was worth it, too. There was plenty other farmer-preachers like that, and done the same way, down South.

In about half an hour Tom's wagon drove up to the front stile, and Aunt Sally she see it through the window, because it was only about fifty yards, and says:

"Why, there's somebody come! I wonder who 'tis? Why, I do believe it's a stranger. Jimmy" (that's one of the children), "run and tell Lize to put on another plate for dinner."

Everybody made a rush for the front door, because, of course, a starnger don't come *every* year, and so he lays over the yaller-fever, for interest, when he does come. Tom was over the stile and starting for the house; the wagon was spinning up the road for the village, and we was all bunched in the front door. Tom had his store clothes on, and an audience—and that was always nuts for Tom Sawyer. In them circumstances it warn't no trouble to him to throw in an amount of style that was suitable. He warn't a boy to meeky along up that yard like a sheep; no, he come ca'm and important, like the ram. When he got a-front of us he lifts his hat ever so gracious and dainty, like it was the lid of a box that had butterflies asleep in it and he didn't want to disturb them, and says:

"Mr. Archibald Nichols, I presume?"

"No, my boy," says the old gentleman, "I'm sorry to say 't your driver has deceived you; Nichols's place is down a matter of three mile more. Come in, come in."

Tom he took a look back over his shoulder, and says, "Too late—he's out of sight."

"Yes, he's gone, my son, and you must come in and eat your dinner with us; and then we'll hitch up and take you down to Nichols's."

"Oh, I *can't* make you so much trouble; I couldn't think of it. I'll walk—I don't mind the distance."

"But we won't *let* you walk—it wouldn't be Southern hospitality to do it. Come right in."

"Oh, *do*," says Aunt Sally; "it ain't a bit of trouble to us, not a bit in the world. You *must* stay. It's a long, dusty three mile, and we *can't* let you walk. And, besides, I've already told 'em to put on another plate when I see you coming; so you mustn't disappoint us. Come right in and make yourself at home."

So Tom he thanked them very hearty and handsome, and let himself be persuaded, and come in; and when he was in he said he was a stranger from Hicksville, Ohio, and his name was William Thompson—and he made another bow.

Well, he run on, and on, and on, making up stuff about Hicksville and everybody in it he could invent, and I getting a little nervious, and wondering how this was going to help me out of my scrape; and at last, still talking along, he reached over and kissed Aunt Sally right on the mouth, and then settled back again in his chair comfortable, and was going on talking; but she jumped up and wiped it off with the back of her hand, and says:

"You owdacious puppy!"

He looked kind of hurt, and says:

"I'm surprised at you, m'am."

"You're s'rp— Why, what do you reckon *I* am? I've a good notion to take and —Say, what do you mean by kissing me?"

He looked kind of humble, and says:

"I didn't mean nothing, m'am. I didn't mean no harm. I—I—thought you'd like it."

"Why, you born fool!" She took up the spinning-stick, and it looked like it was all she could do to keep from giving him a crack with it. "What made you think I'd like it?"

"Well, I don't know. Only, they—they—told me you would."

"*They* told you I would. Whoever told you's *another* lunatic. never heard the beat of it. Who's *they?*"

"Why, everybody. They all said so, m'am."

It was all she could do to hold in; and her eyes snapped, and he fingers worked like she wanted to scratch him; and she says:

"Who's 'everybody'? Out with their names, or ther'll be an idio short."

He got up and looked distressed, and fumbled his hat, and says

"I'm sorry, and I warn't expecting it. They told me to. They a told me to. They all said, kiss her; and said she'd like it. They all sai it—every one of them. But I'm sorry, m'am, and I won't do it n more—I won't, honest."

"You won't, won't you? Well, I sh'd *reckon* you won't!"

"No'm, I'm honest about it; I won't ever do it again—till you as me."

"Till I *ask* you! Well, I never see the beat of it in my born days I lay you'll be the Methusalem-numskull of creation before ever ask you—or the likes of you."

"Well," he says, "it does surprise me so. I can't make it ou somehow. They said you would, and I thought you would. But— He stopped and looked around slow, like he wished he could ru across a friendly eye somewheres, and fetched up on the old gentle men's, and says, "Didn't *you* think she'd like me to kiss her, sir?"

"Why, no; I—I—well, no, I b'lieve I didn't."

Then he looks on around the same way to me, and says:

"Tom, didn't *you* think Aunt Sally 'd open out her arms and say 'Sid Sawyer—' "

"My land!" she says, breaking in and jumping for him, "you impudent young rascal, to fool a body so—" and was going to hug him but he fended her off, and says:

"No, not till you've asked me first."

So she didn't lose no time, but asked him; and hugged him an kissed him over and over again, and then turned him over to th old man, and he took what was left. And after they got a little quie again she says:

"Why, dear me, I never see such a surprise. We warn't looking fo *you* at all, but only Tom. Sis never wrote to me about anybody coming but him."

"It's because it warn't *intended* for any of us to come but Tom," he says; "but I begged and begged, and at the last minute she let me come, too; so, coming down the river, me and Tom thought it would be a first-rate surprise for him to come here to the house first, and for me to by and by tag along and drop in, and let on to be a stranger. But it was a mistake, Aunt Sally. This ain't no healthy place for a stranger to come."

"No—not impudent whelps, Sid. You ought to had your jaws boxed; I hain't been so put out since I don't know when. But I don't care, I don't mind the terms—I'd be willing to stand a thousand such jokes to have you here. Well, to think of that performance! I don't deny it, I was most putrified with astonishment when you give me that smack."

We had dinner out in that broad open passage betwixt the house and the kitchen; and there was things enough on that table for seven families—and all hot, too; none of your flabby, tough meat that's laid in a cupboard in a damp cellar all night and tastes like a hunk of old cold cannibal in the morning. Uncle Silas he asked a pretty long blessing over it, but it was worth it; and it didn't cool it a bit, neither, the way I've seen them kind of interruptions do lots of times.

There was a considerable good deal of talk all the afternoon, and me and Tom was on the lookout all the time; but it warn't no use, they didn't happen to say nothing about any runaway nigger, and we was afraid to try to work up to it. But at supper, at night, one of the little boys says:

"Pa, mayn't Tom and Sid and me go to the show?"

"No," says the old man, "I reckon there ain't going to be any; and you couldn't go if there was; because the runaway nigger told Burton and me all about that scandalous show, and Burton said he would tell the people; so I reckon they've drove the owdacious loafers out of town before this time."

So there it was!—but *I* couldn't help it. Tom and me was to sleep in the same room and bed; so, being tired, we bid good night and went up to bed right after supper, and clumb out of the window and down the lightning-rod, and shoved for the town; for I didn't believe anybody was going to give the king and the duke a hint, and so if

I didn't hurry up and give them one they'd get into troubl sure.

On the road Tom he told me all about how it was reckoned I wa murdered, and how pap disappeared pretty soon, and didn't com back no more, and what a stir there was when Jim run away; and told Tom all about our "Royal Nonesuch" rapscallions, and as muc of the raft voyage as I had time to; and as we struck into the tow and up through the middle of it—it was as much as half after eigh then—here comes a raging rush of people with torches, and an awfu whooping and yelling, and banging tin pans and blowing horns; an we jumped to one side to let them go by; and as they went by I se they had the king and the duke astraddle of a rail—that is, I knowe it *was* the king and duke, though they was all over tar and feather and didn't look like nothing in the world that was human—ju looked like a couple of monstrous big soldier-plumes. Well, it mad me sick to see it; and I was sorry for them poor pitiful rascals, seemed like I couldn't ever feel any hardness against them any mo in the world. It was a dreadful thing to see. Human beings *can* b awful cruel to one another.

We see we was too late—couldn't do no good. We asked som stragglers about it, and they said everybody went to the show look ing very innocent; and laid low and kept dark till the poor old kin was in the middle of his cavortings on the stage; then somebody giv a signal, and the house rose up and went for them.

So we poked along back home, and I warn't feeling so brash as was before, but kind of ornery, and humble, and to blame, someho —though *I* hadn't done nothing. But that's always the way; it don make no difference whether you do right or wrong, a person's con science ain't got no sense, and just goes for him *anyway*. If I had yaller dog that didn't know no more than a person's conscience doe I would pison him. It takes up more room than all the rest of a pe son's insides, and yet ain't no good, nohow. Tom Sawyer he says th same.

34 *The Hut by the Ash-hopper—Outrageous —Climbing the Lightning-rod— Troubled with Witches*

We stopped talking, and got to thinking. By and by Tom says:

"Looky here, Huck, what fools we are to not think of it before! I bet I know where Jim is."

"No! Where?"

"In that hut down by the ash-hopper. Why, looky here. When we was at dinner, didn't you see a nigger man go in there with some vittles?"

"Yes."

"What did you think the vittles was for?"

"For a dog."

"So 'd I. Well, it wasn't for a dog."

"Why?"

"Because part of it was watermelon."

"So it was—I noticed it. Well, it does beat all that I never thought about a dog not eating watermelon. It shows how a body can see and don't see at the same time."

"Well, the nigger unlocked the padlock when he went in, and he locked it again when he came out. He fetched uncle a key about the time we got up from table—same key, I bet. Watermelon shows man, lock shows prisoner; and it ain't likely there's two prisoners on such a little plantation, and where the people's all so kind and good. Jim's the prisoner. All right—I'm glad we found it out detective fashion; I wouldn't give shucks for any other way. Now you work your mind, and study out a plan to steal Jim, and I will study out one, too; and we'll take the one we like the best."

What a head for just a boy to have! If I had Tom Sawyer's head I wouldn't trade it off to be a duke, nor mate of a steamboat, nor clown in a circus, nor nothing I can think of. I went to thinking out a plan, but only just to be doing something; I knowed very well where the right plan was going to come from. Pretty soon Tom says:

"Ready?"

"Yes," I says.

"All right—bring it out."

"My plan is this," I says. "We can easy find out if it's Jim in there Then get up my canoe to-morrow night, and fetch my raft ove from the island. Then the first dark night that comes steal the ke out of the old man's britches after he goes to bed, and shove off dow the river on the raft with Jim, hiding daytimes and running nights the way me and Jim used to do before. Wouldn't that plan work?"

"*Work?* Why, cert'nly it would work, like rats a-fighting. But it' too blame' simple; there ain't nothing *to* it. What's the good of plan that ain't no more trouble than that? It's as mild as goose-milk Why, Huck, it wouldn't make no more talk than breaking into soap factory."

I never said nothing, because I warn't expecting nothing different but I knowed mighty well that whenever he got *his* plan ready i wouldn't have none of them objections to it.

And it didn't. He told me what it was, and I see in a minute i was worth fifteen of mine for style, and would make Jim just as fre a man as mine would, and maybe get us all killed besides. So I wa satisfied, and said we would waltz in on it. I needn't tell what it wa here, because I knowed it wouldn't stay the way it was. I knowed h would be changing it around every which way as we went along, and heaving in new bullinesses wherever he got a chance. And that i what he done.

Well, one thing was dead sure, and that was that Tom Sawye was in earnest, and was actuly going to help steal that nigger out o slavery. That was the thing that was too many for me. Here was a boy that was respectable and well brung up; and had a character to lose; and folks at home that had characters; and he was bright and not leather-headed; and knowing and not ignorant; and not mean, but kind; and yet here he was, without any more pride, or rightness, or feeling, than to stoop to this business, and make himself a shame, and his family a shame, before everybody. I *couldn't* understand it no way at all. It was outrageous, and I knowed I ought to just up and tell him so; and so be his true friend, and let him quit the thing right where he was and save himself. And I *did* start to tell him; but he shut me up, and says:

"Don't you reckon I know what I'm about? Don't I generly know what I'm about?"

"Yes."

"Didn't I *say* I was going to help steal the nigger?"

"Yes."

"*Well*, then."

That's all he said, and that's all I said. It warn't no use to say any more; because when he said he'd do a thing, he always done it. But *I* couldn't make out how he was willing to go into this thing; so I just let it go, and never bothered no more about it. If he was bound to have it so, *I* couldn't help it.

When we got home the house was all dark and still; so we went on down to the hut by the ash-hopper for to examine it. We went through the yard so as to see what the hounds would do. They knowed us, and didn't make no more noise than country dogs is always doing when anything comes by in the night. When we got to the cabin we took a look at the front and the two sides; and on the side I warn't acquainted with—which was the north side—we found a square window-hole, up tolerable high, with just one stout board nailed across it. I says:

"Here's the ticket. This hole's big enough for Jim to get through if we wrench off the board."

Tom says:

"It's as simple as tit-tat-toe, three-in-a-row, and as easy as playing hooky. I should *hope* we can find a way that's a little more complicated than *that*, Huck Finn."

"Well, then," I says, "how'll it do to saw him out, the way I done before I was murdered that time?"

"That's more *like*," he says. "It's real mysterious, and troublesome, and good," he says; "but I bet we can find a way that's twice as long. There ain't no hurry; le's keep on looking around."

Betwixt the hut and the fence, on the back side, was a lean-to that joined the hut at the eaves, and was made out of plank. It was as long as the hut, but narrow—only about six foot wide. The door to it was at the south end, and was padlocked. Tom he went to the soap-kettle and searched around, and fetched back the iron thing they lift the lid with; so he took it and prized out one of the staples. The chain fell down, and we opened the door and went in, and shut it, and struck a match, and see the shed was only built against a cabin and hadn't no connection with it; and there warn't no floor to the shed, nor nothing in it but some old rusty played-out hoes and spades and picks and a crippled plow. The match went out, and so did we, and shoved in the staple again, and the door was locked as good as ever. Tom was joyful. He says;

"Now we're all right. We'll *dig* him out. It'll take about a week!"

Then we started for the house, and I went in the back door—you only have to pull a buckskin latchstring, they don't fasten the doors—but that warn't romantical enough for Tom Sawyer; no way would do him but he must climb up the lightning-rod. But after he got up half-way about three times, and missed fire and fell every time, and the last time most busted his brains out, he thought he'd got to give it up; but after he was rested he allowed he would give her one more turn for luck, and this time he made the trip.

In the morning we was up at break of day, and down to the nigger cabins to pet the dogs and make friends with the nigger that fed Jim—if it *was* Jim that was being fed. The niggers was just getting through breakfast and starting for the fields; and Jim's nigger was piling up a tin pan with bread and meat and things; and whilst the others was leaving, the key come from the house.

This nigger had a good-natured, chuckle-headed face, and his wool was all tied up in little bunches with thread. That was to keep witches off. He said the witches was pestering him awful these nights, and making him see all kinds of strange things, and hear all kinds of strange words and noises, and he didn't believe he was ever witched so long before in his life. He got so worked up, and got to running on so about his troubles, he forgot all about what he'd been a-going to do. So Tom says:

"What's the vittles for? Going to feed the dogs?"

The nigger kind of smiled around graduly over his face, like when you heave a brickbat in a mud-puddle, and he says:

"Yes, Mars Sid, *a* dog. Cur'us dog, too. Does you want to go en look at 'im?"

"Yes."

I hunched Tom, and whispers:

"You going, right here in the daybreak? *That* warn't the plan."

"No, it warn't; but it's the plan *now*."

So, drat him, we went along, but I didn't like it much. When we got in we couldn't hardly see anything, it was so dark; but Jim was there, sure enough, and could see us; and he sings out:

"Why, *Huck*! En good *lan'*! ain't dat Misto Tom?"

I just knowed how it would be; I just expected it. *I* didn't know nothing to do; and if I had I couldn't 'a' done it, because that nigger busted in and says:

"Why, de gracious sakes! do he know you genlmen?"

We could see pretty well now. Tom he looked at the nigger, steady and kind of wondering, and says:

"Does *who* know us?"

"Why, dis-yer runaway nigger."

"I don't reckon he does; but what put that into your head?"

"What *put* it dar? Didn' he jis' dis minute sing out like he knowed you?"

Tom says, in a puzzled-up kind of way:

"Well, that's mighty curious. *Who* sung out? *When* did he sing out? *What* did he sing out?" And turns to me, perfectly ca'm, and says, "Did *you* hear anybody sing out?"

Of course there warn't nothing to be said but the one thing; so I says:

"No; *I* ain't heard nobody say nothing."

Then he turns to Jim, and looks him over like he never see him before, and says:

"Did you sing out?"

"No, sah," says Jim; "*I* hain't said nothing, sah."

"Not a word?"

"No, sah, I hain't said a word."

"Did you ever see us before?"

"No, sah; not as *I* knows on."

So Tom turns to the nigger, which was looking wild and distressed, and says, kind of severe:

"What do you reckon's the matter with you, anyway? What made you think somebody sung out?"

"Oh, it's de dad-blame' witches, sah, en I wisht I was dead, I do. Dey's awluz at it, sah, en dey do mos' kill me, dey sk'yers me so. Please to don't tell nobody 'bout it sah, er ole Mars Silas he'll scole me; 'kase he say dey ain't no witches. I jis' wish to goodness he was heah now—*den* what would he say! I jis' bet he couldn't fine no way to git aroun' it *dis* time. But it's awluz jis' so; people dat's *sot*, stays sot; dey won't look into noth'n' en fine it out f'r deyselves, en when *you* fine it out en tell um 'bout it, dey doan' b'lieve you."

Tom give him a dime, and said he wouldn't tell nobody; and told him to buy some more thread to tie up his wool with; and then look at Jim, and says:

"I wonder if Uncle Silas is going to hang this nigger. If I was t catch a nigger that was ungrateful enough to run away, *I* wouldn give him up, I'd hang him." And whilst the nigger stepped to th door to look at the dime and bite it to see if it was good, he whispe to Jim and says:

"Don't ever let on to know us. And if you hear any digging goin on nights, it's us; we're going to set you free."

Jim only had time to grab us by the hand and squeeze it; then th nigger come back, and we said we'd come again some time if th nigger wanted us to; and he said he would, more particular if it wa dark, because the witches went for him mostly in the dark, and it wa good to have folks around then.

35 *Escaping Properly—Dark Schemes—Discrimination in Stealing—A Deep Hole*

It would be most an hour yet till breakfast, so we left and struc down into the woods; because Tom said we got to have *some* ligh to see how to dig by, and a lantern makes too much, and might ge us into trouble; what we must have was a lot of them rotten chunk that's called foxfire, and just makes a soft kind of a glow when yo lay them in a dark place. We fetched an armful and hid it in th weeds, and set down to rest, and Tom says, kind of dissatisfied:

"Blame it, this whole thing is just as easy and awkward as it ca be. And so it makes it so rotten difficult to get up a difficult pla There ain't no watchman to be drugged—now there *ought* to be watchman. There ain't even a dog to give a sleeping-mixture to. An there's Jim chained by one leg, with a ten-foot chain, to the leg of h bed: why, all you got to do is to lift up the bedstead and slip off th chain. And Uncle Silas he trusts everybody; sends the key to th punkin-headed nigger, and don't send nobody to watch the nigger. Jim could 'a' got out of that window-hole before this, only there wouldn't be no use trying to travel with a ten-foot chain on his leg. Why, drat it, Huck, it's the stupidest arrangement I ever see. You got to invent *all* the difficulties. Well, we can't help it; we got to do the best we can with the materials we've got. Anyhow, there's one thing—there's more honor in getting him out through a lot of difficulties and dangers, where there warn't one of them furnished to you by the people who it was their duty to furnish them, and you had to contrive them all out of your own head. Now look at just that one thing of the lantern. When you come down to the cold facts, we simply got to *let on* that a lantern's resky. Why, we could work with a torchlight procession if we wanted to, *I* believe. Now, whilst I think of it, we got to hunt up something to make a saw out of the first chance we get."

"What do we want of a saw?"

"What do we *want* of a saw? Hain't we got to saw the leg of Jim's bed off, so as to get the chain loose?"

"Why, you just said a body could lift up the bedstead and slip the chain off."

"Well, if that ain't just like you, Huck Finn. You *can* get up the infant-schooliest ways of going at a thing. Why, hain't you ever read any books at all?—Baron Trenck, nor Casanova, nor Benvenuto Chelleeny, nor Henri IV., nor none of them heroes? Who ever heard of getting a prisoner loose in such an old-maidy way as that? No; the way all the best authorities does is to saw the bed-leg in two, and leave it just so, and swallow the sawdust, so it can't be found, and put some dirt and grease around the sawed place so the very keenest seneskal can't see no sign of its being sawed, and thinks the bed-leg is perfectly sound. Then, the night you're ready, fetch the leg a kick, down she goes; slip off your chain, and there you are. Nothing to do but hitch your rope ladder to the battlements, shin down it, break your leg in the moat—because a rope ladder is nineteen foot too short, you know—and there's your horses and your trusty vassels, and they scoop you up and fling you across a saddle, and away you go to your native Langudoc, or Navarre, or wherever it is. It's gaudy, Huck. I wish there was a moat to this cabin. If we get time, the night of the escape, we'll dig one."

I says:

"What do we want of a moat when we're going to snake him o from under the cabin?"

But he never heard me. He had forgot me and everything else. H had his chin in his hand, thinking. Pretty soon he sighs and shak his head; then sighs again, and says:

"No, it wouldn't do—there ain't necessity enough for it."

"For what?" I says.

"Why, to saw Jim's leg off," he says.

"Good land!" I says; "why, there ain't *no* necessity for it. And wh would you want to saw his leg off for?"

"Well, some of the best authorities has done it. They couldn't g the chain off, so they just cut their hand off and shoved. And a l would be better still. But we got to let that go. There ain't necessi enough in this case; and, besides, Jim's a nigger, and wouldn't und stand the reasons for it, and how it's the custom in Europe; so we let it go. But there's one thing—he can have a rope ladder; we c tear up our sheets and make him a rope ladder easy enough. And can send it to him in a pie; it's mostly done that way. And I've worse pies."

"Why, Tom Sawyer, how you talk," I says; "Jim ain't got no u for a rope ladder."

"He *has* got use for it. How *you* talk, you better say; you do know nothing about it. He's *got* to have a rope ladder; they all do"

"What in the nation can he *do* with it?"

"*Do* with it? He can hide it in his bed, can't he? That's what th all do; and *he's* got to, too. Huck, you don't ever seem to want to anything that's regular; you want to be starting something fresh the time. S'pose he *don't* do nothing with it? ain't it there in his be for a clue, after he's gone? and don't you reckon they'll want clue Of course they will. And you wouldn't leave them any? That wou be a *pretty* howdy-do, *wouldn't* it! I never heard of such a thing."

"Well," I says, "if it's in the regulations, and he's got to have all right, let him have it; because I don't wish to go back on no reg lations; but there's one thing, Tom Sawyer—if we go to tearing our sheets to make Jim a rope ladder, we're going to get into tro ble with Aunt Sally, just as sure as you're born. Now, the way I lo at it, a hickry-bark ladder don't cost nothing, and don't waste nothi and is just as good to load up a pie with, and hide in a straw ti as any rag ladder you can start; and as for Jim, he ain't had no experience, and so *he* don't care what kind of a—"

"Oh, shucks, Huck Finn, if I was as ignorant as you I'd keep still —that's what *I'd* do. Who ever heard of a state prisoner escaping by a hickry-bark ladder? Why, it's perfectly ridiculous."

"Well, all right, Tom, fix it your own way; but if you'll take my advice, you'll let me borrow a sheet off of the clothes-line."

He said that would do. And that gave him another idea, and he says:

"Borrow a shirt, too."

"What do we want of a shirt, Tom?"

"Want it for Jim to keep a journal on."

"Journal your granny—*Jim* can't write."

"S'pose he *can't* write—he can make marks on the shirt, can't he, if we make him a pen out of an old pewter spoon or a piece of an old iron barrel-hoop?"

"Why, Tom, we can pull a feather out of a goose and make him a better one; and quicker, too."

"*Prisoners* don't have geese running around the donjon-keep to pull pens out of, you muggins. They *always* make their pens out of the hardest, toughest, troublesomest piece of old brass candlestick or something like that they can get their hands on; and it takes them weeks and weeks and months and months to file it out, too, because they've got to do it by rubbing it on the wall. *They* wouldn't use a goose-quill if they had it."

"Well, then, what 'll we make him the ink out of?"

"Many makes it out of iron-rust and tears; but that's the common sort and women; the best authorities uses their own blood. Jim can do that; and when he wants to send any little common ordinary mysterious message to let the world know where he's captivated, he can write it on the bottom of a tin plate with a fork and throw it out of the window. The Iron Mask always done that, and it's a blame' good way, too."

"Jim ain't got no tin plates. They feed him in a pan."

"That ain't nothing; we can get him some."

"Can't nobody *read* his plates."

"That ain't got anything to *do* with it, Huck Finn. All *he's* got to do is to write on the plate and throw it out. You don't *have* to be able to read it. Why, half the time you can't read anything a prisoner writes on a tin plate, or anywhere else."

"Well, then, what's the sense in wasting the plates?"

"Why, blame it all, it ain't the *prisoner's* plates."

"But it's *somebody's* plates, ain't it?"

"Well, spos'n it is? What does the *prisoner* care whose—"

He broke off there, because we heard the breakfast-horn blowing So we cleared out for the house.

Along during the morning I borrowed a sheet and a white shirt o of the clothes-line; and I found an old sack and put them in it, an we went down and got the fox-fire, and put that in too. I called i borrowing, because that was what pap always called it; but Tom sai it warn't borrowing, it was stealing. He said we was representin prisoners; and prisoners don't care how they get a thing so they ge it, and nobody don't blame them for it, either. It ain't no crime i a prisoner to steal the thing he needs to get away with, Tom said it's his right; and so, as long as we was representing a prisoner, we ha a perfect right to steal anything on this place we had the least us for to get ourselves out of prison with. He said if we warn't prisoner it would be a very different thing, and nobody but a mean, orner person would steal when he warn't a prisoner. So we allowed w would steal everything there was that come handy. And yet he mad a mighty fuss, one day, after that, when I stole a watermelon out o the nigger patch and eat it; and he made me go and give the nigger a dime without telling them what it was for. Tom said that what h meant was, we could steal anything we *needed*. Well, I says, I needed the watermelon. But he said I didn't need it to get out o prison with; there's where the difference was. He said if I'd 'a wanted it to hide a knife in, and smuggle it to Jim to kill the seneska with, it would 'a' been all right. So I let it go at that, though I couldn't see no advantage in my representing a prisoner if I got t set down and chaw over a lot of gold-leaf distinctions like that ever time I see a chance to hog a watermelon.

Well, as I was saying, we waited that morning till everybody wa settled down to business, and nobody in sight around the yard; then Tom he carried the sack into the lean-to whilst I stood off a piece t keep watch. By and by he come out, and we went and set down on the woodpile to talk. He says:

"Everything's all right now except tools; and that's easy fixed."

"Tools?" I says.

"Yes."

"Tools for what?"

"Why, to dig with. We ain't a-going to *gnaw* him out, are we?"

"Ain't them old crippled picks and things in there good enough to dig a nigger out with?" I says.

He turns on me, looking pitying enough to make a body cry, and says:

"Huck Finn, did you *ever* hear of a prisoner having picks and shovels, and all the modern conveniences in his wardrobe to dig himself out with? Now I want to ask you—if you got any reasonableness in you at all—what kind of a show would *that* give him to be a hero? Why, they might as well lend him the key and done with it. Picks and shovels—why, they wouldn't furnish 'em to a king."

"Well, then," I says, "if we don't want the picks and shovels, what do we want?"

"A couple of case-knives."

"To dig the foundations out from under that cabin with?"

"Yes."

"Confound it, it's foolish, Tom."

"It don't make no difference how foolish it is, it's the *right* way—and it's the regular way. And there ain't no *other* way, that ever *I* heard of, and I've read all the books that gives any information about these things. They always dig out with a case-knife—and not through dirt, mind you; generly it's through solid rock. And it takes them weeks and weeks and weeks, and for ever and ever. Why, look at one of them prisoners in the bottom dungeon of the Castle Deef, in the harbor of Marseilles, that dug himself out that way; how long was *he* at it, you reckon?"

"I don't know."

"Well, guess."

"I don't know. A month and a half."

"*Thirty-seven year*—and he come out in China. *That's* the kind. I wish the bottom of *this* fortress was solid rock."

"*Jim* don't know nobody in China."

"What's *that* got to do with it? Neither did that other fellow. But you're always a-wandering off on a side issue. Why can't you stick to the main point?"

"All right—*I* don't care where he comes out, so he *comes* out; and

Jim don't, either, I reckon. But there's one thing, anyway—Jim's too old to be dug out with a case-knife. He won't last."

"Yes he will *last* too. You don't reckon it's going to take thirty-seven years to dig out through a *dirt* foundation, do you?"

"How long will it take, Tom?"

"Well, we can't resk being as long as we ought to, because it mayn't take very long for Uncle Silas to hear from down there by New Orleans. He'll hear Jim ain't from there. Then his next move will be to advertise Jim, or something like that. So we can't resk being as long digging him out as we ought to. By rights I reckon we ought to be a couple of years; but we can't. Things being so uncertain, what I recommend is this: that we really dig right in, as quick as we can; and after that, we can *let* on, to ourselves, that we was at it thirty-seven years. Then we can snatch him out and rush him away the first time there's an alarm. Yes, I reckon that 'll be the best way."

"Now, there's *sense* in that," I says. "Letting on don't cost nothing; letting on ain't no trouble; and if it's any object, I don't mind letting on we was at it a hundred and fifty year. It wouldn't strain me none, after I got my hand in. So I'll mosey along now, and smouch a couple of case-knives."

"Smouch three," he says; "we want one to make a saw out of."

"Tom, if it ain't unregular and irreligious to sejest it," I says, "there's an old rusty saw-blade around yonder sticking under the weather-boarding behind the smokehouse."

He looked kind of weary and discouraged-like, and says:

"It ain't no use to try to learn you nothing, Huck. Run along and smouch the knives—three of them." So I done it.

36 The Lightning-rod—His Level Best—A Bequest to Posterity—A High Figure

As soon as we reckoned everybody was asleep that night we went down the lightning-rod, and shut ourselves up in the lean-to, and got out our pile of foxfire, and went to work. We cleared everything out of the way, about four or five foot along the middle of the bottom log. Tom said we was right behind Jim's bed now, and we'd dig in under it, and when we got through there couldn't nobody in the cabin ever know there was any hole there, because Jim's counterpin hung down most to the ground, and you'd have to raise it up and look under to see the hole. So we dug and dug with the case-knives till most midnight; and then we was dog-tired, and our hands was blistered, and yet you couldn't see we'd done anything hardly. At last I says:

"This ain't no thirty-seven-year job; this is a thirty-eight-year job, Tom Sawyer."

He never said nothing. But he sighed, and pretty soon he stopped digging, and then for a good little while I knowed that he was thinking. Then he says:

"It ain't no use, Huck, it ain't a-going to work. If we was prisoners it would, because then we'd have as many years as we wanted, and no hurry; and we wouldn't get but a few minutes to dig, every day, while they was changing watches, and so our hands wouldn't get blistered, and we could keep it up right along, year in and year out, and do it right, and the way it ought to be done. But *we* can't fool along; we got to rush; we ain't got no time to spare. If we was to put in another night this way we'd have to knock off for a week to let our hands get well—couldn't touch a case-knife with them sooner."

"Well, then, what we going to do, Tom?"

"I'll tell you. It ain't right, and it ain't moral, and I wouldn't like it to get out; but there ain't only just the one way: we got to dig him out with the picks, and *let on* it's case-knives."

"*Now* you're *talking!*" I says; "your head gets leveler and leveler all the time, Tom Sawyer," I says. "Picks is the thing, moral or no moral; and as for me, I don't care shucks for the morality of it, nohow. When I start in to steal a nigger, or a watermelon, or a Sunday-school book, I ain't no ways particular how it's done so it's done. What I want is my nigger; or what I want is my watermelon; or what I want is my Sunday-school book; and if a pick's the handiest thing, that's the thing I'm a-going to dig that nigger or that watermelon or that Sunday-school book out with; and I don't give a dead rat what the authorities thinks about it nuther."

"Well," he says, "there's excuse for picks and letting on in a case like this; if it warn't so, I wouldn't approve of it, nor I wouldn't stand by and see the rules broke—because right is right, and wrong is wrong, and a body ain't got no business doing wrong when he ain't ignorant and knows better. It might answer for *you* to dig Jim out with a pick, *without* any letting on, because you don't know no better; but it wouldn't for me, because I do know better. Gimme a case-knife."

He had his own by him, but I handed him mine. He flung it down, and says:

"Gimme a *case-knife*."

I didn't know just what to do—but then I thought. I scratched around amongst the old tools, and got a pickax and give it to him, and he took it and went to work, and never said a word.

He was always just that particular. Full of principle.

So then I got a shovel, and then we picked and shoveled, turn about, and made the fur fly. We stuck to it about a half an hour, which was as long as we could stand up; but we had a good deal of a hole to show for it. When I got up-stairs I looked out at the window and see Tom doing his level best with the lightning-rod, but he couldn't come it, his hands was so sore. At last he says:

"It ain't no use, it can't be done. What you reckon I better do? Can't you think of no way?"

"Yes," I says, "but I reckon it ain't regular. Come up the stairs, and let on it's a lightning-rod."

So he done it.

Next day Tom stole a pewter spoon and a brass candlestick in the house, for to make some pens for Jim out of, and six tallow candles; and I hung around the nigger cabins and laid for a chance, and stole three tin plates. Tom says it wasn't enough; but I said nobody wouldn't ever see the plates that Jim throwed out, because they'd fall in the dog-fennel and jimpson weeds under the window-hole—then we could tote them back and he could use them over again. So Tom was satisfied. Then he says:

"Now, the thing to study out is, how to get the things to Jim."

"Take them in through the hole," I says, "when we get it done."

He only just looked scornful, and said something about nobody ever heard of such an idiotic idea, and then he went to studying. By and by he said he had ciphered out two or three ways, but there warn't no need to decide on any of them yet. Said we'd got to post Jim first.

That night we went down the lightning-rod a little after ten, and took one of the candles along, and listened under the window-hole, and heard Jim snoring; so we pitched it in, and it didn't wake him. Then we whirled in with the pick and shovel, and in about two hours and a half the job was done. We crept in under Jim's bed and into the cabin, and pawed around and found the candle and lit it, and stood over Jim awhile, and found him looking hearty and healthy, and then we woke him up gentle and gradual. He was so glad to see us he most cried; and called us honey, and all the pet names he could think of; and was for having us hunt up a cold-chisel to cut the chain off of his leg with right away, and clearing out without losing any time. But Tom he showed him how unregular it would be, and set down and told him all about our plans, and how we could alter them in a minute any time there was an alarm; and not to be the least afraid, because we would see he got away, *sure*. So Jim he said it was all right, and we set there and talked over old times awhile, and then Tom asked a lot of questions, and when Jim told him Uncle Silas come in every day or two to pray with him, and Aunt Sally come in to see if he was comfortable and had plenty to eat, and both of them was kind as they could be, Tom says:

"*Now* I know how to fix it. We'll send you some things by them."

I said, "Don't do nothing of the kind; it's one of the most jackass ideas I ever struck"; but he never paid no attention to me; went right on. It was his way when he'd got his plans set.

So he told Jim how we'd have to smuggle in the rope-ladder pie and other large things by Nat, the nigger that fed him, and he must be on the lookout, and not be surprised, and not let Nat see him open them; and we would put small things in uncle's coat pockets and he must steal them out; and we would tie things to aunt's apron-strings or put them in her apron pocket, if we got a chance; and told him what they would be and what they was for. And told him hov to keep a journal on the shirt with his blood, and all that. He tol him everything. Jim he couldn't see no sense in the most of it, bu he allowed we was white folks and knowed better than him; so h was satisfied, and said he would do it all just as Tom said.

Jim had plenty corn-cob pipes and tobacco; so we had a righ down good sociable time; then we crawled out through the hole, an so home to bed, with hands that looked like they'd been chawed Tom was in high spirits. He said it was the best fun he ever had i his life, and the most intellectural; and said if he only could see hi way to it we would keep it up all the rest of our lives and leave Jin to our children to get out; for he believed Jim would come to lik it better and better the more he got used to it. He said that in tha way it could be strung out to as much as eighty year, and would b the best time on record. And he said it would make us all celebrate that had a hand in it.

In the morning we went out to the woodpile and chopped up th brass candlestick into handy sizes, and Tom put them and the pewte spoon in his pocket. Then we went to the nigger cabins, and while I got Nat's notice off, Tom shoved a piece of candlestick into the middle of a corn-pone that was in Jim's pan, and we went along with Nat to see how it would work, and it just worked noble; when Jim bit into it it most mashed all his teeth out; and there warn't ever anything could 'a' worked better. Tom said so himself. Jim he never let on but what it was only just a piece of rock or something like that that's always getting into bread, you know; but after that he never bit into nothing but what he jabbed his fork into it in three or four places first.

And whilst we was a-standing there in the dimmish light, here comes a couple of the hounds bulging in from under Jim's bed; and they kept on piling in till there was eleven of them, and there warn't hardly room in there to get your breath. By jings, we forgot to fasten that lean-to door! The nigger Nat he only just hollered "Witches" once, and keeled over onto the floor amongst the dogs, and begun to groan like he was dying. Tom jerked the door open and flung out a slab of Jim's meat, and the dogs went for it, and in two seconds he was out himself and back again and shut the door, and I knowed he'd fixed the other door too. Then he went to work on the nigger, coaxing him and petting him, and asking him if he'd been imagining he saw something again. He raised up, and blinked his eyes around, and says:

"Mars Sid, you'll say I's a fool, but if I didn't b'lieve I see most a million dogs, er devils, er some'n, I wisht I may die right heah in dese tracks. I did, mos' sholy. Mars Sid, I *felt* um—I *felt* um, sah; dey was all over me. Dad fetch it, I jis' wisht I could git my han's on one er dem witches jis' wunst—on'y jis' wunst—it's all *I'd* ast. But mos'ly I wisht dey'd lemme 'lone, I does."

Tom says:

"Well, I tell you what *I* think. What makes them come here just at this runaway nigger's breakfast-time? It's because they're hungry; that's the reason. You make them a witch pie; that's the thing for *you* to do."

"But my lan', Mars Sid, how's I gwyne to make 'm a witch pie. I doan' know how to make it. I hain't ever hearn er sich a thing b'fo'."

"Well, then, I'll have to make it myself."

"Will you do it, honey?—will you? I'll wusshup de groun' und' yo' foot, I will!"

"All right, I'll do it, seeing it's you, and you've been good to us and showed us the runaway nigger. But you got to be mighty careful. When we come around, you turn your back; and then whatever we've put in the pan, don't you let on you see it at all. And don't you look when Jim unloads the pan—something might happen, I don't know what. And above all, don't you *handle* the witch things."

"*Hannel* 'm, Mars Sid? What *is* you a-talkin' 'bout? I wouldn' lay de weight er my finger on um, not f'r ten hund'd thous'n billion dollars, I wouldn't."

37 *The Last Shirt—Mooning Around—Sailing Orders—The Witch Pie*

That was all fixed. So then we went away and went to the rubbage-pile in the back yard, where they keep the old boots, and rags, and pieces of bottles, and wore-out tin things, and all such truck, and scratched around and found an old tin washpan, and stopped up the holes as well as we could, to bake the pie in, and took it down cellar and stole it full of flour and started for breakfast, and found a couple of shingle-nails that Tom said would be handy for a prisoner to scrabble his name and sorrows on the dungeon walls with, and dropped one of them in Aunt Sally's apron pocket which was hanging on a chair, and t'other we stuck in the band of Uncle Silas's hat, which was on the bureau, because we heard the children say their pa and ma was going to the runaway nigger's house this morning, and then went to breakfast, and Tom dropped the pewter spoon in Uncle Silas's coat pocket, and Aunt Sally wasn't come yet, so we had to wait a little while.

And when she come she was hot and red and cross, and couldn't hardly wait for the blessing; and then she went to sluicing out coffee with one hand and cracking the handiest child's head with her thimble with the other, and says:

"I've hunted high and I've hunted low, and it does beat all what *has* become of your other shirt."

My heart fell down amongst my lungs and livers and things, and a hard piece of corn-crust started down my throat after it and got met on the road with a cough, and was shot across the table, and took one of the children in the eye and curled him up like a fishing-worm, and let a cry out of him the size of a war-whoop, and Tom he turned kinder blue around the gills, and it all amounted to a considerable state of things for about a quarter of a minute or as much as that, and I would 'a' sold out for half price if there was a bidder. But after that we was all right again—it was the sudden surprise of it that knocked us so kind of cold. Uncle Silas he says:

"It's most uncommon curious, I can't understand it. I know perfectly well I took it *off*, because—"

"Because you hain't got but one *on*. Just *listen* at the man! *I* know you took it off, and know it by a better way than your wool-gethering memory, too, because it was on the clo's-line yesterday—I see it there myself. But it's gone, that's the long and the short of it, and you'll just have to change to a red flann'l one till I can get time to make a new one. And it 'll be the third I've made in two years. It just keeps a body on the jump to keep you in shirts; and whatever you do manage to *do* with 'm all is more'n *I* can make out. A body'd think you *would* learn to take some sort of care of 'em at your time of life."

"I know it, Sally, and I do try all I can. But it oughtn't to be altogether my fault, because, you know, I don't see them nor have nothing to do with them except when they're on me; and I don't believe I've ever lost one of them *off* of me."

"Well, it ain't *your* fault if you haven't, Silas; you'd 'a' done it if you could, I reckon. And the shirt ain't all that's gone, nuther. Ther's a spoon gone; and *that* ain't all. There was ten, and now ther's only nine .The calf got the shirt, I reckon, but the calf never took the spoon, *that's* certain."

"Why, what else is gone, Sally?"

"Ther's six *candles* gone—that's what. The rats could 'a' got the candles, and I reckon they did; I wonder they don't walk off with the whole place, the way you're always going to stop their holes and don't do it; and if they warn't fools they'd sleep in your hair, Silas —*you'd* never find it out; but you can't lay the *spoon* on the rats, and that I *know*."

"Well, Sally, I'm in fault, and I acknowledge it; I've been remiss; but I won't let to-morrow go by without stopping up them holes."

"Oh, I wouldn't hurry; next year 'll do. Matilda Angelina Araminta *Phelps!*"

Whack comes the thimble, and the child snatches her claws out of the sugar-bowl without fooling around any. Just then the nigger woman steps onto the passage, and says:

"Missus, dey's a sheet gone."

"A *sheet* gone! Well, for the land's sake!"

"I'll stop up them holes to-day," says Uncle Silas, looking sorrowful.

"Oh, *do* shet up!—s'pose the rats took the *sheet? Where's* it gone, Lize?"

"Clah to goodness I hain't no notion, Miss' Sally. She wuz on de clo's-line yistiddy, but she done gone: she ain' dah no mo' now."

"I reckon the world *is* coming to an end. I *never* see the beat of it in all my born days. A shirt, and a sheet, and a spoon, and six can—"

"Missus," comes a young yaller wench, "dey's a brass cannelstick miss'n."

"Cler out from here, you hussy, er I'll take a skillet to ye!"

Well, she was just a-biling. I begun to lay for a chance; I reckoned I would sneak out and go for the woods till the weather moderated. She kept a-raging right along, running her insurrection all by herself, and everybody else mighty meek and quiet; and at last Uncle Silas, looking kind of foolish, fishes up that spoon out of his pocket. She stopped, with her mouth open and her hands up; and as for me, I wished I was in Jeruslem or somewheres. But not long, because she says:

"It's *just* as I expected. So you had it in your pocket all the time; and like as not you've got the other things there, too. How'd it get there?"

"I reely don't know, Sally," he says, kind of apologizing, "or you know I would tell. I was a-studying over my text in Acts Seventeen before breakfast, and I reckon I put it in there, not noticing, meaning to put my Testament in, and it must be so, because my Testament ain't in; but I'll go and see; and if the Testament is where I had it, I'll know I didn't put it in, and that will show that I laid the Testament down and took up the spoon, and—"

"Oh, for the land's sake! Give a body a rest! Go 'long now, the whole kit and biling of ye; and don't come nigh me again till I've got back my peace of mind."

I'd 'a' heard her if she'd 'a' said it to herself, let alone speaking it out; and I'd 'a' got up and obeyed her if I'd 'a' been dead. As we was passing through the setting-room the old man he took up his hat, and the shingle-nail fell out on the floor, and he just merely picked it up and laid it on the mantel-shelf, and never said nothing, and went out. Tom see him do it, and remembered about the spoon, and says:

"Well, it ain't no use to send things by *him* no more, he ain't reliable." Then he says: "But he done us a good turn with the spoon, anyway, without knowing it, and so we'll go and do him one without *him* knowing it—stop up his rat-holes."

There was a noble good lot of them down cellar, and it took us a whole hour, but we done the job tight and good and shipshape. Then we heard steps on the stairs, and blowed out our light and hid; and here comes the old man, with a candle in one hand and a bundle of stuff in t'other, looking as absent-minded as year before last. He went a-mooning around, first to one rat-hole and then another, till he'd been to them all. Then he stood about five minutes, picking tallow-drip off of his candle and thinking. Then he turns, saying:

"Well, for the life of me I can't remember when I done it. I could show her now that I warn't to blame on account of the rats. But never mind—let it go. I reckon it wouldn't do no good."

And so he went on a-mumbling up-stairs, and then we left. He was a mighty nice old man. And always is.

Tom was a good deal bothered about what to do for a spoon, but he said we'd got to have it; so he took a think. When he had ciphered it out he told me how we was to do; then we went and waited around the spoon-basket till we see Aunt Sally coming, and then Tom went to counting the spoons and laying them out to one side, and I slid one of them up my sleeve, and Tom says:

"Why, Aunt Sally, there ain't but nine spoons *yet*."

She says:

"Go 'long to your play, and don't bother me. I know better, I counted 'm myself."

"Well, I've counted them twice, Aunty, and *I* can't make but nine."

She looked out of all patience, but of course she come to count—anybody would.

"I declare to gracious ther' *ain't* but nine!" she says. "Why, what in the world—plague *take* the things, I'll count 'm again."

So I slipped back the one I had, and when she got done counting, she says:

"Hang the troublesome rubbage, ther's *ten* now!" and she looked huffy and bothered both. But Tom says:

"Why, Aunty, *I* don't think there's ten."

"You numskull, didn't you see me *count* 'im?"

"I know, but—"

"Well, I'll count 'm again."

So I smouched one, and they come out nine, same as the other time. Well, she *was* in a tearing way—just a-trembling all over, she was so mad. But she counted and counted till she got that addled she'd start to count in the *basket* for a spoon sometimes; and so three times they come out right, and three times they come out wrong. Then she grabbed up the basket and slammed it across the house and knocked the cat galley-west; and she said cler out and let her have some peace, and if we come bothering around her again betwixt that and dinner she'd skin us. So we had the odd spoon, and dropped it in her apron pocket whilst she was a-giving us our sailing orders, and Jim got it all right, along with her shingle-nail, before noon. We was very well satisfied with this business, and Tom allowed it was worth twice the trouble it took, because he said *now* she couldn't ever count them spoons twice alike again to save her life and wouldn't believe she'd counted them right if she *did;* and said that after she'd about counted her head off for the next three days he judged she'd give it up and offer to kill anybody that wanted her to ever count them any more.

So we put the sheet back on the line that night, and stole one out of her closet; and kept on putting it back and stealing it again for a couple of days till she didn't know how many sheets she had any more, and she didn't *care,* and warn't a-going to bullyrag the rest of her soul out about it, and wouldn't count them again not to save her life; she druther die first.

So we was all right now, as to the shirt and the sheet and the spoon and the candles, by the help of the calf and the rats and the mixed-up counting; and as to the candlestick, it warn't no consequence, it would blow over by and by.

But that pie was a job; we had no end of trouble with that pie. We fixed it up away down in the woods, and cooked it there; and we got it done at last, and very satisfactory too; but not all in one day; and we had to use up three washpans full of flour before we got through and we got burnt pretty much all over, in places, and eyes put out with the smoke; because, you see, we didn't want nothing but a crust and we couldn't prop it up right, and she would always cave in. But of course we thought of the right way at last—which was to cook the ladder, too, in the pie. So then we laid in with Jim the second night and tore up the sheet all in little strings and twisted them together and long before daylight we had a lovely rope that you could 'a' hung a person with. We let on it took nine months to make it.

And in the forenoon we took it down to the woods, but it wouldn't go into the pie. Being made of a whole sheet, that way, there was rope enough for forty pies if we'd 'a' wanted them, and plenty left over for soup, or sausage, or anything you choose. We could 'a' had a whole dinner.

But we didn't need it. All we needed was just enough for the pie, and so we throwed the rest away. We didn't cook none of the pies in the washpan—afraid the solder would melt; but Uncle Silas he had a noble brass warming-pan which he thought considerable of, because it belonged to one of his ancesters with a long wooden handle that come over from England with William the Conqueror in the *Mayflower* or one of them early ships and was hid away up garret with a lot of other old pots and things that was valuable, not on account of being any account, because they warn't, but on account of them being relicts, you know, and we snaked her out, private, and took her down there, but she failed on the first pies, because we didn't know how, but she come up smiling on the last one. We took and lined her with dough, and set her in the coals, and loaded her up with rag rope, and put on a dough roof, and shut down the lid, and put hot embers on top, and stood off five foot, with the long handle, cool and comfortable, and in fifteen minutes she turned out a pie that was a satisfaction to look at. But the person that et it would want to fetch a couple of kags of toothpicks along, for if that rope ladder wouldn't cramp him down to business I don't know nothing what I'm talking about, and lay him in enough stomach-ache to last him till next time, too.

Nat didn't look when he put the witch pie in Jim's pan; and we put the three tin plates in the bottom of the pan under the vittles; and so Jim got everything all right, and as soon as he was by himself he busted into the pie and hid the hope ladder inside of his straw tick, and scratched some marks on a pin plate and throwed it out of the window-hole.

38 *The Coat of Arms—A Skilled Superintendent—Unpleasant Glory—A Tearful Subject*

Making them pens was a distressid tough job, and so was the saw; and Jim allowed the inscription was going to be the toughest of all. That's the one which the prisoner has to scrabble on the wall. But he had to have it; Tom said he'd *got* to; there warn't no case of a state prisoner not scrabbling his inscription to leave behind, and his coat of arms.

"Look at Lady Jane Grey," he says; "look at Gilford Dudley; look at old Northumberland! Why, Huck, s'pose it *is* considerable trouble?—what you going to do?—how you going to get around it? Jim's *got* to do his inscription and coat of arms. They all do."

Jim says:

"Why, Mars Tom, I hain't got no coat o' arm; I hain't got nuffn but dish yer ole shirt, en you knows I got to keep de journal on dat."

"Oh, you don't understand, Jim; a coat of arms is very different."

"Well," I says, "Jim's right, anyway, when he says he ain't got no coat of arms, because he hain't."

"I reckon *I* knowed that," Tom says, "but you bet he'll have one before he goes out of this—because he's going out *right*, and there aint going to be no flaws in his record."

So whilst me and Jim filed away at the pens on a brickbat apiece, Jim, a-making his'n out of the brass and I making mine out of the spoon, Tom set to work to think out the coat of arms. By and by he said he'd struck so many good ones he didn't hardly know which to take, but there was one which he reckoned he'd decide on. He says:

"On the scutcheon we'll have a bend *or* in the dexter base, a saltire *murrey* in the fess, with a dog, couchant, for common charge, and under his foot a chain embattled, for slavery, with a chevron *vert* in a chief engrailed, and three invected lines on a field *azure*, with the nombril points rampant on a dancette indented; crest, a runaway nigger, *sable*, with his bundle over his shoulder on a bar sinister; and a couple of gules for supporters, which is you and me; motto, *Maggiore fretta, minore atto*. Got it out of a book—means the more haste the less speed."

"Geewhillikins," I says, "but what does the rest of it mean?"

"We ain't got no time to bother over that," he says; "we got to dig in like all git-out."

"Well, anyway," I says, "what's *some* of it? What's a fess?"

"A fess—a fess is—*you* don't need to know what a fess is. I'll show him how to make it when he gets to it."

"Shucks, Tom," I says, "I think you might tell a person. What's a bar sinister?"

"Oh, *I* don't know. But he's got to have it. All the nobility does."

That was just his way. If it didn't suit him to explain a thing to you, he wouldn't do it. You might pump at him a week, it wouldn't make no difference.

He'd got all that coat-of-arms business fixed, so now he started in to finish up the rest of that part of the work, which was to plan out a mournful inscription—said Jim got to have one, like they all done. He made up a lot, and wrote them out on a paper, and read them off, so:

1. *Here a captive heart busted.*

2. *Here a poor prisoner, forsook by the world and friends, fretted his sorrowful life.*

3. *Here a lonely heart broke, and a worn spirit went to its rest, after thirty-seven years of solitary captivity.*

4. *Here, homeless and friendless, after thirty-seven years of bitter captivity, perished a noble stranger, natural son of Louis XIV.*

Tom's voice trembled whilst he was reading them, and he most broke down. When he got done he couldn't no way make up his mind which one for Jim to scrabble onto the wall, they was all so good; but at last he allowed he would let him scrabble them all on. Jim said it would take him a year to scrabble such a lot of truck onto the logs with a nail, and he didn't know how to make letters, besides; but Tom said he would block them out for him, and then he wouldn't have nothing to do but just follow the lines. Then pretty soon he says:

"Come to think, the log ain't a-going to do; they don't have log walls in a dungeon: we got to dig the inscriptions into a rock. We'll fetch a rock."

Jim said the rock was worse than the logs; he said it would take him such a pison long time to dig them into a rock he wouldn't ever get out. But Tom said he would let me help him do it. Then he took a look to see how me and Jim was getting along with the pens. It was most pesky tedious hard work and slow, and didn't give my hands no show to get well of the sores, and we didn't seem to make no headway, hardly; so Tom says:

"I know how to fix it. We got to have a rock for the coat of arms and mournful inscriptions, and we can kill two birds with that same rock. There's a gaudy big grindstone down at the mill, and we'll smouch it, and carve the things on it, and file out the pens and the saw on it, too."

It warn't no slouch of an idea; and it warn't no slouch of a grindstone nuther; but we allowed we'd tackle it. It warn't quite midnight yet, so we cleared out for the mill, leaving Jim at work. We smouched the grindstone, and set out to roll her home, but it was a most nation tough job. Sometimes, do what we could, we couldn't keep her from falling over, and she come mighty near mashing us every time. Tom said she was going to get one of us, sure before we got through. We got her halfway; and then we was plumb played out, and most drownded with sweat. We see it warn't no use; we got to go and fetch Jim. So he raised up his bed and slid the chain off of the bed-leg, and wrapt it round and round his neck, and we crawled out through our hole and down there, and Jim and me laid into that grindstone and walked her along like nothing; and Tom superintended. He could outsuperintend any boy I ever see. He knowed how to do everything.

Our hole was pretty big, but it warn't big enough to get the grindstone through; but Jim he took the pick and soon made it big enough. Then Tom marked out them things on it with the nail, and Jim set to work on them, with the nail for a chisel and an iron bolt from the rubbage in the lean-to for a hammer, and told him to work till the rest of his candle quit on him, and then he could go to bed, and hide the grindstone under his straw tick and sleep on it. Then we helped him fix his chain back on the bed-leg, and was ready for bed ourselves. But Tom thought of something, and says:

"You got any spiders in here, Jim?"

"No, sah, thanks to goodness I hain't, Mars Tom."

"All right, we'll get you some."

"But bless you, honey, I doan' *want* none. I's afeard un um. I jis' 's soon have rattlesnakes aroun'."

Tom thought a minute or two, and says:

"It's a good idea. And I reckon it's been done. It *must* 'a' been done; it stands to reason. Yes, it's a prime good idea. Where could you keep it?"

"Keep what, Mars Tom?"

"Why, a rattlesnake."

"De goodness gracious alive, Mars Tom! Why, if dey was a rattlesnake to come in heah I'd take en bust right out thoo dat log wall, I would, wid my head."

"Why, Jim, you wouldn't be afraid of it after a little. You could tame it."

"*Tame* it!"

"Yes—easy enough. Every animal is grateful for kindness and petting, and they wouldn't *think* of hurting a person that pets them. Any book will tell you that. You try—that's all I ask; just try for two or three days. Why, you can get him so in a little while that he'll love you; and sleep with you; and won't stay away from you a minute; and will let you wrap him around your neck and put his head in your mouth."

"*Please*, Mars Tom—*doan'* talk so! I can't *stan'* it! He'd *let* me shove his head in my mouf—fer a favor, hain't it? I lay he'd wait a pow'ful long time 'fo' I *ast* him. En mo' en dat, I doan' *want* him to sleep wid me."

"Jim, don't act so foolish. A prisoner's *got* to have some kind of a dumb pet, and if a rattlesnake hain't ever been tried, why, there's more glory to be gained in your being the first to ever try it than any other way you could ever think of to save your life."

"Why, Mars Tom, I doan' *want* no sich glory. Snake take 'n bite Jim's chin off, den *whah* is de glory? No, sah, I doan' want no sich doin's."

"Blame it, can't you *try*? I only *want* you to try—you needn't keep it up if it don't work."

"But de trouble all *done* ef de snake bite me while I's a'tryin' him. Mars Tom, I's willin' to tackle mos' anything 'at aint onreasonable, but ef you en Huck fetches a rattlesnake in heah for me to tame, I's gwyne to *leave*, dat's *shore*."

"Well, then, let it go, let it go, if you're so bullheaded about it. We can get you some garter snakes, and you can tie some buttons on their tails, and let on they're rattlesnakes, and I reckon that'll have to do."

"I k'n stan' *dem*, Mars Tom, but blame' 'f I couldn' get along wid-out um, I tell you dat. I never knowed b'fo' 'twas so much bother and trouble to be a prisoner."

"Well, it *always* is when it's done right. You got any rats around here?"

"No, sah, I hain't seed none."

"Well, we'll get you some rats."

"Why, Mars Tom, I doan' *want* no rats. Dey's de dadblamedest creturs to 'sturb a body, en rustle roun' over 'im, en bite his feet, when he's try'in to sleep, I ever see. No, sah, gimme y'garter snakes, 'f I's got to have 'm, but doan' gimme no rats; I hain't got no use f'r um, skasely."

"But, Jim, you *got* to have 'em—they all do. So don't make no more fuss about it. Prisoners ain't ever without rats. There ain't no instance of it. And they train them, and pet them, and learn them tricks, and they get to be as sociable as flies. But you got to play music to them. You got anything to play music on?"

"I ain't got nuffn but a coase comb en a piece o' paper, en a juice-harp; but I reck'n dey wouldn't take no stock in a juice-harp."

"Yes they would. *They* don't care what kind of music 'tis. A jew's harp's plenty good enough for a rat. All animals like music—in a prison they dote on it. Specially, painful music; and you can't get no other kind out of a jew's harp. It always interests them; they come out to see what's the matter with you. Yes, you're all right; you're fixed very well. You want to set on your bed nights before you go to sleep, and early in the mornings, and play your jew's-harp; play 'The Last Link is Broken'—that's the thing that 'll scoop a rat quicker 'n any-thing else; and when you've played about two minutes you'll see all the rats, and the snakes, and spiders and things begin to feel worried about you, and come. And they'll just fairly swarm over you, and have a noble good time."

"Yes, *dey* will, I reck'n, Mars Tom, but what kine er time is *Jim* havin'? Blest if I kin see de pint. But I'll do it ef I got to. I reck'n I better keep de animals satisfied, en not have no trouble in de house."

Tom waited to think it over, and see if there wasn't nothing else; and pretty soon he says:

"Oh, there's one thing I forgot. Could you raise a flower here, do you reckon?"

"I doan' know but maybe I could, Mars Tom; but it's tolable dark in heah, en I ain't got no use f'r no flower, nohow, en she'd be a pow'-ful sight o' trouble."

"Well, you try it, anyway. Some other prisoners has done it."

"One er dem big cat-tail-lookin' mullen-stalks would grow in heah, Mars Tom, I reck'n, but she wouldn't be wuth half de trouble she'd coss."

"Don't you believe it. We'll fetch you a little one, and you plant it in the corner over there, and raise it. And don't call it mullen, call it Pitchiola—that's its right name when it's in a prison. And you want to water it with your tears."

"Why, I got plenty spring water, Mars Tom."

"You don't *want* spring water; you want to water it with your tears. It's the way they always do."

"Why, Mars Tom, I lay I kin raise one er dem mullen-stalks twyste wid spring water while another man's a *start'n* one wid tears."

"That ain't the idea. You *got* to do it with tears."

"She'll die on my han's, Mars Tom, she sholy will; kase I doan' skasely ever cry."

So Tom was stumped. But he studied it over, and then said Jim would have to worry along the best he could with an onion. He promised he would go to the nigger cabins and drop one, private, in Jim's coffee-pot, in the morning. Jim said he would "jis' 's soon have tobacker in his coffee"; and found so much fault with it, and with the work and bother of raising the mullen, and jew's-harping the rats, and petting and flattering up the snakes and spiders and things, on top of all the other work he had to do on pens, and inscriptions, and journals, and things, which made it more trouble and worry and responsibility to be a prisoner than anything he ever undertook, that Tom most lost all patience with him; and said he was just loaded down with more gaudier chances than a prisoner ever had in the world to make a name for himself, and yet he didn't know enough to appreciate them, and they was just about wasted on him. So Jim he was sorry, and said he wouldn't behave so no more, and then me and Tom shoved for bed.

39 *Rats—Lively Bedfellows— The Straw Dummy*

In the morning we went up to the village and bought a wire rat-trap and fetched it down, and unstopped the best rat-hole, and in about an hour we had fifteen of the bulliest kind of ones; and then we took it and put it in a safe place under Aunt Sally's bed. But while we was gone for spiders little Thomas Franklin Benjamin Jefferson Elexander Phelps found it there, and opened the door of it to see if the rats would come out, and they did, and Aunt Sally she come in, and when we got back she was a-standing on top of the bed raising Cain, and the rats was doing what they could to keep off the dull times for her. So she took and dusted us both with the hickry, and we was as much as two hours catching another fifteen or sixteen, drat that meddlesome cub, and they warn't the likeliest, nuther, because the first haul was the pick of the flock. I never see a likelier lot of rats than what that first haul was.

We got a splendid stock of sorted spiders, and bugs, and frogs, and caterpillars, and one thing or another; and we like to got a hornet's nest, but we didn't. The family was at home. We didn't give it right up, but stayed with them as long as we could; because we allowed we'd tire them out or they'd got to tire us out, and they done it. Then we got allycumpain and rubbed on the places, and was pretty near all right again, but couldn't set down convenient. And so we went for the snakes, and grabbed a couple of dozen garters and house-snakes, and put them in a bag, and put it in our room, and by that time it was supper-time, and a rattling good honest day's work: and hungry?—oh, no, I reckon not! And there warn't a blessed snake up there when we went back—we didn't half tie the sack, and they worked out somehow, and left. But it didn't matter much, because they was still on the premises somewheres. So we judged we could get some of them again. No, there warn't no real scarcity of snakes about the house for a considerable spell. You'd see them dripping from the rafters and places every now and then; and they generly landed in your plate, or down the back of your neck, and most of the time where you didn't want them. Well, they was handsome and striped, and there warn't no harm in a million of them; but that never made no difference to Aunt Sally; she despised snakes, be the breed what they might, and she couldn't stand them no way you could fix it; and every time one of them flopped down on her, it didn't make no difference what she was doing, she would just lay that work down and light out. I never see such a woman. And you could hear her whoop to Jericho. You couldn't get her to take a-holt of one of them with the tongs. And if she turned over and found one in bed she would scramble out and lift a howl that you would think the house was afire. She disturbed the old man so that he said he could most wish there hadn't ever been no snakes created. Why, after every last snake had been gone clear out of the house for as much as a week Aunt Sally warn't over it yet; she warn't near over it; when she was setting thinking about something you could touch her on the back of her neck with a feather and she would jump right out of her stockings. It was very curious. But Tom said all women was just so. He said they was made that way for some reason or other.

We got a licking every time one of our snakes come in her way, and she allowed these lickings warn't nothing to what she would do if we ever loaded up the place again with them. I didn't mind the lickings, because they didn't amount to nothing; but I minded the trouble we had to lay in another lot. But we got them laid in, and all the other things; and you never see a cabin as blithesome as Jim's was when they'd all swarm out for music and go for him. Jim didn't like the spiders, and the spiders didn't like Jim; and so they'd lay for him, and make it mighty warm for him. And he said that between the rats and the snakes and the grindstone there warn't no room in bed for him, skasely; and when there was, a body couldn't sleep, it was so lively, and it was always lively, he said, because *they* never all slept at one time, but took turn about, so when the snakes was asleep the rats was on deck, and when the rats turned in the snakes came on watch, so he always had one gang under him, in his way, and t'other gang having a circus over him, and if he got up to hunt a new place the spiders would take a chance at him as he crossed over. He said if he ever got out this time he wouldn't ever be a prisoner again, not for a salary.

Well, by the end of three weeks everything was in pretty good shape. The shirt was sent in early, in a pie, and every time a rat bit Jim he would get up and write a line in his journal whilst the ink was fresh; the pens was made, the inscriptions and so on was all carved on the grindstone; the bed-leg was sawed in two, and we had et up the sawdust, and it give us a most amazing stomach-ache. We reckoned we was all going to die, but didn't. It was the most undigestible sawdust I ever see; and Tom said the same. But as I was saying. we'd got all the work done now, at last; and we was all pretty much fagged out, too, but mainly Jim. The old man had wrote a couple of times to the plantation below Orleans to come and get their runaway nigger, but hadn't got no answer, because there warn't no such plantation; so he allowed he would advertise Jim in the St. Louis and New Orleans papers; and when he mentioned the St. Louis ones it give me the cold shivers, and I see we hadn't no time to lose. So Tom said, now the the nonnamous letters.

"What's them?" I says.

"Warnings to the people that something is up. Sometimes it's done one way, sometimes another. But there's always somebody spying around that gives notice to the governor of the castle. When Louis XVI was going to light out of the Tooleries a servant-girl done it. It's a very good way, and so is the nonnamous letters. We'll use them both. And it's usual for the prisoner's mother to change clothes with him, and she stays in, and he slides out in her clothes. We'll do that, too."

"But looky here, Tom, what do we want to *warn* anybody for that something's up? Let them find it out for themselves—it's their lookout."

"Yes, I know; but you can't depend on them. It's the way they've acted from the very start—left us to do *everything*. They're so confiding and mullet-headed they don't take notice of nothing at all. So if we don't *give* them notice there won't be nobody nor nothing to interfere with us, and so after all our hard work and trouble this escape 'll go off perfectly flat; won't amount to nothing—won't be nothing *to* it."

"Well, as for me, Tom, that's the way I'd like."

"Shucks!" he says, and looked disgusted. So I says:

"But I ain't going to make no complaint. Any way that suits you suits me. What you going to do about the servant-girl?"

"You'll be her. You slide in, in the middle of the night, and hook that yaller girl's frock."

"Why, Tom, that 'll make trouble next morning; because, of course, she prob'bly hain't got any but that one."

"I know; but you don't want it but fifteen minutes, so carry the nonnamous letter and shove it under the front door."

"All right, then, I'll do it; but I could carry it just as handy in my own togs."

"You wouldn't look like a servant-girl *then*, would you?"

"No, but there won't be nobody to see what I look like, *anyway*."

"That ain't got nothing to do with it. The thing for us to do is just to do our *duty*, and not worry about whether anybody *sees* us do it or not. Hain't you got no principle at all?"

"All right, I ain't saying nothing; I'm the servant-girl. Who's Jim's mother?"

"I'm his mother. I'll hook a gown from Aunt Sally."

"Well, then, you'll have to stay in the cabin when me and Jim leaves."

"Not much. I'll stuff Jim's clothes full of straw and lay it on his bed to represent his mother in disguise, and Jim 'll take the nigger woman's gown off of me and wear it, and we'll all evade together. When a prisoner of style escapes it's called an evasion. It's always called so when a king escapes, f'rinstance. And the same with a king's son; it don't make no difference whether he's a natural one or an unnatural one."

So Tom he wrote the nonnamous letter, and I smouched the yaller wench's frock that night, and put it on, and shoved it under the front door, the way Tom told me to. It said:

Beware. Trouble is brewing. Keep a sharp lookout.

UNKNOWN FRIEND.

Next night we stuck a picture, which Tom drawed in blood, of a skull and crossbones on the front door; and next night another one of a coffin on the back door. I never see a family in such a sweat. They couldn't 'a' been worse scared if the place had 'a' been full of ghosts laying for them behind everything and under the beds and shivering through the air. If a door banged, Aunt Sally she jumped and said "ouch!" if anything fell, she jumped and said "ouch!" if you happened to touch her, when she warn't noticing, she done the same; she couldn't face no way and be satisfied, because she allowed there was something behind her every time—so she was always a-whirling around sudden, and saying "ouch," and before she'd got two-thirds around she'd whirl back again, and say it again; and she was afraid to go to bed, but she dasn't set up. So the thing was working very well, Tom said; he said he never see a thing work more satisfactory. He said it showed it was done right.

So he said, now for the grand bulge! So the very next morning at the streak of dawn we got another letter ready, and was wondering what we better do with it, because we heard them say at supper they was going to have a nigger on watch at both doors all night. Tom he went down the lightning-rod to spy around; and the nigger at the back door was asleep, and he stuck it in the back of his neck and come back. This letter said:

Don't betray me, I wish to be your friend. There is a desprate gang of cutthroats from over in the Indian Territory going to steal your runaway nigger to-night, and they have been trying to scare you so as you will stay in the house and not bother them. I am one of the gang, but have got religgion and wish to quit it and lead an honest life again, and will betray the helish design. They will sneak down from northards, along the fence, at midnight exact, with a false key, and go in the nigger's cabin to get him. I am to be off a piece and blow a tin horn if I see any danger; but stead of that I will BA *like a sheep soon as they get in and not blow at all; then whilst they are getting his chains loose, you slip there and lock them in, and can kill them at your leasure. Don't do anything but just the way I am telling you; if you do they will suspicion something and raise whoopjamboreehoo. I do not wish any reward but to know I have done the right thing.*

UNKNOWN FRIEND.

40 *Fishing—The Vigilance Committee— A Lively Run—Jim Adivses a Doctor*

We was feeling pretty good after breakfast, and took my canoe and went over the river a-fishing, with a lunch, and had a good time, and took a look at the raft and found her all right, and got home late to supper, and found them in such a sweat and worry they didn't know which end they was standing on, and made us go right off to bed the minute we was done supper, and wouldn't tell us what the trouble was, and never let on a word about the new letter, but didn't need to, because we knowed as much about it as anybody did, and as soon as we was half up-stairs and her back was turned we slid for the cellar cubboard and loaded up a good lunch and took it up to our room and went to bed, and got up about half past eleven, and Tom put on Aunt Sally's dress that he stole and was going to start with the lunch, but says:

"Where's the butter?"

"I laid out a hunk of it," I says, "on a piece of a corn-pone."

"Well, you *left* it laid out, then—it ain't here."

"We can get along without it," I says.

"We can get along *with* it, too," he says; "just you slide down the cellar and fetch it. And then mosey right down the lightning-rod and come along. I'll go and stuff the straw into Jim's clothes to represent his mother in disguise, and be ready to *ba* like a sheep and shove soon as you get there."

So out he went, and down cellar went I. The hunk of butter, big as a person's fist, was where I had left it, so I took up the slab of corn-pone with it on, and blowed out my light, and started up-stairs very stealthy, and got up to the main floor all right, but here comes Aunt Sally with a candle, and I clapped the truck in my hat, and clapped my hat on my head, and the next second she see me; and she says:

"You been down cellar?"

"Yes'm."

"What you been doing down there?"

"Noth'n."

"*Noth'n!*"

"No'm."

"Well, then, what possessed you to go down there this time of night?"

"I don't know 'm."

"You don't *know?* Don't answer me that way. Tom, I want to know what you been *doing* down there."

"I hain't been doing a single thing, Aunt Sally, I hope to gracious if I have."

I reckoned she'd let me go now, and as a generl thing she would; but I s'pose there was so many strange things going on she was just in a sweat about every little thing that warn't yard-stick straight; so she says, very decided:

"You just march into that setting-room and stay there till I come. You been up to something you no business to, and I lay I'll find out what it is before *I'm* done with you."

So she went away as I opened the door and walked into the setting-room. My, but there was a crowd there! Fifteen farmers, and every one of them had a gun. I was most powerful sick, and slunk to a chair and set down. They was setting around, some of them talking a little, in a low voice, and all of them fidgety and uneasy, but trying to look like they warn't; but I knowed they was, because they was always takin off their hats, and putting them on, and scratching their heads, and changing their seats, and fumbling with their buttons. I warn't easy myself, but I didn't take my hat off, all the same.

I did wish Aunt Sally would come, and get done with me, and lick me, if she wanted to, and let me get away and tell Tom how we'd overdone this thing, and what a thundering hornet's nest we'd got ourselves into, so we could stop fooling around straight off, and clear out with Jim before these rips got out of patience and come for us.

At last she come and begun to ask me questions, but I *couldn't* answer them straight, I didn't know which end of me was up; because these men was in such a fidget now that some was wanting to start right *now* and lay for them desperadoes, and saying it warn't but a few minutes to midnight; and others was trying to get them to hold on and wait for the sheep-signal; and here was Aunty pegging away at the questions, and me a-shaking all over and ready to sink down in my tracks I was that scared; and the place getting hotter and hotter, and the butter beginning to melt and run down my neck and behind my ears; and pretty soon, when one of them says, "*I'm* for going and getting in the cabin *first* and right *now*, and catching them when they come," I most dropped; and a streak of butter come a-trickling down my forehead, and Aunt Sally she see it, and turns white as a sheet, and says:

"For the land's sake, what *is* the matter with the child? He's got the brain-fever as shore as you're born, and they're oozing out!"

And everybody runs to see, and she snatches off my hat, and out comes the bread and what was left of the butter, and she grabbed me, and hugged me, and says:

"Oh, what a turn you did give me! and how glad and grateful I am it ain't no worse; for luck's against us, and it never rains but it pours, and when I see that truck I thought we'd lost you, for I knowed by the color and all it was just like your brains would be if—Dear, dear, whyd'nt you *tell* me that was what you'd been down there for, *I* wouldn't 'a' cared. Now cler out to bed, and don't you lemme see no more of you till morning!"

I was up-stairs in a second, and down the lightning-rod in another one, and shinning through the dark for the lean-to. I couldn't hardly get my words out, I was so anxious; but I told Tom as quick as I could we must jump for it now, and not a minute to lose—the house full of men, yonder, with guns!

His eyes just blazed; and he says:

"No!—is that so? *Ain't* it bully! Why, Huck, if it was to do over again, I bet I could fetch two hundred! If we could put it off till—"

"Hurry! *hurry!*" I says. "Where's Jim?"

"Right at your elbow; if you reach out your arm you can touch him. He's dressed, and everything's ready. Now we'll slide out and give the sheep-signal."

But then we heard the tramp of men coming to the door, and heard them begin to fumble with the padlock, and heard a man say:

"I *told* you we'd be too soon; they haven't come—the door is locked. Here, I'll lock some of you into the cabin, and you lay for 'em in the dark and kill 'em when they come; and the rest scatter around a piece, and listen if you can hear 'em coming."

So in they come, but couldn't see us in the dark, and most trod on us whilst we was hustling to get under the bed. But we got under all right, and out through the hole, swift but soft—Jim first, me next, and Tom last, which was according to Tom's orders. Now we was in the lean-to, and heard trampings close by outside. So we crept to the door, and Tom stopped us there and put his eye to the crack, but couldn't make out nothing, it was so dark; and whispered and said he would listen for the steps to get further, and when he nudged us Jim must glide out first, and him last. So he set his ear to the crack and listened, and listened, and listened, and the steps a-scraping around out there all the time; and at last he nudged us, and we slid out, and stooped down, not breathing, and not making the least noise, and slipped stealthily towards the fence in Injun file, and got to it all right, and me and Jim over it; but Tom's britches catched fast on a splinter on the top rail, and then he hear the steps coming, so he had to pull loose, which snapped the splinter and made a noise; and as he dropped in our tracks and started somebody sings out:

"Who's that? Answer, or I'll shoot!"

But we didn't answer; we just unfurled our heels and shoved. Then there was a rush, and a *bang, bang, bang!* and the bullets fairly whizzed around us! We heard them sing out:

"Here they are! They've broke for the river! After 'em, boys, and turn loose the dogs!"

So here they come, full tilt. We could hear them because they wore boots and yelled, but we didn't wear no boots and didn't yell. We was in the path to the mill; and when they got pretty close onto us we dodged into the bush and let them go by, and then dropped in behind them. They'd had all the dogs shut up, so they wouldn't scare off the robbers; but by this time somebody had let them loose, and here they come making powwow enough for a million; but they was our dogs; so we stopped in our tracks till they catched up; and when they see it warn't nobody but us, and no excitement to offer them, they only just said howdy, and tore right ahead towards the shouting and clattering; and then we up-stream again, and whizzed along after them till we was nearly to the mill, and then struck up through the bush to where my canoe was tied, and hopped in and pulled for dear life towards the middle of the river, but didn't make no more noise than we was obleeged to. Then we struck out, easy and comfortable, for the island where my raft was; and we could hear them yelling and barking at each other all up and down the bank, till we was so far away the sounds got dim and died out. And when we stepped onto the raft I says:

"*Now*, old Jim, you're a free man *again*, and I bet you won't ever be a slave no more."

"En a mighty good job it wuz, too, Huck. It 'uz planned beautiful, en it 'uz *done* beautiful; en dey ain't *nobody* kin git up a plan dat's mo' mixed up en splendid den what dat one wuz."

We was all glad as we could be, but Tom was the gladdest of all because he had a bullet in the calf of his leg.

When me and Jim heard that we didn't feel as brash as what we did before. It was hurting him considerable, and bleeding; so we laid him in the wigwam and tore up one of the duke's shirts for to bandage him, but he says:

"Gimme the rags; I can do it myself. Don't stop now; don't fool around here, and the evasion booming along so handsome; man the sweeps, and set her loose! Boys, we done it elegant!—'deed we did. I wish *we'd* 'a' had the handling of Louis XVI, there wouldn't 'a' been no 'Son of Saint Louis, ascend to heaven!' wrote down in *his* biography; no, sir, we'd 'a' whooped him over the *border*—that's what we'd 'a' done with *him*—and done it just as slick as nothing at all, too. Man the sweeps—man the sweeps!"

But me and Jim was consulting—and thinking. And after we'd thought a minute, I says:

"Say it, Jim."

So he says:

"Well, den, dis is de way it look to me, Huck. Ef it wuz *him* dat 'uz bein' sot free, en one er de boys wuz to git shot, would he say, 'Go on en save me, nemmine 'bout a doctor f'r to save dis one'? Is dat like Mars Tom Sawyer? Would he say dat? You *bet* he wouldn't! *Well*, den, is Jim gwyne to say it? No, sah—I doan' budge a step out'n dis place 'dout a *doctor*; not if it's forty year!"

I knowed he was white inside, and I reckoned he'd say what he did say—so it was all right now, and I told Tom I was a-going for a doctor. He raised considerable row about it, but me and Jim stuck to it and wouldn't budge; so he was for crawling out and setting the raft loose himself; but we wouldn't let him. Then he gave us a piece of his mind, but it didn't do no good.

So when he sees me getting the canoe ready, he says:

"Well, then, if you're bound to go, I'll tell you the way to do when you get to the village. Shut the door and blindfold the doctor tight and fast, and make him swear to be silent as the grave, and put a purse full of gold in his hand, and then take and lead him all around the back alleys and everywheres in the dark, and then fetch him here in the canoe, in a roundabout way amongst the islands, and search him and take his chalk away from him, and don't give it back to him till you get him back to the village, or else he will chalk this raft so he can find it again. It's the way they all do."

So I said I would, and left, and Jim was to hide in the woods when he see the doctor coming till he was gone again.

41 The Doctor—Uncle Silas—Sister Hotchkiss—Aunt Sally in Trouble

The doctor was an old man; a very nice, kind-looking old man when I got him up. I told him me and my brother was over on Spanish Island hunting yesterday afternoon, and camped on a piece of a raft we found, and about midnight he must 'a' kicked his gun in his dreams, for it went off and shot him in the leg, and we wanted him to go over there and fix it and not say nothing about it, nor let anybody know, because we wanted to come home this evening and surprise the folks.

"Who is your folks?" he says.

"The Phelpses, down yonder."

"Oh," he says. And after a minute, he says:

"How'd you say he got shot?"

"He had a dream," I says, "and it shot him."

"Singular dream," he says.

So he lit up his lantern, and got his saddle-bags, and we started. But when he see the canoe he didn't like the look of her—said she was big enough for one, but didn't look pretty safe for two. I says:

"Oh, you needn't be afeard, sir, she carried the three of us easy enough."

"What three?"

"Why, me and Sid, and—and—and *the guns*; that's what I mean."

"Oh," he says.

But he puts his foot on the gunnel and rocked her, and shook his head, and said he reckoned he'd look around for a bigger one. But they was all locked and chained; so he took my canoe, and said for me to wait till he come back, or I could hunt around further, or maybe I better go down home and get them ready for the surprise if I wanted to. But I said I didn't; so I told him just how to find the raft, and then he started.

I struck an idea pretty soon. I says to myself, spos'n he can't fix that leg just in three shakes of a sheep's tail, as the saying is? Spos'n it takes him three or four days? What are we going to do?—lay around there till he lets the cat out of the bag? No, sir; I know what *I'll* do. I'll wait, and when he comes back if he says he's got to go any more I'll get down there, too, if I swim; and we'll take and tie him, and keep him, and shove out down the river; and when Tom's done with him we'll give him what it's worth, or all we got, and then let him get ashore.

So then I crept into a lumber-pile to get some sleep; and next time I waked up the sun was away up over my head! I shot out and went for the doctor's house, but they told me he'd gone away in the night some time or other, and warn't back yet. Well, thinks I, that looks powerful bad for Tom, and I'll dig out for the island right off. So away I shoved, and turned the corner and nearly rammed my head into Uncle Silas's stomach! He says:

"Why, *Tom!* Where you been all this time, you rascal?"

"*I* hain't been nowheres," I says, "only just hunting for the runaway nigger—me and Sid."

"Why, where ever did you go?" he says. "Your aunt's been mighty uneasy."

"She needn't," I says, "because we was all right. We followed the men and the dogs, but they outrun us, and we lost them; but we thought we heard them on the water, so we got a canoe and took out after them and crossed over, but couldn't find nothing of them; so we cruised along up-shore till we got kind of tired and beat out; and tied up the canoe and went to sleep, and never waked up till about an hour ago; then we paddled over here to hear the news, and Sid's at the post-office to see what he can hear, and I'm a-branching out to get something to eat for us, and then we're going home."

So then we went to the post-office to get "Sid"; but just as I suspicioned, he warn't there; so the old man he got a letter out of the office, and we waited awhile longer, but Sid didn't come; so the old man said, come along, let Sid foot it home, or canoe it, when he got done fooling around—but we would ride. I couldn't get him to let me stay and wait for Sid; and he said there warn't no use in it, and I must come along, and let Aunt Sally see we was all right.

When we got home Aunt Sally was that glad to see me she laughed and cried both, and hugged me, and give me one of them lickings of hern that don't amount to shucks, and said she'd serve Sid the same when he come.

And the place was plum full of farmers and farmers' wives, to dinner; and such another clack a body never heard. Old Mrs. Hotchkiss was the worst; her tongue was a-going all the time. She says:

"Well, Sister Phelps, I've ransacked that-air cabin over, an' I b'lieve the nigger was crazy. I says to Sister Damrell—didn't I, Sister Damrell?—s'I, he's crazy, s'I—them's the very words I said. You all hearn me: he's crazy, s'I; everything shows it, s'I. Look at that-air grindstone, s'I; want to tell *me't* any cretur 't's in his right mind 's a-goin' to scrabble all them crazy things onto a grindstone? s'I. Here sich 'n' sich a person busted his heart; 'n' here so 'n' so pegged along for thirty-seven year, 'n' all that—natcherl son o' Louis somebody, 'n' sich everlastin' rubbage. He's plumb crazy, s'I; it's what I says in the fust place, it's what I says in the middle 'n' it's what I says last 'n' all the time—the nigger's crazy—crazy's Nebokoodneezer, s'I."

"An' look at that-air ladder made out'n rags, Sister Hotchkiss," says old Mrs. Damrell; "what in the name o' goodness *could* he ever want of—"

"The very words I was a-sayin' no longer ago th'n this minute to Sister Utterback, 'n' she'll tell you so herself. Sh-she, look at that-air rag ladder, sh-she; 'n' s'I, yes, *look* at it, s'I—what *could* he 'a' wanted of it? s'I. Sh-she, Sister Hotchkiss, sh-she—"

"But how in the nation'd they ever *git* that grindstone *in* there, *any*way? 'n' who dug that-air *hole?* 'n' who—"

"My very *words*, Brer Penrod! I was a-sayin'—pass that-air sasser o' m'lasses, won't ye?—I was a'sayin' to Sister Dunlap, jist this minute, how *did* they git that grindstone in there? s'I. Without *help*, mind you— 'thout *help!* Thar's where 'tis. Don't tell *me*, s'I; there *wuz* help, s'I; 'n' ther' wuz a *plenty* help, too, s'I; ther's ben a *dozen* a-helpin' that nigger, 'n' I lay I'd skin every last nigger on this place but *I'd* find out who done it, s'I; 'n' moreover, s'I—

"A *dozen* says you!—*forty* couldn't 'a' done everything that's been done. Look at them case-knife saws and things, how tedious they've been made; look at that bed-leg sawed off with 'm, a week's work for six men: look at that nigger made out'n straw on the bed; and look at—"

"You may *well* say it, Brer Hightower! It's jist as I was a-sayin' to Brer Phelps, his own self. S'e, what do you think of it, Sister Hotchkiss? s'e. Think o' what, Brer Phelps? s'I. Think o' that bed-leg sawed off that way? s'e. *Think* of it? s'I. I lay it never sawed *itself* off, s'I—somebody *sawed* it, s'I; that's my opinion, take it or leave it, it mayn't be no 'count, s'I, but sich as 't is, it's my opinion, s'I, 'n' if anybody k'n start a better one, s'I, let him *do* it, s'I, that's all. I says to Sister Dunlap, s'I.—"

"Why, dog my cats, they must 'a' ben a house-full o' niggers in there every night for four weeks to 'a' done all that work, Sister Phelps. Look at that shirt—every last inch of it kivered over with secret African writ'n done with blood! Must 'a' ben a raft uv 'im at it right along, all the time, amost. Why, I'd give two dollars to have it read to me; 'n' as for the niggers who wrote it, I 'low I'd take 'n' lash 'm t'll—"

"People to *help* him, Brother Marples! Well, I reckon you'd *think* so if you'd 'a' been in this house for a while back. Why, they've stole everything they could lay their hands on—and we a-watching all the time, mind you. They stole that shirt right off o' the line! and as for that sheet they made the rag ladder out of, ther' ain't no telling how many times they *didn't* steal that; and flour, and candles, and candlesticks, and spoons, and the old warming-pan, and most a thousand things that I disremember now, and my new calico dress; and me and Silas and my Sid and Tom on the constant watch day *and* night, as I was a-telling you, and not a one of us could catch hide nor hair nor sight nor sound of them; and here at the last minute, lo and behold you, they slides right in under our noses and fools us, and not only fools *us* but the Injun Territory robbers too, and actuly gets *away* with that nigger safe and sound, and that with sixteen men and twenty-two dogs right on their very heels at that very time! I tell you, it just bangs anything I ever *heard* of. Why, *sperits* couldn't 'a' done better and been no smarter. And I reckon they must 'a' *been* sperits—because, *you* know our dogs, and ther' ain't no better; well, them dogs never even got on the *track* of 'm once! You explain *that* to me if you can!—*any* of you!"

"Well, it does beat—"

"Laws alive, I never—"

"So help me, I wouldn't 'a' be—"

"*House*-thieves as well as—"

"Goodnessgracioussakes, I'd 'a' ben afeard to *live* in sich a—"

" 'Fraid to *live!*—why, I was that scared I dasn't hardly go to bed, or get up, or lay down, or *set* down, Sister Ridgeway. Why, they'd steal the very—why, goodness sakes, you can guess what kind of a fluster *I* was in by the time midnight come last night. I hope to gracious if I warn't afraid they'd steal some o' the family! I was just to that pass I didn't have no reasoning faculties no more. It looks foolish enough *now*, in the daytime; but I says to myself, there's my two poor boys asleep, 'way upstairs in that lonesome room, and I declare to goodness I was that uneasy 't I crep' up there and locked 'em in! I *did*. And anybody would. Because, you know, when you get scared that way, it keeps running on, and getting worse and worse all the time, and your wits gets to addling, and you get to doing all sorts o' wild things, and by and by you think to yourself, spos'n *I* was a boy and was away up there, and the door ain't locked, and you—" She stopped, looking kind of wondering, and then she turned her head around slow, and when her eye lit on me—I got up and took a walk.

Says I to myself, I can explain better how we come to not be in that room this morning if I go out to one side and study over it a little. So I done it. But I dasn't go fur, or she'd 'a' sent for me. And when it was late in the day the people all went, and then I come in and told her the noise and shooting waked up me and "Sid," and the door was locked, and we wanted to see the fun, so we went down the lightning-rod, and both of us got hurt a little, and we didn't never want to try *that* no more. And then I went on and told her all what I told Uncle Silas before; and then she said she'd forgive us, and maybe it was all right enough anyway, and about what a body might expect of boys, for all boys was a pretty harum-scarum lot as fur as she could see; and so, as long as no harm hadn't come of it, she judged she better put in her time being grateful we was alive and well and she had us still, stead of fretting over what was past and done. So then she kissed me, and patted me on the head, and dropped into a kind of a brown-study; and pretty soon jumps up, and says:

"Why, lawsamercy, it's most night, and Sid not come yet? What *has* become of that boy?"

I see my chance; so I skips up and says:

"I'll run right up to town and get him," I says.

"No you won't," she says. "You'll stay right wher' you are; *one's* enough to be lost at a time. If he ain't here to supper, your uncle 'll go."

Well, he warn't there to supper; so right after supper uncle went.

He come back about ten a little bit uneasy; hadn't run across Tom's track. Aunt Sally was a good *deal* uneasy; but Uncle Silas he said there warn't no occasion to be—boys will be boys, he said, and you'll see this one turn up in the morning all sound and right. So she had to be satisfied. But she said she'd set up for him awhile anyway, and keep a light burning so he could see it.

And then when I went up to bed she come up with me and fetched her candle, and tucked me in, and mothered me so good I felt mean, and like I couldn't look her in the face; and she set down on the bed and talked with me a long time, and said what a splendid boy Sid was, and didn't seem to want to ever stop talking about him; and kept asking me every now and then if I reckoned he could 'a' got lost, or hurt, or maybe drownded, and might be laying at this minute somewheres suffering or dead, and she not by him to help him, and so the tears would drip down silent, and I would tell her that Sir was all right, and would be home in the morning, sure; and she would squeeze my hand, or maybe kiss me, and tell me to say it again, and keep on saying it, because it done her good, and she was in so much trouble. And when she was going away she looked down in my eyes so steady and gentle, and says:

"The door ain't going to be locked, Tom, and there's the window and the rod; but you'll be good, *won't* you? And you won't go? For *my* sake."

Laws knows I *wanted* to go bad enough to see about Tom, and was all intending to go; but after that I wouldn't 'a' went, not for kingdoms.

But she was on my mind and Tom was on my mind, so I slept very restless. And twice I went down the rod away in the night, and slipped around front, and see her setting there by her candle in the window with her eyes towards the road and the tears in them; and I wished I could do something for her, but I couldn't, only to swear that I wouldn't never do nothing to grieve her any more. And the third time I waked up at dawn, and slid down, and she was there yet, and her candle was most out, and her old gray head was resting on her hand, and she was asleep.

42 *Tom Sawyer Wounded—The Doctor's Story—Tom Confesses—Aunt Polly Arrives—Hand Out Them Letters*

The old man was up-town again before breakfast, but couldn't get no track of Tom; and both of them set at the table thinking, and not saying nothing, and looking mournful, and their coffee getting cold, and not eating anything. And by and by the old man says:

"Did I give you the letter?"

"What letter?"

"The one I got yesterday out of the post-office."

"No, you didn't give me no letter."

"Well, I must 'a' forgot it."

So he rummaged his pockets, and then went off somewheres where he had laid it down, and fetched it, and give it to her. She says:

"Why, it's from St. Petersburg—it's from Sis."

I allowed another walk would do me good; but I couldn't stir. But before she could break it open she dropped it and run—for she see something. And so did I. It was Tom Sawyer on a mattress; and that old doctor; and Jim, in *her* calico dress, with his hands tied behind him; and a lot of people. I hid the letter behind the first thing that come handy, and rushed. She flung herself at Tom, crying, and says:

"Oh, he's dead, he's dead, I know he's dead!"

And Tom he turned his head a little, and muttered something or other, which showed he warn't in his right mind; then she flung up her hands, and says:

"He's alive, thank God! And that's enough!" and she snatched a kiss of him, and flew for the house to get the bed ready, and scattering orders right and left at the niggers and everybody else, as fast as her tongue could go, every jump of the way.

I followed the men to see what they was going to do with Jim; and the old doctor and Uncle Silas followed after Tom into the house. The men was very huffy, and some of them wanted to hang Jim for an example to all the other niggers around there, so they wouldn't be trying to run away like Jim done, and making such a raft of trouble, and keeping a whole family scared most to death for days and nights. But the others said, don't do it, it wouldn't answer at all; he ain't our nigger, and his owner would turn up and make us pay for him, sure. So that cooled them down a little, because the people that's always the most anxious for to hang a nigger that hain't done just right is always the very ones that ain't the most anxious to pay for him when they've got their satisfaction out of him.

They cussed Jim considerable, though, and give him a cuff or two side the head once in a while, but Jim never said nothing, and he never let on to know me, and they took him to the same cabin, and put his own clothes on him, and chained him again, and not to no bed-leg this time, but to a big staple drove into the bottom log, and chained his hands, too, and both legs, and said he warn't to have nothing but bread and water to eat after this till his owner come, or he was sold at auction because he didn't come in a certain length of time, and filled up our hole, and said a couple of farmers with guns must stand watch around about the cabin every night, and a bulldog tied to the door in the daytime; and about this time they was through with the job and was tapering off with a kind of generl good-by cussing, and then the old doctor comes and takes a look, and says:

"Don't be no rougher on him than you're obleeged to, because he ain't a bad nigger. When I got to where I found the boy I see I couldn't cut the bullet out without some help, and he warn't in no condition for me to leave to go and get help; and he got a little worse and a little worse, and after a long time he went out of his head, and wouldn't let me come a-nigh him any more, and said if I chalked his raft he'd kill me, and no end of wild foolishness like that, and I see I couldn't do anything at all with him; so I says, I got to have *help* somehow; and the minute I says it out crawls this nigger from somewheres and says he'll help, and he done it, too, and done it very well. Of course I judged he must be a runaway nigger, and there I *was!* and there I had to stick right straight along all the rest of the day and all night. It was a fix, I tell you! I had a couple of patients with the chills, and of course I'd of liked to run up to town and see them, but I dasn't because the nigger might get away, and then I'd be to blame; and yet never a skiff came close enough for me to hail. So there I had to stick plumb until daylight this morning; and I never see a nigger that was a better nuss or faithfuller, and yet he was risking his freedom to do it, and was all tired out, too, and I see plain enough he'd been worked main hard lately. I liked the nigger for that; I tell you, gentlemen, a nigger like that is worth a thousand dollars—and kind treatment, too. I had everything I needed, and the boy was doing as well there as he would 'a' done at home—better, maybe, because it was so quiet; but there I *was*, with both of 'm on my hands, and there I had to stick till about dawn this morning; then some men in a skiff come by, and as good luck would have it the nigger was setting by the pallet with his head propped on his knees sound asleep; so I motioned them in quiet, and they slipped up on him and grabbed him and tied him before he knowed what he was about, and we never had no trouble. And the boy being in a kind of a flighty sleep, too, we muffled the oars and hitched the raft on, and towed her over very nice and quiet, and the nigger never made the least row nor said a word from the start. He ain't no bad nigger, gentleman; that's what I think about him."

Somebody says:

"Well, it sounds very good, doctor, I'm obleeged to say."

Then the others softened up a little, too, and I was mighty thankful to that old doctor for doing Jim that good turn; and I was glad it was according to my judgment of him, too; because I thought he had a good heart in him and was a good man the first time I see him. Then they all agreed that Jim had acted very well, and was deserving to have some notice took of it, and reward. So every one of them promised, right out hearty, that they wouldn't cuss him no more.

Then they come out and locked him up. I hoped they was going to say he could have one or two of the chains took off, because they was rotten heavy, or could have meat and greens with his bread and water; but they didn't think of it, and I reckoned it warn't the best for me to mix in, but I judged I'd get the doctor's yarn to Aunt Sally somehow or other as soon as I'd got through the breakers that was laying just ahead of me—explanations, I mean, of how I forgot to mention about Sid being shot when I was telling how him and me put in that dratted night paddling around hunting the runaway nigger.

But I had plenty time. Aunt Sally she stuck to the sick-room all day and all night, and every time I see Uncle Silas mooning around I dodged him.

Next morning I heard Tom was a good deal better, and they said Aunt Sally was gone to get a nap. So I slips to the sick-room, and if I found him awake I reckoned we could put up a yarn for the family that would wash. But he was sleeping, and sleeping very peaceful, too; and pale, not fire-faced the way he was when he come. So I set down and laid for him to wake. In about half an hour Aunt Sally comes gliding in, and there I was, up a stump again! She motioned me to be still, and set down by me, and begun to whisper, and said we could all be joyful now, because all the symptoms was first-rate, and he'd been sleeping like that for ever so long, and looking better and peacefuller all the time, and ten to one he'd wake up in his right mind.

So we set there watching, and by and by he stirs a bit, and opened his eyes very natural, and takes a look, and says:

"Hello!—why, I'm at *home!* How's that? Where's the raft?"

"It's all right," I says.

"And *Jim?*"

"The same," I says, but couldn't say it pretty brash. But he never noticed, but says:

"Good! Splendid! *Now* we're all right and safe! Did you tell Aunty?"

I was going to say yes; but she chipped in and says:

"About what, Sid?"

"Why, about the way the whole thing was done."

"What whole thing?"

"Why, *the* whole thing. There ain't but one; how we set the runaway nigger free—me and Tom."

"Good land! Set the run—What *is* the child talking about! Dear, dear, out of his head again!"

"*No*, I ain't out of my HEAD; I know all what I'm talking about. We *did* set him free—me and Tom. We laid out to do it, and we *done* it elegant, too." He'd got a start, and she never checked him up, just set and stared and stared, and let him clip along, and I see it warn't no use for *me* to put in. "Why, Aunty, it cost us a power of work—weeks of it—hours and hours, every night, whilst you was all asleep. And we had to steal candles, and the sheet, and the shirt, and your dress, and spoons, and tin plates, and case-knives, and the warming-pan, and the grindstone, and flour, and just no end of things, and you can't think what work it was to make the saws, and pens, and inscriptions, and one thing or another, and you can't think *half* the fun it was. And we had to make up the pictures of coffins and things, and nonnamous letters from the robbers, and get up and down the lightning rod, and dig the hole into the cabin, and make the rope ladder and send it in cooked up in a pie, and send in spoons and things to work with in your apron pocket—"

"Mercy sakes!"

"—and load up the cabin with rats and snakes and so on, for company for Jim; and then you kept Tom here so long with the butter in his hat that you come near spiling the whole business, because the men come before we was out of the cabin, and we had to rush, and they heard us and let drive at us, and I got my share, and we dodged out of the path and let them go by, and when the dogs come they warn't interested in us, but went for the most noise, and we got our canoe, and made for the raft, and was all safe, and Jim was a free man, and we done it all by ourselves, and *wasn't* it bully, *Aunty!*"

"Well, I never heard the likes of it in all my born days! So it was *you*, you little rapscallions, that's been making all this trouble, and turned everybody's wits clean inside out and scared us all most to death. I've as good a notion as ever I had in my life to take it out o' you this very minute. To think, here I've been, night after night, a—*you* just get well once, you young scamp, and I lay I'll tan the Old Harry out o' both o' ye!"

But Tom, he *was* so proud and joyful, he just *couldn't* hold in, and his tongue just *went* it—she a-chipping in, and spitting fire all along, and both of them going it at once, like a cat convention; and she says:

"*Well*, you get all the enjoyment you can out of it *now*, for mind I tell you if I catch you meddling with him again—"

"Meddling with *who?*" Tom says, dropping his smile and looking surprised.

"With *who?* Why, the runaway nigger, of course. Who'd you reckon?"

Tom looks at me very grave, and says:

"Tom, didn't you just tell me he was all right? Hasn't he got away?"

"*Him?*" says Aunt Sally; "the runaway nigger? 'Deed he hasn't. They've got him back, safe and sound, and he's in that cabin again, on bread and water, and loaded down with chains, till he's claimed or sold!"

Tom rose square up in bed, with his eye hot, and his nostrils opening and shutting like gills, and sings out to me:

"They hain't no *right* to shut him up! *Shove!*—and don't you lose a minute. Turn him loose! he ain't no slave; he's as free as any cretur that walks this earth!"

"What *does* the child mean?"

"I mean every word I *say*, Aunt Sally, and if somebody don't go, *I'll* go. I've knowed him all his life, and so has Tom, there. Old Miss Watson died two months ago, and she was ashamed she ever was going to sell him down the river, and *said* so; and she set him free in her will."

"Then what on earth did *you* want to set him free for, seeing he was already free?"

"Well, that *is* a question, I must say; and *just* like women! Why, I wanted the *adventure* of it; and I'd 'a' waded neck-deep in blood to—goodness alive, AUNT POLLY!"

If she warn't standing right there, just inside the door, looking as sweet and contented as an angel half full of pie, I wish I may never!

Aunt Sally jumped for her, and most hugged the head off of her, and cried over her, and I found a good enough place for me under the bed, for it was getting pretty sultry for *us*, seemed to me. And I peeped out, and in a little while Tom's Aunt Polly shook herself loose and stood there looking across at Tom over her spectacles—kind of grinding him into the earth, you know. And then she says:

"Yes, you *better* turn y'r head away—I would if I was you, Tom."

"Oh, deary me!" says Aunt Sally; "*is* he changed so? Why, that ain't *Tom*, it's Sid; Tom's—Tom's—why, where is Tom? He was here a minute ago."

"You mean where's Huck *Finn*—that's what you mean! I reckon I hain't raised such a scamp as my Tom all these years not to know him when I *see* him. That *would* be a pretty howdy-do. Come out from under that bed, Huck Finn."

So I done it. But not feeling brash.

Aunt Sally she was one of the mixed-upest-looking persons I ever see—except one, and that was Uncle Silas, when he come in and they told it all to him. It kind of made him drunk, as you may say, and he didn't know nothing at all the rest of the day, and preached a prayer-meeting sermon that night that gave him a rattling ruputation, because the oldest man in the world couldn't 'a' understood it. So Tom's Aunt Polly, she told all about who I was, and what; and I had to up and tell how I was in such a tight place that when Mrs. Phelps took me for Tom Sawyer—she chipped in and says, "Oh, go on and call me Aunt Sally, I'm used to it now, and 'taint no need to change"—that when Aunt Sally took me for Tom Sawyer I had to stand it—there warn't no other way, and I knowed he wouldn't mind, because it would be nuts for him, being a mystery, and he'd make an adventure out of it, and be perfectly satisfied. And so it turned out, and he let on to be Sid, and made things as soft as he could for me.

And his Aunt Polly she said Tom was right about old Miss Watson setting Jim free in her will; and so, sure enough, Tom Sawyer had gone and took all that trouble and bother to set a free nigger free! and I couldn't ever understand before, until that minute and that talk, how he *could* help a body set a nigger free with his bringing-up.

Well, Aunt Polly she said that when Aunt Sally wrote to her that Tom and *Sid* had come all right and safe, she says to herself:

"Look at that, now ! I might have expected it, letting him go off that way without anybody to watch him. So now I got to go and trapse all the way down the river, eleven hundred mile, and find out what that creetur's up to *this* time, as long as I couldn't seem to get any answer out of you about it."

"Why, I never heard nothing from you," says Aunt Sally.

"Well, I wonder! Why, I wrote you twice to ask you what you could mean by Sid being here."

"Well, I never got 'em, Sis."

Aunt Polly she turns around slow and severe, and says:

"You, Tom!"

"Well—*what?*" he says, kind of pettish.

"Don't you what *me*, you impudent thing—hand out them letters."

"What letters?"

"*Them* letters. I be bound, if I have to take a-holt of you I'll—"

"They're in the trunk. There, now. And they're just the same as they was when I got them out of the office. I hain't looked into them, I hain't touched them. But I knowed they'd make trouble, and I thought if you warn't in no hurry, I'd—"

"Well, you *do* need skinning, there ain't no mistake about it. And I wrote another one to tell you I was coming; and I s'pose he—"

"No, it come yesterday; I hain't read it yet, but *it's* all right, I've got that one."

I wanted to offer to bet two dollars she hadn't, but I reckoned maybe it was just as safe to not to. So I never said nothing.

43 *Out of Bondage—Paying the Captive—Yours Truly, Huck Finn*

The first time I catched Tom private I asked him what was his idea, time of the evasion?—what it was he'd planned to do if the evasion worked all right and he managed to set a nigger free that was already free before? And he said, what he had planned in his head from the start, if we got Jim out all safe, was for us to run him down the river on the raft, and have adventures plumb to the mouth of the river, and then tell him about his being free, and take him back up home on a steamboat, in style, and pay him for his lost time, and write word ahead and get out all the niggers around, and have them waltz him into town with a torchlight procession and a brass-band, and then he would be a hero, and so would we. But I reckoned it was about as well the way it was.

We had Jim out of the chains in no time, and when Aunt Polly and Uncle Silas and Aunt Sally found out how good he helped the doctor nurse Tom, they made a heap of fuss over him, and fixed him up prime, and give him all he wanted to eat, and a good time, and nothing to do. And we had him up to the sick-room, and had a high talk; and Tom give Jim forty dollars for being a prisoner for us so patient, and doing it up so good, and Jim was pleased most to death, and busted out, and says:

"*Dah*, now, Huck, what I tell you?—what I tell you up dah on Jackson Islan'? I *tole* you I got a hairy breas', en what's de sign un it; en I *tole* you I ben rich wunst, en gwineter to be rich *ag'in;* en it's come true; en heah she *is! Dah,* now! doan' talk to *me*—signs is *signs,* mine I tell you; en I knowed jis' 's well 'at I 'uz gwineter be rich ag'in as I's a-stannin' heah dis minute!"

And then Tom he talked along and talked along, and says, le's all three slide out of here one of these nights and get an outfit, and go for howling adventures amongst the Injuns, over in the territory, for a couple of weeks or two; and I says, all right, that suits me, but I ain't got no money for to buy the outfit, and I reckon I couldn't get none from home, because it's likely pap's been back before now, and got it all away from Judge Thatcher and drunk it up.

"No, he hain't," Tom says; "it's all there yet—six thousand dollars and more; and your pap hain't ever been back since. Hadn't when I come away, anyhow."

Jim says, kind of solemn:

"He ain't a-comin' back no mo', Huck."

I says:

"Why, Jim?"

"Nemmine why, Huck—but he ain't comin' back no mo'."

But I kep at him; so at last he says:

"Doan' you 'member de house dat was float'n down de river, en dey wuz a man in dah, kivered up, en I went in en unkivered him and didn' let you come in? Well, den, you kin git yo' money when you wants it, kase dat wuz him."

Tom's most well now, and got his bullet around his neck on a watch-guard for a watch, and is always seeing what time it is, and so there ain't nothing more to write about, and I am rotten glad of it, because if I'd 'a' knowed what a trouble it was to make a book I wouldn't 'a' tackled it, and ain't a-going to no more. But I reckon I got to light out for the territory ahead of the rest, because Aunt Sally she's going to adopt me and sivilize me, and I can't stand it. I been there before.

The Raftsmen Passage

THE RAFTSMEN PASSAGE

The following is the well-known "raftsmen passage," originally a part of HUCKLEBERRY FINN, *but not included in most editions of the novel. Mark Twain lifted the passage for inclusion in Chapter III of* LIFE ON THE MISSISSIPPI. *When he finished* HUCKLEBERRY FINN, *he was advised by his publisher to delete the passage, in order to make the length of the novel closer to that of* TOM SAWYER. *The passage occurs immediately after the second paragraph of Chapter XVI (page 77 of our text).*

By way of illustrating keelboat talk and manners, and that now-departed and hardly-remembered raft-life, I will throw in, in this place, a chapter from a book which I have been working at, by fits and starts, during the past five or six years, and may possibly finish in the course of five or six more. The book is a story which details some passages in the life of an ignorant village boy, Huck Finn, son of the town drunkard of my time out west, there. He has run away from his persecuting father, and from a persecuting good widow who wishes to make a nice, truth-telling, respectable boy of him; and with him a slave of the widow's has also escaped. They have found a fragment of a lumber raft (it is high water and dead summer time), and are floating down the river by night, and hiding in the willows by day,—bound for Cairo,—whence the negro will seek freedom in the heart of the free States. But in a fog, they pass Cairo without knowing it. By and by they begin to suspect the truth, and Huck Finn is persuaded to end the dismal suspense by swimming down to a huge raft which they have seen in the distance ahead of them, creeping aboard under cover of the darkness, and gathering the needed information by eavesdropping:—

> But you know a young person can't wait very well when he is impatient to find a thing out. We talked it over, and by and by Jim said it was such a black night, now, that it would n't be no risk to swim down to the big raft and crawl aboard and listen,—they would talk about Cairo, because they would be calculating to go ashore there for a spree, maybe, or anyway

they would send boats ashore to buy whiskey or fresh meat or something. Jim had a wonderful level head, for a nigger: he could most always start a good plan when you wanted one.

I stood up and shook my rags off and jumped into the river, and struck out for the raft's light. By and by, when I got down nearly to her, I eased up and went slow and cautious. But everything was all right—nobody at the sweeps. So I swum down along the raft till I was most abreast the camp fire in the middle, then I crawled aboard and inched along and got in amongst some bundles of shingles on the weather side of the fire. There was thirteen men there—they was the watch on deck of course. And a mighty rough-looking lot, too. They had a jug, and tin cups, and they kept the jug moving. One man was singing—roaring, you may say; and it was n't a nice song—for a parlor anyway. He roared through his nose, and strung out the last word of every line very long. When he was done they all fetched a kind of Injun war-whoop, and then another was sung. It begun:—

"There was a woman in our towdn,
  In our towdn did dwed'l (dwell,)
She loved her husband dear-i-lee,
  But another man twyste as wed'l.
Singing too, riloo, riloo, riloo,
  Ri-too, riloo, rilay - - -e,
She loved her husband dear-i-lee,
  But another man twyste as wed'l."

And so on—fourteen verses. It was kind of poor, and when he was going to start on the next verse one of them said it was the tune the old cow died on; and another one said, "Oh, give us a rest." And another one told him to take a walk. They made fun of him till he got mad and jumped up and begun to cuss the crowd, and said he could lam any thief in the lot.

They was all about to make a break for him, but the biggest man there jumped up and says:—

"Set whar you are, gentlemen. Leave him to me; he's my meat."

Then he jumped up in the air three times and cracked his heels together every time. He flung off a buckskin coat that was all hung with fringes, and says, "You lay thar tell the chawin-up's done;" and flung his hat down, which was all over ribbons, and says, "You lay thar tell his sufferins is over."

Then he jumped up in the air and cracked his heels together again and shouted out:—

"Whoo-oop! I'm the old original iron-jawed, brass-mounted, copper-bellied corpse-maker from the wilds of Arkansaw!—Look at me! I 'm the man they call Sudden Death and General Desolation! Sired by a hurricane, dam'd by an earthquake, half-brother to the cholera, nearly related to the small-pox on the mother's side! Look at me! I take nineteen alligators and a bar'l of whiskey for breakfast when I'm in robust health, and a bushel of rattlesnakes and a dead body when I'm ailing! I split the everlasting rocks with my glance, and I squench the thunder when I speak! Whoo-oop! Stand back and give me room according to my strength! Blood's my natural drink, and the wails of the dying is music to my ear! Cast your eye on me, gentlemen!—and lay low and hold your breath, for I'm bout to turn myself loose!"

All the time he was getting this off, he was shaking his head and looking fierce, and kind of swelling around in a little circle, tucking up his wrist-bands, and now and then straightening up and beating his breast with his fist, saying, "Look at me, gentlemen!" When he got through, he jumped up and cracked his heels together three times, and let off a roaring "whoo-oop! I'm the bloodiest son of a wildcat that lives!"

Then the man that had started the row tilted his old slouch hat down over his right eye; then he bent stooping forward, with his back sagged and his south end sticking out far, and his fists a-shoving out and drawing in in front of him, and so went around in a little circle about three times, swelling himself up and breathing hard. Then he straightened, and jumped up and cracked his heels together three times before he lit again (that made them cheer), and he began to shout like this:—

"Whoo-oop! bow your neck and spread, for the kingdom of sorrow's a-coming! Hold me down to the earth, for I feel my powers a-working! whoo-oop! I'm a child of sin, *don't* let me get a start! Smoked glass, here, for all! Don't attempt to look at me with the naked eye, gentlemen! When I'm playful I use the meridians of longitude and parallels of latitude for a seine, and drag the Atlantic Ocean for whales! I scratch my head with the lightning and purr myself to sleep with the thunder! When I'm cold, I bile the Gulf of Mexico and bathe in it; when I'm hot I fan myself with an equinoctial storm; when I'm thirsty I reach up and suck a cloud dry like a sponge; when I range the earth hungry, famine follows in my tracks! Whoo-oop! Bow your neck and spread! I put my hand on the sun's face and make it night in the earth; I bite a piece out of the moon and hurry the seasons; I shake myself and crumble the mountains! Contemplate me through leather—*don't* use the naked eye! I'm the man with a petrified heart and biler-iron bowels! The massacre of isolated communities is the pastime of my idle moments, the destruction of nationalities the serious business of my life! The boundless vastness of the great American desert is my enclosed property, and I bury my dead on my own premises!" He jumped up and cracked his heels together three times before he lit (they cheered him again), and as he come down he shouted out: "Whoo-oop! bow your neck and spread, for the pet child of calamity's a-coming!"

Then the other one went to swelling around and blowing again—the first one—the one they called Bob; next, the Child of Calamity chipped in again, bigger than ever; then they both got at it at the same time, swelling round and round each other and punching their fists most into each other's faces, and whooping and jawing like Injuns; then Bob called the Child names, and the Child called him names back again: next, Bob called him a heap rougher names and the Child come back at him with the very worst kind of language; next, Bob knocked the Child's hat off, and the Child picked it up and kicked Bob's ribbony hat about six foot; Bob went and got it and said never mind, this war n't going to be the last of this thing, because he was a man that never forgot and never forgive, and so the Child better look out, for there was a time a-coming, just as sure as he was a living man, that he would have to answer to him with the best blood in his body. The Child said no man was willinger than he was for that time to come, and he would give Bob fair warning, *now*, never to cross his path again, for he could never rest till he had waded in his blood, for such was his nature, though he was sparing him now on account of his family, if he had one.

Both of them was edging away in different directions, growling and shaking their heads and going on about what they was going to do; but a little black-whiskered chap skipped up and says:—

"Come back here, you couple of chicken-livered cowards, and I'll thrash the two of ye!"

And he done it, too. He snatched them, he jerked them this way and that, he booted them around, he knocked them sprawling faster than they could get up. Why, it war n't two minutes till they begged like dogs—and how the other lot did yell and laugh and clap their hands all the way through, and shout "Sail in, Corpse-Maker!" "Hi! at him again, Child of Calamity!" "Bully for you, little Davy!" Well, it was a perfect pow-wow for a while. Bob and the Child had red noses and black eyes when they got through. Little Davy made them own up that they was sneaks and cowards and not fit to eat with a dog or drink with a nigger; then Bob and the Child shook hands with each other, very solemn, and said they had always respected each other and was willing to let bygones be bygones. So then they washed their faces in the river; and just then there was a loud order to stand by for a crossing, and some of them went forward to man the sweeps there, and the rest went aft to handle the after-sweeps.

I laid still and waited for fifteen minutes, and had a smoke out of a pipe that one of them left in reach; then the crossing was finished, and they stumped back and had a drink around and went to talking and singing again. Next they got out an old fiddle, and one played, and another patted juba, and the rest turned themselves loose on a regular old-fashioned keel-boat break-down. They couldn't keep that up very long without getting winded, so by and by they settled around the jug again.

They sung "jolly, jolly raftsman's the life for me," with a rousing chorus, and then they got to talking about differences betwixt hogs, and their different kinds of habits; and next about women and their different ways; and next about the best ways to put out houses that was afire; and next about what ought to be done with the Injuns; and next about what a king had to do, and how much he got; and next about how to make cats fight; and next about what to do when a man has fits; and next about differences betwixt clear-water rivers and muddy-water ones. The man they called Ed said the muddy Mississippi water was wholesomer to drink than the clear water of the Ohio; he said if you let a pint of this yaller Mississippi water settle, you would have about a half to three quarters of an inch of mud in the bottom, according to the stage of the river, and then it warn't no better then Ohio water—what you wanted to do was to keep it stirred up—and when the river was low, keep mud on hand to put in and thicken the water up the way it ought to be.

The Child of Calamity said that was so; he said there was nutritiousness in the mud, and a man that drunk Mississippi water could grow corn in his stomach if he wanted to. He says:—

"You look at the graveyards; that tells the tale. Trees won't grow worth shucks in a Cincinnati graveyard, but in a Sent Louis graveyard they grow upwards of eight hundred foot high. It's all on account of the water the people drunk before they laid up. A Cincinnati corpse don't richen a soil any."

And they talked about how Ohio water did n't like to mix with Mississippi water. Ed said if you take the Mississippi on a rise when the Ohio is low, you'll find a wide band of clear water all the way down the east side of the Mississippi for a hundred mile or more, and the minute you get out a quarter of a mile from shore and pass the line, it is all thick and yaller the rest of the way across. Then they talked about how to keep tobacco from getting mouldy, and from that they went into ghosts and told about a lot that other folks had seen; but Ed says:—

"Why don't you tell something that you've seen yourselves? Now let me have a say. Five years ago I was on a raft as big as this, and right along here it was a bright moonshiny night, and I was on watch and boss of the stabboard oar forrard, and one of my pards was a man named Dick Allbright, and he come along to where I was sitting, forrard—gaping and stretching, he was—and stooped down on the edge of the raft and washed his face in the river, and come and set down by me and got out his pipe, and had just got it filled, when he looks up and says,—

" 'Why looky-here,' he says, 'ain't that Buck Miller's place, over yander in the bend?'

" 'Yes,' says I, 'it is—why?' He laid his pipe down and leant his head on his hand, and says,—

" 'I thought we'd be furder down.' I says,—

" 'I thought it too, when I went off watch'—we was standing six hours on and six off—'but the boys told me,' I says, 'that the raft didn't seem to hardly move, for the last hour,'—says I, 'though she's a slipping along all right, now,' says I. He give a kind of a groan, and says,—

" 'I've seed a raft act so before, along here,' he says, ' 'pears to me the current has most quit above the head of this bend durin' the last two years,' he says.

"Well, he raised up two or three times, and looked away off and around on the water. That started me at it, too. A body is always doing what he sees somebody else doing, though there may n't be no sense in it. Pretty soon I see a black something floating on the water away off to stabboard and quartering behind us. I see he was looking at it, too. I says,—

" 'What's that?' He says, sort of pettish,—

" 'Tain't nothing but an old empty bar'l.'

" 'An empty bar'l!' says I, 'why,' says I, 'a spy-glass is a fool to *your* eyes. How can you tell it's an empty bar'l?' He says,—

" 'I don't know; I reckon it ain't a bar'l, but I thought it might be,' says he.

" 'Yes,' I says, 'so it might be, and it might be anything else, too; a body can't tell nothing about it, such a distance as that,' I says.

"We hadn't nothing else to do, so we kept on watching it. By and by I says,—

" 'Why looky-here, Dick Allbright, that thing's a-gaining on us, I believe.'

"He never said nothing. The thing gained and gained, and I judged it must be a dog that was about tired out. Well, we swung down into the crossing, and the thing floated across the bright streak of the moonshine, and, by George, it *was* a bar'l. Says I,—

" 'Dick Allbright, what made you think that thing was a bar'l, when it was a half a mile off,' says I. Says he,—

" 'I don't know.' Says I,—

" 'You tell me, Dick Allbright.' He says,—

" 'Well, I knowed it was a bar'l; I've seen it before; lots has seen it; they says it's a hanted bar'l.'

"I called the rest of the watch, and they come and stood there, and I told them what Dick said. It floated right along abreast, now, and did n't gain any more. It was about twenty foot off. Some was for having it aboard, but the rest didn't want to. Dick Allbright said rafts that had fooled with it had got bad luck by it. The captain of the watch said he did n't believe in it. He said he reckoned the bar'l gained on us because it was in a little better current than what we was. He said it would leave by and by.

"So then we went to talking about other things, and we had a song, and then a breakdown; and after that the captain of the watch called for another song; but it was clouding up, now, and the bar'l stuck right thar in the same place, and the song didn't seem to have much warm-up to it, somehow, and so they did n't finish it, and there war n't any cheers, but it sort of dropped flat, and nobody said anything for a minute. Then everybody tried to talk at once, and one chap got off a joke, but it war n't no use, they did n't laugh, and even the chap that made the joke did n't laugh at it, which ain't usual. We all just settled down glum, and watched the bar'l, and was oneasy and oncomfortable. Well, sir, it shut down black and still, and then the wind begin to moan around, and next the lightning begin to play and the thunder to grumble. And pretty soon there was a regular storm, and in the middle of it a man that was running aft stumbled and fell and sprained his ankle so that he had to lay up. This made the boys shake their heads. And every time the lightning come, there was that bar'l with the blue lights winking around it. We was always on the look-out for it. But by and by, towards dawn, she was gone. When the day come we could n't see her anywhere, and we war n't sorry, neither.

"But next night about half-past nine, when there was songs and high jinks going on, here she comes again, and took her old roost on the stabboard side. There war n't no more high jinks. Everybody got solemn; nobody talked; you could n't get anybody to do anything but set around moody and look at the bar'l. It begun to cloud up again. When the watch changed, the off watch stayed up, 'stead of turning in. The storm ripped and roared around all night, and in the middle of it another man tripped and sprained his ankle, and had to knock off. The bar'l left towards day, and nobody see it go.

"Everybody was sober and down in the mouth all day. I don't mean the kind of sober that comes of leaving liquor alone,—not that. They was quiet, but they all drunk more than usual,—not together, —but each man sidled off and took it private, by himself.

"After dark the off watch did n't turn in; nobody sung, nobody talked; the boys did n't scatter around, neither; they sort of huddled together, forrard; and for two hours they set there, perfectly still, looking steady in the one direction, and heaving a sigh once in a while. And then, here comes the bar'l again. She took up her old place. She staid there all night; nobody turned in. The storm come on again, after midnight. It got awful dark; the rain poured down; hail, too; the thunder boomed and roared and bellowed; the wind blowed a hurricane; and the lightning spread over everything in big sheets of glare, and showed the whole raft as plain as day; and the river lashed up white as milk as far as you could see for miles, and there was that bar'l jiggering along, same as ever. The captain ordered the watch to man the after sweeps for a crossing, and nobody would go,—no more sprained ankles for them, they said. They wouldn't even *walk* aft. Well then, just then the sky split wide open, with a crash, and the lightning killed two men of the after watch, and crippled two more. Crippled them how, says you? Why, *sprained their ankles!*

"The bar'l left in the dark betwixt lightnings, towards dawn. Well, not a body eat a bite at breakfast that morning. After that the men loafed around, in twos and threes, and talked low together. But none of them herded with Dick Allbright. They all give him the cold shake. If he come around where any of the men was, they split up and sidled away. They would n't man the sweeps with him. The captain had all the skiffs hauled up on the raft, alongside of his wigwam, and would n't let the dead men be took ashore to be planted; he did n't believe a man that got ashore would come back; and he was right.

"After night come, you could see pretty plain that there was going to be trouble if that bar'l come again; there was such a muttering going on. A good many wanted to kill Dick Allbright, because he'd seen the bar'l on other trips, and that had an ugly look. Some wanted to put him ashore. Some said, let's all go ashore in a pile, if the bar'l comes again.

"This kind of whispers was still going on, the men being bunched together forrard watching for the bar'l, when, lo and behold you, here she comes again. Down she comes, slow and steady, and settles into her old tracks. You could a heard a pin drop. Then up comes the captain, and says:—

" 'Boys, don't be a pack of children and fools; I don't want this bar'l to be dogging us all the way to Orleans, and *you* don't; well, then, how's the best way to stop it? Burn it up,—that's the way. I'm going to fetch it aboard,' he says. And before anybody could say a word, in he went.

"He swum to it, and as he come pushing it to the raft, the men spread to one side. But the old man got it aboard and busted in the head, and there was a baby in it! Yes sir, a stark naked baby. It was Dick Allbright's baby; he owned up and said so.

" 'Yes,' he says, a-leaning over it, 'yes, it is my own lamented darling, my poor lost Charles William Allbright deceased,' says he,—for he could curl his tongue around the bulliest words in the language when he was a mind to, and lay them before you without a jint started, anywheres. Yes, he said he used to live up at the head of this bend, and one night he choked his child, which was crying, not intending to kill it,—which was prob'ly a lie,—and then he was scared, and buried it in a bar'l, before his wife got home, and off he went, and struck the northern trail and went to rafting; and this was the third year that the bar'l had chased him. He said the bad luck always begun light, and lasted till four men was killed, and then the bar'l did n't come any more after that. He said if the men would stand it one more night,—and was a-going on like that,—but the men had got enough. They started to get out a boat and take him ashore and lynch him, but he grabbed the little child all of a sudden and jumped overboard with it hugged up to his breast and shedding tears, and we never see him again in this life, poor old suffering soul, nor Charles William neither."

"*Who* was shedding tears?" says Bob; "was it Allbright or the baby?"

"Why, Allbright, of course; didn't I tell you the baby was dead? Been dead three years—how could it cry?"

"Well, never mind how it could cry—how could it *keep* all that time?" says Davy. "You answer me that."

"I don't know how it done it," says Ed. "It done it though—that's all I know about it."

"Say—what did they do with the bar'l?" says the Child of Calamity.

"Why, they hove it overboard, and it sunk like a chunk of lead."

"Edward, did the child look like it was choked?" says one.

"Did it have its hair parted?" says another.

"What was the brand on that bar'l, Eddy?" says a fellow they called Bill.

"Have you got the papers for them statistics, Edmund?" says Jimmy.

"Say, Edwin, was you one of the men that was killed by the lightning?" says Davy.

"Him? O, no, he was both of 'em," says Bob. Then they all haw-hawed.

"Say, Edward, don't you reckon you 'd better take a pill? You look bad—don't you feel pale?" says the Child of Calamity.

"O, come, now, Eddy," says Jimmy, "show up; you must a kept part of that bar'l to prove the thing by. Show us the bunghole—*do*—and we'll all believe you."

"Say, boys," says Bill, "less divide it up. Thar's thirteen of us. I can swaller a thirteenth of the yarn, if you can worry down the rest."

Ed got up mad and said they could all go to some place which he ripped out pretty savage, and then walked off aft cussing to himself, and they yelling and jeering at him, and roaring and laughing so you could hear them a mile.

"Boy's we'll split a watermelon on that," says the Child of Calamity; and he come rummaging around in the dark amongst the shingle bundles where I was, and put his hand on me. I was warm and soft and naked; so he says "Ouch!" and jumped back.

"Fetch a lantern or a chunk of fire here, boys—there's a snake here as big as a cow!"

So they run there with a lantern and crowded up and looked in on me.

"Come out of that, you beggar!" says one.

"Who are you?" says another.

"What are you after here? Speak up prompt, or overboard you go."

"Snake him out, boys. Snatch him out by the heels."

I began to beg, and crept out amongst them trembling. They looked me over, wondering, and the Child of Calamity says:—

"A cussed thief! Lend a hand and less heave him overboard!"

"No," says Big Bob, "less get out the paint-pot and paint him a sky blue all over from head to heel, and *then* heave him over!"

"Good! that's it. Go for the paint, Jimmy."

When the paint come, and Bob took the brush and was just going to begin, the others laughing and rubbing their hands, I begun to cry, and that sort of worked on Davy, and he says:—

" 'Vast there! He's nothing but a cub. I'll paint the man that tetches him!"

So I looked around on them, and some of them grumbled and growled, and Bob put down the paint, and the others did n't take it up.

"Come here to the fire, and less see what you're up to here," says Davy. "Now set down there and give an account of yourself. How long have you been aboard here?"

"Not over a quarter of a minute, sir," says I.

"How did you get dry so quick?"

"I don't know, sir. I'm always that way, mostly."

"Oh, you are, are you? What's your name?"

I war n't going to tell my name. I did n't know what to say, so I just says:

"Charles William Allbright, sir."

Then they roared—the whole crowd; and I was mighty glad I said that, because maybe laughing would get them in a better humor.

When they got done laughing, Davy says:—

"It won't hardly do, Charles William. You could n't have growed this much in five year, and you was a baby when you come out of the bar'l, you know, and dead at that. Come, now, tell a straight story, and nobody'll hurt you, if you ain't up to anything wrong. What *is* your name?"

"Aleck Hopkins, sir. Aleck James Hopkins."

"Well, Aleck, where did you come from, here?"

"From a trading scow. She lays up the bend yonder. I was born on her. Pap has traded up and down here all his life; and he told me to swim off here, because when you went by he said he would like to get some of you to speak to a Mr. Jonas Turner, in Cairo, and tell him—"

"Oh, come!"

"Yes, sir, it's as true as the world; Pap he says—"

"Oh, your grandmother!"

They all laughed, and I tried again to talk, but they broke in on me and stopped me.

"Now, looky-here," says Davy; "you 're scared, and so you talk wild. Honest, now, do you live in a scow, or is it a lie?"

"Yes, sir, in a trading scow. She lays up at the head of the bend. But I war n't born in her. It's our first trip."

"Now you're talking! What did you come aboard here, for? To steal?"

"No, sir, I did n't.—It was only to get a ride on the raft. All boys does that."

"Well, I know that. But what did you hide for?"

"Sometimes they drive the boys off."

"So they do. They might steal. Looky-here; if we let you off this time, will you keep out of these kind of scrapes hereafter?"

" 'Deed I will, boss. You try me."

"All right, then. You ain't but little ways from shore. Overboard with you, and don't you make a fool of yourself another time this way.—Blast it, boy, some raftsmen would rawhide you till you were black and blue!"

I didn't wait to kiss good-byë, but went overboard and broke for shore. When Jim come along by and by, the big raft was away out of sight around the point. I swum out and got aboard, and was mighty glad to see home again.

QUESTIONS FOR DISCUSSION AND WRITING

1. For what reasons, aesthetic or otherwise, do you suppose this passage was omitted from *Huckleberry Finn?*
2. What does the inclusion of the passage do for—or to—the novel? Consider some of the major concerns of the criticism you have read (structure, characterization, social criticism, etc.).
3. What do you make of the introductory paragraph to this passage?
4. What themes or ideas do you find here that help to relate this passage to the rest of the novel?
5. On what level do you think some of the incidents in this passage (for example, the story of the barrel) are intended to operate? Are they simple reportage? Do they have any symbolic value? Do they illustrate aspects of the American character?
6. Elsewhere Huck says, "It's lovely to live on a raft." Do you think this applies to the raft in this passage? May this raft be useful in any way for comparison or contrast with the raft of Huck and Jim?

The Criticism

REVIEW OF *HUCKLEBERRY FINN*

by Robert Bridges

Mark Twain is a humorist or nothing. He is well aware of this fact himself, for he prefaces the "Adventures of Huckleberry Finn" with a brief notice, warning persons in search of a moral, motive or plot that they are liable to be prosecuted, banished or shot. This is a nice little artifice to scare off the critics—a kind of "trespassers on these grounds will be dealt with according to law."

However, as there is no penalty attached, we organized a search expedition for the humorous qualities of this book with the following hilarious results:

A very refined and delicate piece of narration by Huck Finn, describing his venerable and dilapidated "pap" as afflicted with delirium tremens, rolling over and over, "kicking things every which way," and "saying there was devils ahold of him." This chapter is especially suited to amuse the children on long, rainy afternoons.

An elevating and laughable description of how Huck killed a pig, smeared its blood on an axe and mixed in a little of his own hair, and then ran off, setting up a job on the old man and the community, and leading them to believe him murdered. This little joke can be repeated by any smart boy for the amusement of his fond parents.

A graphic and romantic tale of a Southern family feud, which resulted in an elopement and from six to eight choice corpses.

A polite version of the "Giascutus" story, in which a nude man, striped with the colors of the rainbow, is exhibited as "The King's Camelopard; or, The Royal Nonesuch." This is a good chapter for lenten parlor entertainments and church festivals.

A side-splitting account of a funeral, enlivened by a "sick melodeum," a "long-legged undertaker," and a rat episode in the cellar. /19/

QUESTIONS FOR DISCUSSION AND WRITING

1. Robert Bridges says "Mark Twain is a humorist or nothing." Isn't Twain more than just a humorist? What "more" have critics found in his work?
2. Discuss this notice of the novel as a naïve reading.

Reprinted from *Life,* V (26 February 1885), 19.

MARK TWAIN

by T. S. Perry

Mark Twain's "Tom Sawyer" is an interesting record of boyish adventure; but, amusing as it is, it may yet be fair to ask whether its most marked fault is not too strong adherence to conventional literary models? A glance at the book certainly does not confirm this opinion, but those who recall the precocious affection of Tom Sawyer, at the age when he is losing his first teeth, for a little girl whom he has seen once or twice, will confess that the modern novel exercises a very great influence. What is best in the book, what one remembers, is the light we get into the boy's heart. The romantic devotion to the little girl, the terrible adventures with murderers and in huge caves, have the air of concessions to jaded readers. But when Tom gives the cat Pain-Killer, is restless in church, and is recklessly and eternally deceiving his aunt, we are on firm ground—the author is doing sincere work.

This later book, "Huckleberry Finn," has the great advantage of being written in autobiographical form. This secures a unity in the narration that is most valuable; every scene is given, not described; and the result is a vivid picture of Western life forty or fifty years ago. While "Tom Sawyer" is scarcely more than an apparently fortuitous collection of incidents, and its thread is one that has to do with murders, this story has a more intelligible plot. Huckleberry, its immortal hero, runs away from his worthless father, and floats down the Mississippi on a raft, in company with Jim, a runaway negro. This plot gives great opportunity for varying incidents. The travelers spend some time on an island; they outwit every one they meet; they acquire full knowledge of the hideous fringe of civilization that then adorned that valley; and the book is a most valuable record of an important part of our motley American civilization.

What makes it valuable is the evident truthfulness of the narrative, and where this is lacking and its place is taken by ingenious invention, the book suffers. What is inimitable, however, is the reflection of the whole varied series of adventures in the mind of the young scapegrace

Reprinted from *Century*, XXX (May 1885), 171–172.

of a hero. His undying fertility of invention, his courage, his manliness in every trial, are an incarnation of the better side of the ruffianism that is one result of the independence of Americans, just as hypocrisy is one result of the English respect for civilization. The total absence of morbidness in the book—for the *mal du siecle* has not yet reached Arkansas—gives it a genuine charm; and it is interesting to notice the art with which this is brought out. The best instance is perhaps to be found in the account of the feud between the Shepherdsons and the Grangerfords, which is described only as it would appear to a semi-civilized boy of fourteen, without the slightest condemnation or surprise,—either of which would be bad art,—and yet nothing more vivid can be imagined. That is the way that a story is best told, by telling it, and letting it go to the reader unaccompanied by sign-posts or directions how he shall understand it and profit by it. Life teaches its lessons by implication, not by didactic preaching; and literature is at its best when it is an imitation of life and not an excuse for instruction.

As to the humor of Mark Twain, it is scarcely necessary to speak. It lends vividness to every page. The little touch in "Tom Sawyer," where, after the murder of which Tom was an eye-witness, it seemed "that his schoolmates would never get done holding inquests on dead cats and thus keeping the trouble present to his mind," and that in the account of the spidery six-armed girl of Emmeline's picture in "Huckleberry Finn," are in the author's happiest vein. Another admirable instance is to be seen in Huckleberry Finn's mixed feelings about rescuing Jim, the negro, from slavery. His perverted views regarding the unholiness of his actions are most instructive and /171/ amusing. It is possible to feel, however, that the fun in the long account of Tom Sawyer's artificial imitation of escapes from prison is somewhat forced; everywhere simplicity is a good rule, and while the account of the Southern *vendetta* is a masterpiece, the caricature of books of adventure leaves us cold. In one we have a bit of life; in the other Mark Twain is demolishing something that has no place in the book.

Yet the story is capital reading, and the reason of its great superiority to "Tom Sawyer" is that it is, for the most part, a consistent whole. If Mark Twain would follow his hero through manhood, he would condense a side of American life that, in a few years, will have to be delved out of newspapers, government reports, county histories, and misleading traditions by unsympathetic sociologists. /172/

QUESTIONS FOR DISCUSSION AND WRITING

1. This essay was written the year *Huckleberry Finn* was published. To what extent does it anticipate later criticism? To what extent does it differ from the mainstream of critical opinion? Draw from your answers a conclusion as to the success of Perry's evaluation of *Huckleberry Finn,* remembering that he lacked the perspective of time which later critics have had.
2. What does Perry mean by "truthfulness" (p. 171) in *Huckleberry Finn?* How can a piece of fiction be truthful? How could it possibly be criticized as untruthful?
3. Perry finds that Huck's account of the Shepherdson-Grangerford feud is the best instance of the total absence of morbidness which gives *Huckleberry Finn* a genuine charm. How have other critics assessed the merits of the Shepherdson-Grangerford feud? Why do so many critics mention this one episode so frequently and so prominently?
4. Perry speaks of the Emmeline Grangerford drawing of a six-armed girl as in the "happiest vein" of Twain's humor, but finds the humor of the final episode "somewhat forced." How have other critics evaluated the humor in *Huckleberry Finn?*

HUCK FINN COMES INTO HIS OWN

by Albert Bigelow Paine

In the December *Century* (1884) appeared a chapter from *The Adventures of Huckleberry Finn,* "The Grangerford-Shepherdson Feud," a piece of writing which Edmund Clarence Stedman, Brander Matthews, and others promptly ranked as among Mark Twain's very

"Huck Finn Comes into his Own" from *Mark Twain: A Biography* by Albert Bigelow Paine. Copyright 1912 by Harper & Brothers. 4 vols. Place of publication, New York. This passage is quoted from Volume 2.

best; when this was followed, in the January number, by "King Sollermun," a chapter which in its way delighted quite as many readers, the success of the new book was accounted certain.[1]

The Adventures of Huckleberry Finn was officially published in England and America in December, 1884, but the book was not in the canvassers' hands for delivery until February. By this time the orders were approximately for forty thousand copies, a number which had increased to fifty thousand a few weeks later. Webster's first publication venture was in the nature of a triumph. Clemens wrote to him March 16th:

"Your news is splendid. *Huck* certainly is a success."

He felt that he had demonstrated his capacity as a general director and Webster had proved his efficiency as an executive. He had no further need of an outside publisher.

The story of *Huck Finn* will probably stand as the best /793/ of Mark Twain's purely fictional writings. A sequel to *Tom Sawyer*, it is greater than its predecessor; greater artistically, though perhaps with less immediate interest for the juvenile reader. In fact, the books are so different that they are not to be compared—wherein lies the success of the later one. Sequels are dangerous things when the story is continuous, but in *Huckleberry Finn* the story is a new one, wholly different in environment, atmosphere, purpose, character, everything. The tale of Huck and Nigger Jim drifting down the mighty river on a raft, cross-secting the various primitive aspects of human existence, constitutes one of the most impressive examples of picaresque fiction in any language. It has been ranked greater than *Gil Blas*, greater even than *Don Quixote*; certainly it is more convincing, more human, than either of these tales. Robert Louis Stevenson once wrote, "It is a book I have read four times, and am quite ready to begin again tomorrow."

It is by no means a flawless book, though its defects are trivial enough. The illusion of Huck as narrator fails the least bit here and there; the "four dialects" are not always maintained; the occasional touch of broad burlesque detracts from the tale's reality. We are inclined to resent this. We never wish to feel that Huck is anything *but* a real character. We want him always the Huck who was willing to go to hell if necessary, rather than sacrifice Nigger Jim; the Huck who watched the river through long nights, and, without caring to explain why, felt his soul go out to the sunrise.

[1] Stedman, writing to Clemens of this instalment, said: "To my mind it is not only the most finished and condensed thing you have done, but as dramatic and powerful an episode as I know in modern literature."

> Two or three days and nights went by; I reckon I might say they swum by, they slid along so quiet and smooth and lovely. Here is the way we put in the time. It was a monstrous big river down there—sometimes a mile and a half wide; we run nights and laid up and hid daytimes; soon as the night was most gone we stopped navigating and tied up—nearly always in the dead water under a towhead; and then cut young cottonwoods /794/ and willows and hid the raft with them. Then we set out the lines. Next we slid into the river and had a swim, so as to freshen up and cool off; then we set down on the sandy bottom where the water was about knee deep, and watched the daylight come. Not a sound anywheres—perfectly still—just like the whole world was asleep, only sometimes the bullfrogs a-cluttering, maybe. The first thing to see, *looking* away over the water, was a kind of dull line—that was the woods on t'other side, you couldn't make nothing else out; then a pale place in the sky; then more paleness, spreading around; then the river softened up, away off, and warn't black anymore, but gray; you could see little dark spots drifting along, ever so far away—trading scows, and such things; and long black streaks—rafts; sometimes you could hear a sweep screaking; or jumbled up voices, it was so still, and sounds come so far; and by-and-by you could see a streak on the water which you know by the look of the streak that there's a snag there in a swift current which breaks on it and makes that streak look that way; and you see the mist curl up off the water, and the east reddens up, and the river, and you make out a log-cabin in the edge of the woods, away on the bank on t'other side of the river, being a woodyard, likely, and piled by them cheats so you can throw a dog through it anywheres; then the nice breeze springs up, and comes fanning you over there, so cool and fresh, and sweet to smell, on account of the woods and the flowers. . . . And next you've got the full day, and everything smiling in the sun, and the song-birds just going it!

This is the Huck we want, and this is the Huck we usually have, and that the world has long been thankful for.

Take the story as a whole, it is a succession of startling and unique pictures. The cabin in the swamp which Huck and his father used together in their weird, ghastly relationship; the night adventure with Jim on the wrecked steamboat; Huck's night among the towheads; the Grangerford-Shepherdson battle; the killing of Boggs—to name a few of the many vivid presentations—these are of no time or literary fashion and will never lose their /795/ flavor nor their freshness so long as humanity itself does not change. The terse, unadorned Grangerford-Shepherdson episode—built out of the Darnell-Watson feuds [2]—is simply classic in its vivid casualness, and the same may be said of almost every incident on that long river-drift; but this is the strength, the very essence of picaresque narrative. It is the way things happen in reality; and the quiet, unexcited frame of mind in which Huck is prompted to set them down would seem to be the last word in literary art. To Huck, apparently, the killing of Boggs and Colonel Sherburn's defiance of the mob are of about the same historical importance as any other incidents of the day's travel. When Colonel Sherburn threw his shotgun across his arm and bade the crowd disperse Huck says:

> The crowd washed back sudden, and then broke all apart and went tearing off every which way, and Buck Harkness he heeled it after them, looking tolerable cheap. I could a staid if I'd a wanted to, but I didn't want to.
>
> I went to the circus, and loafed around the back side till the watchman went by, and then dived in under the tent.

That is all. No reflections, no hysterics; a murder and a mob dispersed, all without a single moral comment. And when the Shepherdsons had got done killing the Grangerfords, and Huck had tugged the two bodies ashore and covered Buck Grangerford's face with a handkerchief, crying a little because Buck had been good to him, he spent no time in sentimental reflection or sermonizing, but promptly hunted up Jim and the raft and sat down to a meal of corn-dodgers, buttermilk, pork and cabbage, and greens:

> There ain't nothing in the world so good, when it is cooked right; and while I eat my supper we talked, and had a good /796/ time. I was powerful glad to get away from the feuds, and so was Jim to get away from the swamp. We said there warn't no home like a raft, after all. Other places do seem so cramped up and smothery, but a raft don't; you feel mighty free and easy and comfortable on a raft.

It was Huck Finn's morality that caused the book to be excluded from the Concord Library, and from other libraries here and there at a later day. The orthodox mental attitude of certain directors of juvenile literature could not condone Huck's looseness in the matter of statement and property rights, and in spite of New England tradi-

[2] See *Life on the Mississippi*, chap. xxvi. Mark Twain himself, as a cub pilot, came near witnessing the battle he describes.

tions Massachusetts librarians did not take any too kindly to his uttered principle that, after thinking it over and taking due thought on the deadly sin of abolition, he had decided that he'd go to hell rather than give Jim over to slavery. Poor vagrant Ben Blankenship, hiding his runaway negro in an Illinois swamp, could not dream that his humanity would one day supply the moral episode of an immortal book.

Able critics have declared that the psychology of Huck Finn is the book's large feature: Huck's moral point of view—the struggle between his heart and his conscience concerning the sin of Jim's concealment, and his final decision of self-sacrifice. Time may show that as an epic of the river, the picture of a vanished day, it will rank even greater. The problems of conscience we have always with us, but periods once passed are gone forever. Certainly Huck's loyalty to that lovely soul Nigger Jim was beautiful, though after all it may not have been so hard for Huck, who could be loyal to anything. Huck was loyal to his father, loyal to Tom Sawyer of course, loyal even to those two river tramps and frauds, the King and the Duke, for whom he lied prodigiously, only weakening when a new and lovelier loyalty came into view—loyalty to Mary Wilks.

The King and the Duke, by the way, are not elsewhere /797/ matched in fiction. The Duke was patterned after a journeyman-printer Clemens had known in Virginia City, but the King was created out of refuse from the whole human family—"all tears and flapdoodle," the very ultimate of disrepute and hypocrisy—so perfect a specimen that one must admire, almost love, him. "Hain't we all the fools in town on our side? and ain't that a big enough majority in any town?" he asks in a critical moment—a remark which stamps him as a philosopher of classic rank. We are full of pity at last when this pair of rapscallions ride out of the history on a rail, and feel some of Huck's inclusive loyalty and all the sorrowful truth of his comment: "Human beings *can* be awful cruel to one another."

The "poor old king" Huck calls him, and confesses how he felt "ornery and humble and to blame, somehow," for the old scamp's misfortunes. "A person's conscience ain't got no sense," he says, and Huck is never more real to us, or more lovable, than in that moment. Huck is what he is because, being made so, he cannot well be otherwise. He is a boy throughout—such a boy as Mark Twain had known and in some degree had been. One may pettily pick a flaw here and there in the tale's construction if so minded, but the moral character of Huck himself is not open to criticism. And indeed any criticism of this the greatest of Mark Twain's tales of modern life would be as the mere scratching of the granite of an imperishable structure. *Huck Finn* is a monument that no puny pecking will destroy. It is built of indestructible blocks of human nature; and if the blocks do not always fit, and the ornaments do not always agree, we need not fear. Time will blur the incongruities and moss over the mistakes. The edifice will grow more beautiful with the years. /798/

QUESTIONS FOR DISCUSSION AND WRITING

1. What does the word "primitive" mean as applied to the "aspects of human existence," as Paine does? (p. 794)
2. Paine says that the "illusion of Huck as narrator fails the least bit here and there." (p. 794) What does Paine mean by "illusion"? Using other criticism in your text, agree or disagree with Paine's comment.
3. Why does Paine say of the passage quoted on pages 794–795, "This is the Huck we want . . ."?
4. What role does loyalty play in the novel?
5. Paine says, "Able critics have declared that the psychology of Huck Finn is the book's large feature." (p. 797) Discuss Huck's psychology. What does Paine mean by "large feature"?
6. Paine mentions flaws in the book. What flaws have he and other critics found? How destructive to the novel are these flaws?

THE ORDEAL OF MARK TWAIN

by Van Wyck Brooks

In fact, the more one scans the later pages of Mark Twain's history the more one is forced to the conclusion that there was something gravely amiss with his inner life. There was that frequently noted fear of solitude, that dread of being alone with himself which made him, for example, beg for just one more game of billiards at 4 o'clock in the morning. There were those "daily self-chidings" that led him to slay his own conscience in one of the most ferocious of his humorous tales. That conscience of his—what was it? Why do so many of his jokes turn upon an affectation, let us say, of moral cowardice in himself? How does it happen that when he reads "Romola" the only thing that "hits" him "with force" is Tito's compromise with his conscience? Why those continual fits of remorse, those fantastic self-accusations in which he charged himself, we are told, with having filled Mrs. Clemens's life with privations, in which he made himself responsible first for the death of his younger brother and later for that of his daughter Susy, writing to his wife, according to Mr. Paine, that he was "wholly and solely responsible for the tragedy, detailing step by step with fearful reality his mistakes and weaknesses which had led to their downfall, the separation from Susy, and this final, incredible disaster"? Was there any reason why, humorously or otherwise, he should have spoken of himself as a liar, why he should have said, in reply to his own idea of writing a book about Tom Sawyer's after-life: "If I went on now and took him into manhood, he would just lie, like all the one-horse men in literature, and the reader would conceive a hearty contempt for him"? That morbid feeling of having lived in sin, which made him come to think of literature as primarily, perhaps, the confession of sins—was there anything in the moral point of view of his generation to justify it, in this greatly-loved writer, this honorable man of business, this zealous reformer, this loyal friend? "Be weak, be /12/ water, be characterless, be cheaply persuadable" was, he said, the first command the Deity ever issued to a human being on this planet, the only command Adam would never be able to disobey. And he noted on the margin of one of his books: "What a man sees in the human race is merely himself in the deep and honest privacy of his own heart. Byron despised the race because he despised himself. I feel as Byron did and for the same reason."

A strange enigma! "You observe," wrote Mark Twain once, almost at the beginning of his career, "that under a cheerful exterior I have got a spirit that is angry with me and gives me freely its contempt." That spirit remained with him, grew in him, to the last. The restless movement of his life, those continual journeys to Bermuda, where "the deep peace and quiet of the country sink into one's body and bones and give his conscience a rest," that consuming desire to write an autobiography "as caustic, fiendish and devilish as possible," which would "make people's hair curl" and get "his heirs and assigns burnt alive" if they ventured to print it within a hundred years, the immense relief of his seventieth birthday, to him "the scriptural statute of limitations—you have served your term, well or less well, and you are mustered out"—how are we to read the signs of all this hidden tragedy? For Mark Twain was right—things do not happen by chance, and the psychological determinism of the present day bears out in certain respects that other sort of determinism in which he so almost fanatically believed. There is no figure for the human being like the ship, he sometimes said. Well, was he not, in the eyes of his contemporaries, just as he proudly, gratefully suggested, in the glory of that last English welcome, the *Begum* of Bengal, stateliest of Indiamen, plowing the great seas under a cloud of canvas? Can we call it merely an irony of circumstance that in his own eyes he was a bit of storm-beaten /13/ human drift, a derelict, washing about on a forlorn sea?

No, there was a reason for Mark Twain's pessimism, a reason for that chagrin, that fear of solitude, that tortured conscience, those fantastic self-accusations, that indubitable self-contempt. It is an established fact, if I am not mistaken, that these morbid feelings of sin, which have no evident cause, are the result of having transgressed some inalienable life-demand peculiar to one's nature. It is as old as Milton that there are talents which are "death to hide," and I suggest that Mark Twain's "talent" was just so hidden. That bitterness of his was the effect of a certain miscarriage in his creative life, a balked personality, an arrested development of which he was himself almost wholly unaware, but which for him destroyed the meaning of life. The spirit of the artist in him, like the genie at last released from the bottle, overspread in a gloomy vapor the mind it had never quite been able to possess. /14/

What a social setting it was, that little world into which Mark Twain was born! It was drab, it was tragic. In "Huckleberry Finn" and "Tom Sawyer" we see it in the color of rose; and besides, we see there only a later phase of it, after Mark Twain's family had settled in Hannibal, on the Mississippi. He was five at the time; his eyes had opened on such a scene as we find in the early pages of "The Gilded Age." That weary, discouraged father, struggling against conditions amid which, as he says, a man can do nothing but rot away, that kind, worn, wan, desperately optimistic, fanatically energetic mother, those ragged, wretched little children, sprawling on the floor, "sopping corn-bread in some gravy left in the bottom of a frying-pan"—it is the epic not only of Mark Twain's infancy but of a whole phase /28/ of American civilization. How many books have been published of late years letting us behind the scenes of the glamorous myth of pioneering! There is E. H. Howe's "Story of a Country Town," for instance, that Western counterpart in sodden misery of "Ethan Frome"—a book which has only begun to find its public. This astonishing Mr. Howe, who is so painfully honest, tells us in so many words that in all his early days he never saw a woman who was not anæmic and fretful, a man who was not moody and taciturn, a child who was not stunted from hard labor or under-nourishment. No wonder he has come to believe, as he tells us frankly in a later book, that there is no such thing as love in the world! Think of those villages Mark Twain himself has pictured for us, with their shabby, unpainted shacks, dropping with decay, the broken fences, the litter of rusty cans and foul rags, how like the leavings of some vast over-turned scrap-basket, some gigantic garbage-can! Human nature was not responsible for this débris of a too unequal combat with circumstance, nor could human nature rise above it. "Gambling, drinking and murder," we are told, were the diversions of the capital city of Nevada in the days of the gold-rush. It was not very different in normal times along the Mississippi. Hannibal was a small place; yet Mr. Paine records four separate murders which Mark Twain actually witnessed as a boy: every week he would see some drunken ruffian run amuck, he saw negroes struck down and killed, he saw men shot and stabbed in the streets. "How many gruesome experiences," exclaims Mr. Paine, "there appear to have been in those early days!" But let us be moderate: every one was not violent. As for the majority of the settlers, it is to the honor of mankind that history calls them heroes; and if that is an illusion, justice will never be realistic. The gods of Greece would have gone unwashed and turned gray at forty and lost /29/ their digestion and neglected their children if they had been pioneers: Apollo himself would have relapsed into an irritable silence.

A desert of human sand!—the barrenest spot in all Christendom, surely, for the seed of genius to fall in. John Hay, revisiting these regions after having lived for several years in New England, wrote in one of his letters: "I am removed to a colder mental atmosphere. . . . I find only a dreary waste of heartless materialism, where great and heroic qualities may indeed bully their way up into the glare, but the flowers of existence inevitably droop and wither."

Here Mark Twain was born, and in a loveless household: the choice of his mother's heart, Mr. Paine tells us, had been "a young physician of Lexington with whom she had quarreled, and her prompt engagement with John Clemens was a matter of temper rather than tenderness." Mark Twain "did not remember ever having seen or heard his father laugh, we are told, and only once, when his little brother Benjamin lay dying, had he seen one member of his family kiss another. His father, absorbed in a perpetual motion machine, "seldom devoted any time to the company of his children." No wonder, poor man; the palsy of a long defeat lay upon him; besides, every spring he was prostrated with a nerve-racking "sun-pain" that would have checked the humane impulses of an archangel. Even his mother, the backbone of the family, was infatuated with patent medicines, "pain-killers," health periodicals—we have it from "Tom Sawyer"—"she was an inveterate experimenter in these things." They were all, we see, living on the edge of their nerves, a harsh, angular, desiccated existence, like so many rusty machines, without enough oil, without enough power, grating on their own metal.

Little Sam, as every one called him, was the fifth child in this household, "a puny baby with a wavering promise of life"; it is suggested that he was not wanted. Mr. /30/ Paine speaks of him somewhere as "high-strung and neurotic." We are not surprised, therefore, to find him at three and four "a wild-headed, impetuous child of sudden ecstasies that sent him capering and swinging his arms, venting his emotions in a series of leaps and shrieks and somersaults, and spasms of laughter as he lay rolling in the grass." This is the child who is to retain through life that exquisite sensibility of which so many observers have spoken. "Once when I met him in the country," says Mr. Howells, for example, of his later life, "he had just been sickened by the success of a gunner in bringing down a blackbird; and he described the poor, stricken, glossy thing, how it lay throbbing its life out on the grass, with such pity as he might have given a wounded child." Already, in his infancy, his gentle, winning manner and smile make him every one's favorite. A very special little flower of life, you see, capable of such feeling that at twenty-three his hair is to turn gray in the tragic experience of his brother's death. A flower of life, a wild flower, and infinitely fragile: the doctor is always being called in his behalf. Before he grows up he is to have prophetic dreams, but now another neurotic symptom manifests itself. In times of family crisis, at four, when one of his sisters is dying, at twelve, after the death of his father, he walks in his sleep: often the rest of the household get up in the middle of the night to find this delicate little waif with his eyes shut "fretting with cold in some dark corner."

Can we not already see in this child the born, predestined artist? And what sort of nurture will his imagination have? He is abandoned to the fervid influences of the negro slaves,—for his father had moments of a relative prosperity. Crouching in their cabins, he drinks in wild, weird tales of blood-curdling African witchcraft. "Certainly," says Mr. Paine, "an atmosphere like this meant a tropic development for the imagination of a delicate child." One thinks in- /31/ deed of an image that would have pleased Heine, the image of a frail snow-plant of the North quivering, flaming in the furnace of the jungle. Mark Twain appears to have been from the outset a center of interest, radiating a singular potency; and the more his spirit was subjected to such a fearful stimulus the more urgently he required for his normal development the calm, clairvoyant guidance a pioneer child could never have had. The negroes were "in real charge of the children and supplied them with entertainment." What other influence was there to counterbalance this?

One, and one only, an influence tragic in its ultimate consequences, the influence of Mark Twain's mother. That poor, taciturn, sunstruck failure, John Clemens, was a mere pathetic shadow beside the woman whose portrait Mark Twain has drawn for us in the Aunt Polly of "Tom Sawyer." She who was regarded as a "character" by all the town, who was said to have been "the handsomest girl and the wittiest, as well as the best dancer, in all Kentucky," who was still able to dance at 80, and lived to be 87, who belonged, in short, to "the long-lived, energetic side of the house," directed her children, we are told —and we can believe it—"with considerable firmness." And what was the inevitable relationship between her and this little boy? "She had a weakness," says Mr. Paine, "for the child that demanded most of her mother's care . . . All were tractable and growing in grace but little Sam . . . a delicate little lad to be worried over, mothered, or spanked and put to bed." In later life, "you gave me more uneasiness than any child I had," she told him. In fact, she was always scolding him, comforting him, forgiving him, punishing and pleading with him, fixing her attention upon him, exercising her emotions about him, impressing it upon his mind for all time, as we shall come to see, /32/ that woman is the inevitable seat of authority and the fount of wisdom.

We know that such excessive influences are apt to deflect the growth of any spirit. Men are like planets in this, that for them to sail clear in their own orbits the forces of gravity have to be disposed with a certain balance on all sides: how often, when the father counts for nothing, a child becomes the satellite of its mother, especially when that mother's love has not found its normal expression in her own youth! We have seen that Mark Twain's mother did not love her husband; that her capacity for love, however, was very great is proved by the singular story revealed in one of Mark Twain's letters: more than sixty years after she had quarreled with that young Lexington doctor, and when her husband had long been dead, she, a woman of eighty or more, took a railway journey to a distant city where there was an Old Settlers' convention because among the names of those who were to attend it she had noticed the name of the lover of her youth. "Who could have imagined such a heart-break as that?" said Mr. Howells, when he heard the story. "Yet it went along with the fulfillment of every-day duty and made no more noise than a grave under foot." It made no noise, but it undoubtedly had a prodigious effect upon Mark Twain's life. When an affection as intense as that is balked in its direct path and repressed it usually, as we know, finds an indirect outlet; and it is plain that the woman as well as the mother expressed itself in the passionate attachment of Jane Clemens to her son. We shall note many consequences of this fact as we go on with our story. We can say at least at this point that Mark Twain was, quite definitely, in his mother's leading-strings.

What was the inevitable result? I have said, not, I hope, with too much presumption, that Mark Twain had /33/ already shown himself the born, predestined artist, that his whole nature manifested what is called a tendency toward the creative life. For that tendency to become conscious, to become purposive, two things were necessary: it must be able, in the first place, to assert itself and in the second place to embody itself in a vocation; to realize itself and then to educate itself, to realize itself in educating itself. And, as we know, the influences of early childhood are, in these matters, vitally important. If Jane Clemens had been a woman of wide experience and independent mind, in proportion to the strength of her character, Mark Twain's career might have been wholly different. Had she been catholic in her sympathies, in her understanding of life, then, no matter how more than maternal her attachment to her son was, she might have placed before him and encouraged him to pursue interests and activities amid which he could eventually have recovered his balance, reduced the filial bond to its normal measure and stood on his own feet. But that is to wish for a type of woman our old pioneer society could never have produced. We are told that the Aunt Polly of "Tom Sawyer" is a speaking portrait of Jane Clemens, and Aunt Polly, as we know, was the symbol of all the taboos. The stronger her will was, the more comprehensive were her repressions, the more certainly she became the inflexible guardian of tradition in a social régime where tradition was inalterably opposed to every sort of personal deviation from the accepted type. "In their remoteness from the political centers of the young Republic," says Mr. Howells, in "The Leatherwood God," of these old Middle Western settlements, "they seldom spoke of the civic questions stirring the towns of the East; the commercial and industrial problems which vex modern society were unknown to them. Religion was their chief interest." And in the slave States it was not the abolitionist alone whose name was held, as Mr. Paine says, "in horror," /34/ but every one who had the audacity to think differently from his neighbors. Jane Clemens, in short, was the embodiment of that old-fashioned, cast-iron Calvinism which had proved so favorable to the life of enterprising action but which perceived the scent of the devil in any least expression of what is now known as the creative impulse. She had a kind heart, she was always repenting and softening and forgiving; it is said that whenever she had to drown kittens, she warmed the water first. But this, without opening any channel in a contrary direction, only sealed her authority! She won her points as much by kindness as by law. Besides, tradition spoke first in her mind; her hand was quicker than her heart; in action she was the madonna of the hairbrush. And what, specifically, was it that she punished? Those furtive dealings of Huck and Tom with whitewash and piracy were nothing in the world—and that is why all the world loves them—but the first stirrings of the normal æsthetic sense, the first stirrings of individuality.

Already I think we divine what was bound to happen in the soul of Mark Twain. The story of "Huckleberry Finn" turns, as we remember, upon a conflict: "the author," says Mr. Paine, "makes Huck's struggle a psychological one between conscience and the law, on one side, and sympathy on the other." In the famous episode of Nigger Jim, "sympathy," the cause of individual freedom, wins. Years later, in "The Mysterious Stranger," Mark Twain presented the parallel situation we noted in the last chapter: "we found," says the boy who tells that story, "that we were not manly enough nor brave enough to do a generous action when there was a chance that it could get us into trouble." Conscience and the law, we see, had long since prevailed in the spirit of Mark Twain, but what is the conscience of a boy who checks a humane impulse but "boy terror," as Mr. Paine calls it, an instinctive fear of custom, of tribal authority? The conflict in "Huckleberry Finn" /35/ is simply the conflict of Mark Twain's own childhood. He solved it successfully, he fulfilled his desire, in the book, as an author can. In actual life he did not solve it at all; he surrendered. /36/

Now, whatever was true of America during the Gilded Age was doubly true of Nevada, where, as Mr. Paine says, "all human beings, regardless of previous affiliations and convictions, were flung into the common fusing-pot and recast into the general mold of pioneer." Life in the gold-fields was, in fact, an infinite intensification of pioneering, it was a sort of furnace in which all the elements of human nature were transmuted into /74/ a single white flame, an incandescence of the passion of avarice. If we are to accept Mark Twain's description in "Roughing It" of the "flush times" in Virginia City, we can see that the spirit of the artist had about as good a chance of survival and development there as a butterfly in a blazing chimney: "Virginia had grown to be the 'livest' town, for its age and population, that America had ever produced. The side-walks swarmed with people. The streets themselves were just as crowded with quartz-wagons, freight-teams, and other vehicles. . . . Joy sat on every countenance, and there was a glad, almost fierce, intensity in every eye that told of the money-getting schemes that were seething in every brain and the high hope that held sway in every heart. Money was as plenty as dust. . . . There were military companies, fire companies, brass bands, banks, hotels, theaters, 'hurdy-gurdy houses,' wide-open gambling palaces, political pow-wows, civic processions, street-fights, murders, inquests, riots, a whiskey mill every fifteen steps, a dozen breweries, and half a dozen jails and station-houses in full operation, and some talk of building a church. The 'flush times' were in magnificent flower! . . . The great 'Comstock lode' stretched its opulent length straight through the town from North to South, and every mine on it was in diligent process of development."

This was the spirit of Mark Twain's new environment, a spirit inflexibly opposed, as we can see, to the development of individuality. Had Mark Twain been free, it might have been a matter of indifference to him; he might have gone his own way and amused himself with the astonishing spectacle of the gold-fields and then taken himself off again. But Mark Twain was not free; he was, on the contrary, bound in such a way that, far from being able to stand aloof from his environment, he had to make terms with it. For what obligations had he not incurred! To become such a conventional citizen /75/ as his father would have approved of, to make money and restore the fallen fortunes of his family—that old pledge was fixed in the back of his mind, where it had been confirmed by his failure to discover and assert any independent principle of his own. Furthermore, he now had his own financial record to live up to. It was the lucrativeness and prestige of the pilot's career that had originally enabled him to adopt it, and we know what pride he had had in his "great triumph," in being a somebody at last: his brother Orion had considered it a "disgrace" to descend to the trade of printing: they were gentleman's sons, these Clemenses! He had had, in short, a chance to exercise and educate his creative instinct while at the same time doing what was expected of him. And now, when he had lost his guiding-line, more was expected of him than ever! His salary, at twenty-three, on the river, had been $250 a month, a vastly greater income certainly than his father had ever earned: at once and of course, we are told, he had become, owing to this fact, the head of the Clemens family. "His brother Orion was ten years older," says Mr. Paine, "but he had not the gift of success. By common consent, the young brother assumed permanently the position of family counselor and financier." These circumstances, I say, compelled Mark Twain to make terms with public opinion. He could not fall too far behind the financial pace his piloting life had set for him, he was bound to recover the prestige that had been his and to shine once more as a conspicuous and important personage, he had to "make good" again, quickly and spectacularly: that was a duty which had also become a craving. How strongly he felt it we can see from one of his Nevada letters in which he declares earnestly that he will never look upon his mother's face again, or his sister's, or get married, or revisit the "Banner State," until he is a rich man.

What chance was there now for the artist in Mark /76/ Twain to find itself? A unique opportunity had led him for four years into the channel of inner development through a special vocation; but it was only the indispensability of the pilot to the Mississippi river folk that had obliged them to give him such lordly freedom. No special vocation was indispensable in Nevada; consequently, no special vocation was tolerated. There, the pioneer law of which Mr. Croly speaks held absolute sway: "the man who persisted in one job interfered with the rough good-fellowship which naturally arises among a group of men who submit good-naturedly and uncritically to current standards: his higher standards and peculiar ways constituted an implied criticism upon the easy methods of his neighbors" and he himself impaired "the consistency of feeling upon which the pioneers rightly placed such a high value." Even if Mark Twain had been fully aware of the demands of his creative instinct, therefore—and he was anything but fully aware of them—he could not have fulfilled them now and at the same time fulfilled his craving for wealth and prestige. Accordingly, he was obliged to acquiesce in the repression of his individuality. His frank freedom of sentiment, his love of reading, his constant desire for privacy—all those qualities that revealed his natural creative instinct—were, from the point of view of his comrades, just so many "pretensions": precisely in so far as they were "different" or "superior," they had to be taken down. The frequency and the force of these manifestations, and the tenacity with which, up to a certain point, he persisted in indulging in them, made him, as we know, a general butt. Many and "cruel," to use his own word, were the tricks his comrades played on him. Knowing his highly organized nervous system, they devised the most complicated methods of torturing him. There was the incident of the false Meerschaum pipe, which cut him to the quick, this man who had been betrayed into uttering words of heartfelt grati- /77/ tude; there were the diabolical monkey-tricks of Steve Gillis who, with his "fiendish tendency to mischief," was always finding means to prevent him from reading; there was the famous hold-up on the Divide on the night of his lecture: "Mark didn't see it our way," said one of the perpetrators of this last practical joke. "He was mad clear through." In short, every revelation of his individuality was mercilessly ridiculed, and Mark Twain was reminded a dozen times a day that his natural instincts and desires and tendencies were incompatible with pioneer life and fatal to the chances of any man who was pledged to succeed in it. That is why, though he always retaliated at first, he always yielded in the end. /78/

Only in the light of this general subjugation of Mark Twain's character can we understand his literary subjugation. From the moment of his marriage his artistic integrity, already compromised, had, as a matter of fact, been irreparably destroyed: quite literally, as a man of letters, his honor rooted in dishonor stood and faith unfaithful kept him falsely true. He had accepted his father-in-law's financial assistance; he had /117/ bought his post on the Buffalo *Express;* in return, he had solemnly pledged the freedom of his mind. In these words of his Salutatory he made his pledge public: "Being a stranger it would be immodest for me to suddenly and violently assume the associate editorship of the Buffalo *Express* without a single word of comfort or encouragement to the unoffending patrons of this paper, who are about to be exposed to constant attacks of my wisdom and learning. But the word shall be as brief as possible. I only want to assure parties having a friendly interest in the prosperity of the journal that I am not going to hurt the paper deliberately and intentionally at any time. I am not going to introduce any startling reforms, nor in any way attempt to make trouble. . . . Such is my platform. I do not see any use in it, but custom is law and must be obeyed." Never, surely, was a creative will more innocently, more painlessly surrendered than in those words; marriage had been, for Mark Twain's artistic conscience, like the final whiff of chloroform sealing a slumber that many a previous whiff had already induced. With that promise to be "good," to refrain from hurting "parties having a friendly interest in the prosperity" of his journal, the artist in Mark Twain had fallen into a final trance: anybody could manipulate him now. We have seen that his wife, who had become his chief censor, having no more independence of judgment than he, simply exposed him to the control of public opinion. This, in all matters of culture, meant New England, and especially Boston, and accordingly to please Boston—impossible, terrifying task!—had become as obligatory upon Mark Twain as to please Elmira. /118/

It is only after some such explanation as this that we can understand the supremacy among all Mark Twain's writings of "Huckleberry Finn." Through the character of Huck, that disreputable, illiterate little /194/ boy, as Mrs. Clemens no doubt thought him, he was licensed to let himself go. We have seen how indifferent his sponsors were to the writing and the fate of this book: "nobody," says Mr. Paine, "appears to have been especially concerned about Huck, except, possibly, the publisher." The more indifferent they were, the freer was Mark Twain! Anything that little vagabond said might be safely trusted to pass the censor, just because he was a little vagabond, just because, as an irresponsible boy, he could not, in the eyes of the mighty ones of this world, know anything in any case about life, morals and civilization. That Mark Twain was almost, if not quite, conscious of his opportunity we can see from his introductory note to the book: "Persons attempting to find a motive in this narrative will be prosecuted; persons attempting to find a moral in it will be banished; persons attempting to find a plot in it will be shot." He feels so secure of himself that he can actually challenge the censor to accuse him of having a motive! Huck's illiteracy, Huck's disreputableness and general outrageousness are so many shields behind which Mark Twain can let all the cats out of the bag with impunity. He must, I say, have had a certain sense of his unusual security when he wrote some of the more cynically satirical passages of the book, when he permitted Colonel Sherburn to taunt the mob, when he drew that picture of the audience who had been taken in by the Duke proceeding to sell the rest of their townspeople, when he has the King put up the notice, "Ladies and Children not Admitted," and add: "There, if that line don't fetch them, I don't know Arkansaw!" The withering contempt for humankind expressed in these episodes was of the sort that Mark Twain expressed more and more openly, as time went on, in his own person; but he was not indulging in that costly kind of cynicism in the days when he wrote "Huckleberry Finn." He must, therefore, have appreciated the /195/ license that little vagabond, like the puppet on the lap of a ventriloquist, afforded him. This, however, was only a trivial detail in his general sense of happy expansion, of ecstatic liberation. "Other places do seem so cramped up and smothery, but a raft don't," says Huck, on the river; "you feel mighty free and easy and comfortable on a raft." Mark Twain himself was free at last!—that raft and that river to him were something more than mere material facts. His whole unconscious life, the pent-up river of his own soul, had burst its bonds and rushed forth, a joyous torrent! Do we need any other explanation of the abandon, the beauty, the eternal freshness of "Huckleberry Finn"? Perhaps we can say that a lifetime of moral slavery and repression was not too much to pay for it. Certainly, if it flies like a gay, bright, shining arrow through the tepid atmosphere of American literature, it is because of the straining of the bow, the tautness of the string, that gave it its momentum.

Yes, if we did not know, if we did not feel, that Mark Twain was intended for a vastly greater destiny, for the rôle of a demiurge, in fact, we might have been glad of all those petty restrictions and misprisions he had undergone, restrictions that had prepared the way for this joyous release. No smoking on Sundays! No "swearing" allowed! Neckties having to be bothered over! That everlasting diet of Ps and Qs, petty Ps and pettier Qs, to which Mark Twain had had to submit, the domestic diet of Mrs. Clemens, the literary diet of Mr. Howells, those second parents who had taken the place of his first—we have to thank it, after all, for the vengeful solace we find in the promiscuous and general revolt of Huckleberry Finn:

> "Don't talk about it, Tom. I've tried it and it don't work; it don't work, Tom. It ain't for me; I ain't used to it. The widder's good to me, and friendly; but I can't stand them ways. She makes me git up just at the same time every morning; she /196/ makes me wash, they comb me all to thunder; she won't let me sleep in the woodshed; I got to wear them blamed clothes that just smothers me, Tom; they don't seem to any air git through 'em, somehow; and they're so rotten nice that I can't set down, nor lay down, nor roll around anywher's; I hain't slid on a cellar door for—well, it 'pears to be years; I got to go to church and sweat and sweat—I hate them ornery ser-

mons! I can't ketch a fly in there, I can't chaw, I got to wear shoes all Sunday. The widder eats by a bell; she goes to bed by a bell; she gits up by a bell—everything's so awful reg'lar a body can't stand it."

"Well, everybody does that way, Huck."

"Tom, it don't make no difference. I ain't everybody, and I can't *stand* it. It's awful to be tied up so. And grub comes too easy. I don't take no interest in vittles, that way. I got to ask to go a-fishing; I got to ask to go in a-swimming—dern'd if I hain't got to ask to do everything. Well, I'd got to talk so nice it wasn't no comfort—I'd got to go up in the attic and rip out a while, every day, to git a taste in my mouth, or I'd a died, Tom. The widder wouldn't let me smoke; she wouldn't let me yell, she wouldn't let me gape, nor stretch, nor scratch, before folks. . . . I *had* to shove, Tom—I just had to. . . . Now these clothes suits me, and this bar'l suits me, and I ain't ever going to shake 'em any more. . . ."

This chapter began with the analogy of the lion in the circus. You see what happens with Mark Twain when the trainer turns his back. /197/

QUESTIONS FOR DISCUSSION AND WRITING

1. Reread what Brooks says on page 12, and then write an essay on *Huckleberry Finn* as a confession of its author's sins.
2. What evidence of bitterness do you find in *Huckleberry Finn?*
3. Using the information Brooks supplies about the social background into which Mark Twain was born, write a paper suggesting the ways in which he has used such material in *Huckleberry Finn.*
4. Find further "cynical satirical passages" in *Huckleberry Finn,* and determine the nature and object of the satire.

HUCKLEBERRY FINN

by John Erskine

"You don't know about me without you have read a book by the name of 'The Adventures of Tom Sawyer'; but that ain't no matter," says Huckleberry Finn. He is quite right. We can understand his masterly story even if we have not read the book to which it is the sequel, but most Americans have read both, and a comparison of them helps us to see the greatness of the later one. In the preface to *Tom Sawyer* Mark Twain tells us he is drawing on his own memories of boyhood, and hopes to entertain young readers, but he adds that older folk may be interested in the picture of the Middle West, around 1850, and in the incidental record of the odd supersitions which were then prevalent among children and slaves.

In *Huckleberry Finn* the superstitions still appear, and the story certainly fascinates boys and girls, but mature readers value it for the rich picture of human nature, a satirical picture, if you will, but mellow and kind. In the preface to this book Mark Twain calls our attention to the various dialects the characters use, but it is hard not to believe his own interest was chiefly in providing us with our first and still our best account of Main Street—of the small community, narrow as to their virtues and their vices, and starved in their imaginations, all but the children and the most childlike among them.

Since the *Adventures of Tom Sawyer* and the later book have the same background and much the same char- /263/ acters, it looks as though Mark Twain must have discovered his true subject during the eight years which separated the stories. Huckleberry Finn tells us far more than he knows; through his naive confessions we see the panorama of his world and become sophisticated. We are really studying ourselves. In the earlier books, however, we have episodes of boyhood, rather loosely strung together, with one terrific stroke of melodrama to help out the plot. No doubt *Tom Sawyer* would be enjoyed by young people even if *Huckleberry Finn* did not lend it fame and keep it alive, but taken by itself it now seems a rather poorly constructed

Reprinted from *Delight of Great Books*. Indianapolis: 1928. Originally printed in the *Delineator* (February, 1927), 94–97.

book. The story is built up with anecdotes, each one complete in itself, and none developed beyond the point of the joke.

In this early book Tom Sawyer interests us by his love of mischief and by his exuberant fancy. He contrives more than the usual share of histrionics; other boys make believe, but Tom dramatizes his boyish sentimentality on the grand scale, and we have the suspicion that by emphasizing and isolating the boy, Mark Twain gets the total picture of life out of focus, and makes it difficult for us to interpret the exceptional events in terms of the normal parts of his story.

These comments on the earlier book may help us to see why we instinctively admire *Huckleberry Finn.* The same elements reappear, the same characters, though new persons enter the tale, the same scene is described, though Huckleberry and the negro Jim have their chief adventures down the river on a raft, and the spirit of adventure in boyhood again is the central theme of the book. But this time the elements are arranged in a proportion which convinces us, and we are sure the picture is true. /264/

When you sit down to write a novel, you find you must have something besides characters and a plot; you must have a philosophy of life. You must decide, for example, what parts of experience are worth writing about, and then you must make up your mind how to dispose of the other parts. Most men and women will take sides on the question whether it is the exceptional experience we should consider important, or whether any experience would seem exceptional if we attached importance to it. Our temperament dictates the answer, but we usually frame it in some kind of philosophy. There are novelists who believe that humdrum experience, the typical daily round of all of us, is the proper material for fiction, and that the novelists, by bearing down hard on it, may bring out the grain of significance under the smoothworn surface. Another kind of artist portrays the average life remorselessly, to show that it is even less significant than it seems. He is the satirist, and he shows himself frequently in American literature to-day, a strong critic of narrowness and meanness, especially as observed in village life. A third kind of story-teller, with perhaps the same dislike of what is familiar and trite, turns resolutely to fresh material, to the unusual event; he looks, as we say, for an escape from the world which shuts him in.

In *Huckleberry Finn* Mark Twain is all three kinds of story-teller at once. He gives us a kindly picture of men and women in very small towns along the river, people with no heroic experience, who yet find their lives of considerable importance to themselves.

There is a satiric picture, too, an intermittent glimpse into the smallness of human nature. Huckleberry has /265/ learned how to make use of men by appealing to their mean side. When the two oarsmen come near the raft and almost discover the runaway slave, Huckleberry saves Jim by inviting them to come on board and minister to the crew. There's a mild case of smallpox, he explains, and the two men row away, after giving him forty dollars, to salve their conscience for thus denying the appeal of the sick.

The way in which the realistic elements and the satiric are combined with extraordinary adventure might well be the envy and the admiration of any novelist. The quiet river towns which Mark Twain remembered from his youth had something of the frontier still; violent death varied the monotony, from time to time, and the outcasts of older parts of the world chanced along, for shelter, or for a last opportunity to play their tricks in a place where they weren't known. The law-abiding portions of the community would condemn such interruptions of the peace, but they would also be fairly hardened to them. If a novelist tried to tell us now that the performance of the two quacks in *Romeo and Juliet*, or in the *Royal Nonesuch*, was ever accepted by any American community we should probably decline to believe him. But when we watch these rascals and their doings through the eyes of Huckleberry Finn, we are free to believe them as exceptional as we please, yet we understand perfectly why the boy took them for granted. Huckleberry has had a bringing-up which has prepared him to be surprised at nothing. We know that his approach to life is peculiar; if his judgments are not those of the average person, we know why they aren't, and we know just how far they depart from the normal, and he has our sympathy. Mark Twain man- /266/ ipulated his material, therefore, so that the most outrageous melodrama could present itself as matter of fact, through the medium of Huckleberry's temperament, and even while we are rearranging the values, and discerning what the boy was blind to, we like him, and concede that he is true to life.

He is not supposed to be an average boy, like Tom Sawyer; he is the son of the village drunkard, a waif who grows up uneducated and uncared for, so far as the community can see. Parents warn their children not to play with him; the schoolmaster whips any boy who is caught in his society. He frankly smokes a corn-cob pipe; he always wears a tattered hat; trousers and shirt are all his dress; he carries a dead cat by the tail, because he considers a dead cat a treasure, and believes it is good magic.

Huckleberry is explained by his father. The elder Finn is as thorough a study of good-for-nothing propensities as we are likely to find in literature. Whenever he can, he drinks himself into a mad fit, and becomes rather dangerous. Huckleberry sits up all night in the hut on the island, with his father's gun in hand, for fear it may be necessary to blow his father's brains out. But in his sober moments the man is even uglier; when he asks Huckleberry next morning what he is doing with the gun, the boy knows he had better invent at once an elaborate lie about a thief who tried to get in during the night.

This extraordinary parent just escapes being lynched for a crime which, oddly enough, he didn't commit, but afterward he is shot in the back during a drunken brawl in a disorderly house. Huckleberry is rather fond of his father—thoroughly afraid of him, of course, and critical of his worst excesses, yet disposed to enjoy the less dan- /267/ gerous periods of his society. From him and from nature has come all the boy's education. His father's temper taught Huckleberry the advantages of falsehood; lying is the better part of discourse, he thinks, one's natural protection against society. He is modest about it, he always believes that Tom Sawyer could make up a far handsomer story, being a superior boy who has had advantages, but we can't see much room for improvement in the gorgeous fables Huckleberry improvises at the slightest challenge of fate. His father's changeable moods taught him also to expect anything of life.

Huckleberry's mother does not exist, so far as the story is concerned. We may imagine her the victim of her husband's brutality, if we are so inclined, and we may endow her with enough virtues to account for her son's kind heart and gentle instincts. But Mark Twain is at his best when he leaves her history a blank. Huckleberry's isolation is complete, and we are under no compulsion to measure him by the accustomed traditions of society.

The handling of the romantic or melodramatic elements in the story can be admired from another angle also. Though the life of the small village may seem unduly quiet, it is the person from the city who chiefly finds it dull; the people involved in it often are aware of excitements. Of course the excitements come at long intervals, and they are cherished most often as scandal. Every small community has its stories about this woman or that man, stories which are often wild enough and improbable, but they really happened. But if a whole and steady view of life seems to us desirable, we can admire the way in which Mark Twain allows us to enjoy the wild /268/ adventures of Huckleberry, and at the same time shows us, in the not too remote background, a just picture of the folks who will talk about such experiences, but to whom they will never come. It is extraordinary that this balance is preserved through so long a succession of wild episodes; but even at the end, we still are aware of some surprise when a new accident occurs, we still consider ourselves the inhabitants of a quite normal world.

Several technical devices for securing this sense of the normal, for convincing us that the eccentric character is eccentric, no matter how often he appears, can easily be recognized by any one who knows the formulas of literary criticism. We can see, for example, that the characters speak for themselves. Though Huckleberry is telling the story, he reports conversations fully, and rarely makes a comment. This is the ancient rule for rendering character vividly, but it is easier to state the principle than to follow it. When the two rascals, driven out of town simultaneously by enraged mobs, happen to meet on the raft, Huck and Jim are wise enough to say nothing until the new arrivals disclose themselves. The younger man, diagnosing their simplicity, as he thinks, breaks the news that he is a duke in disguise, and that his rank entitles him to the only comfortable bed in the raft. Jim and Huck don't care; they know he isn't a duke, but he might as well have the bed. The older man, however, is not so complacent, and in a few moments he has confessed that he is really the lost Dauphin of France, by rights a king. The conversations of the king and the duke are among the great passages of dramatic satire. They know they are not fooling each other, they pretend to be deceiving the negro and the boy, and yet we half /269/ think they would have kept up the nonsense even if they had been alone, so strong in them was the instinct for imposture. The device is the strictly dramatic one of omitting comment and letting the characters talk, but the formula is used here by a genius.

It would be in the sound tradition of criticism to say also that Mark Twain established a human scale throughout by descriptions of nature. The broad and changing river, the starry nights, the fogs, the glorious storms, refer us constantly to a scheme of things against which man even at his best would seem small. When the first heavy rain makes the river rise, and sweeps away whole villages in the flood, Huck and Jim paddle over to a rather substantial wreck of a house and climb in through the window. Wise as he is in much wickedness, Huckleberry seems not to know what sort of house this was before it was swept away, but we see clearly enough. At the time he doesn't know that the murdered man they find in a corner of the room is his own father. We are too much interested ourselves, perhaps, in the description of the room and in the finding of the corpse to grasp the full irony, but later it comes upon us, the contrast between that mighty flood and the wretched occupations it put an end to.

But when we have said this about the descriptions of nature in the story, we ought to add that perhaps Mark Twain put them in for no other reason than his love of them. The joy in grand aspects of weather is so evident that their effect on the story may well have been a happy result, not altogether intended. It is a pagan love of nature—and we might say, a typically American love of the thing for itself, without asking what it means. /270/

The book owes more of its fame than we sometimes recognize to the portrait of the negro, Jim, who runs away from a good home and from the neighborhood of his wife and children because he has reason to fear he may be sold down the river. He is the one elaborate picture we have of the negro slave before the war, and in a community in which owner and slave alike take slavery very much for granted. Mrs. Stowe's famous book is full of correct observation; she gives us no doubt a fair account of slavery at its happiest—along with other reports which some Southerners will always think exaggerated. But *Uncle Tom's Cabin* remains a discussion of slavery as an issue in justice; the problem colors every sentence in the book. There must have been thousands of families in which the issue never suggested itself. That is the version of slavery which Mark Twain has given us—the picture of good Christian homes in which the slaves were as natural an incident as any other human relation. Even as propaganda, if *Huckleberry Finn* had been written early enough to serve that purpose, it would have been more subtly convincing than Mrs. Stowe's book, for the dramatic method, without preaching of any kind, here stirs the emotions deeply.

One of the moving themes of the story is Huck's uneasiness over the fact that by accident he is helping a "nigger" to run away. He has his own code of morality, where property is concerned; he doesn't wish to be a thief. The refinements of honesty, so to speak, he had learned from his father, who always said it was wrong to take what was another man's, unless you had the intention of paying it back sometime. When he and Jim found themselves obliged to rob orchards and gardens, in /271/ order to maintain life, they quieted their conscience by making it a rule never to steal all they could. Crab-apples, for instance, they always left untouched. But when it came to stealing niggers! On the other hand, when he thought of Jim's kindness to him, of the negro's terror of the plantations from which he could never hope to return to his wife and children, Huckleberry was in a tangle. He did go so far as to write Miss Watson and tell her where Jim could be found, but he couldn't bring himself to post the letter. "It was a tight place. I took it up and held it in my hand. I was a-trembling, because I'd got to decide, forever, betwixt two things, and I knowed it. I studied a minute, sort of holding my breath, and then says to myself:

" 'All right, then, I'll *go* to hell,' and tore it up."

Though our sympathy for the slave is profound, we are allowed to see the negro on more sides of his character than Mrs. Stowe may have been aware of. She knew that the colored race was deeply religious, but she took religion to mean the reading of the Bible and the attendance on a Christian church. Uncle Tom is religious in this sense. What we have more recently learned to appreciate, the wealth of folk-lore, superstition and mysticism which still seems to be the inheritance of negroes, even when they live among the whites, Mrs. Stowe did not portray. Mark Twain makes the most of it; he shows us the African in Jim, the ignorance which to the casual white seems absurd, but which really is connected with powers the white does not share. Altogether he is a wonderful creation, the more remarkable for the matter-of-fact way in which he is presented, without emphasis or exaggeration. He does not take the important place in /272/ the scene—Huckleberry remains the hero of the story, but when we have laid the book down, the patient inscrutable black, with his warm heart and his childlike wisdom, remains not the least vivid of our memories.

Whether the portrait of the Grangerfords and the Shepherdsons, in their famous feud, is true to historical fact, those must decide who know the regions of the South before the war where this feud is supposed to occur. But there is no question that the persons seem real, and that the satire on the follies of human nature bites rather deep in this part of the story. Here again the fact that Huckleberry is telling the story serves to secure a splendid literary effect. Nothing in the book is told with greater restraint, and nothing is quite so tragic. The restraint is art, but it seems the work of nature, because Huck wishes, as he says, to hurry over the details—he tries not to remember them for fear they may spoil his sleep. Yet out of the tragedy the reader seizes a noble emotion. When you reflect on the wickedness of feuds and duels, as on the wickedness of war, you may be troubled that a noble emotion should be roused by such material, but when you let yourself go uncritically you can enjoy the courage, the chivalry, the romance which Mark Twain has put into this episode.

At the end of the story Tom Sawyer reappears. He comes to the place where Jim has been captured as a runaway slave, and Huck is hoping to contrive an escape. Tom happens to know that Jim is no longer a slave, but a freeman. The idea of getting him out of his prison, however, is too fruitful to be resisted; Tom begins to make believe—the log cabin becomes a dungeon—the methods of release must be as elaborate as though there /273/ were a moat and high walls to cross, and valiant guards to beat down. From this point on, the story lags. The adventures which Tom imagines are cheap after the real dangers Huck and Jim have gone through. We wonder whether this effect of anticlimax was accidental or intended. Did Mark Twain wish to draw this comparison between the genuine experience and the fanciful? Whether he did or not, the contrast is there.

For that reason I have thought it not unjust to compare the two stories to the advantage of *Huckleberry Finn.* We always think of them together, and here at the close of his masterpiece the author sets the two boys side by side for us to look at. *Tom Sawyer* is a fine story, but the other is one of those books which occur all too rarely in a national literature, a book so close to the life of the people that it can hold any reader, and yet so subtle in its art that the craftsman tries to find out how it was done. I don't see why we shouldn't recognize it as a masterpiece now, without waiting for posterity to cast any more votes. Indeed, we thought a while ago that the ballot was closed. But recently it has been suggested that Mark Twain, poor man, missed his full development as an artist, that American life in his time was not sophisticated enough in matters of art to demand of him perfect workmanship, or to applaud when he gave it. Well, that sort of argument breaks down when we ask to see what men have written who were more fortunately placed than he, and when we set their work beside his. Some things he wrote will suffer by the comparison, but not the *Adventures of Huckleberry Finn.* /274/

QUESTIONS FOR DISCUSSION AND WRITING

1. Erskine applies the adjective "mellow" to *Huckleberry Finn.* (p. 263) Does this seem valid to you? What proportions of the novel do and do not merit such an adjective?
2. "Huckleberry Finn tells us more than he knows." (p. 264) Explain this statement, using material from the novel to support your answer.
3. In what sense are we "really studying ourselves" (p. 264) when we read *Huckleberry Finn?* Are we like Huck or any of the people he encounters?
4. Do you think the criticism Erskine applies to *Tom Sawyer* can also be applied to those sections of *Huckleberry Finn* where Tom appears? If so, are they equally harmful there? If not, why not? What is the opinion of the critics?
5. On page 265 Erskine discusses the selection of material in *Huckleberry Finn,* something very important in a novel. Examine the novel carefully, and determine what Mark Twain has not put into the book about Huck's trip . . . then explain why he has omitted these things.

6. In what ways is Huck unusual beyond those mentioned by Erskine on page 267?
7. Explore the relationship between Huck and his father which Erskine discusses briefly. Is this relationship important to the rest of the novel in any way?
8. For what artistic reasons may Twain have deprived Huck of a mother?
9. What significance do you find in the statements of the last paragraph on page 270? For example, how does Erskine know what Twain's reasons were for putting descriptions of nature into *Huckleberry Finn?* Does this paragraph suggest anything about Mark Twain as a literary artist?
10. Decide to what extent Erskine's comments on slavery in *Huckleberry Finn* are valid.
11. Argue for or against Erskine's comments on the Grangerfords and the Shepherdsons.

[THE REAL MARK TWAIN]

by Vernon L. Parrington

He had opened another door to his genius and discovered the satirist. There lay the real Mark Twain. But the wares of the satirist were not in demand at the barbecue, so he closed the door and fell to purveying what the public wanted. *Tom Sawyer* was in part a malicious thrust at the Sunday School tale, and in part a whimsical pronouncement of the natural rights of the small boy. But it is in *Huckleberry Finn*—the one great picaresque tale of the frontier—that the western philosophy of Mark Twain, a philosophy that derives straight from the old naturistic school, crops out most sharply. It is a drama of the struggle between the individual and the village *mores*, set in a loose picturesque framework, and exemplifying the familiar thesis that the stuff of life springs strong and wholesome from the great common stock. Huck Finn is a child of nature who has lived close to the simple facts of life, unperverted by the tyrannies of the village that would make a good boy of him. He had got his schooling from the unfenced woods, from the great river that swept past him as he idly fished, from the folk-tales of negroes and poor whites, from queer adventures with Tom Sawyer; and from such experiences he had got a code of natural ethics. Then he found himself on the raft with Jim the runaway nigger, and his little pagan soul felt the stirrings of the problem of right and wrong. The village code and the natural code clashed and the conflict was terrifying. The village code /94/ warned him that hell yawned for one who helped a slave escape, and the human code warned him that betrayal was a blackguardly thing. With the fear of hell upon him he wrote to Miss Watson, and then his sense of the kindliness of Jim, the honest humanity under the black skin, rose up in fierce protest.

> It was a close place. I took [the letter] up, and held it in my hands. I was a-trembling, because I'd got to decide, forever, betwixt two things, and I knowed it. I studied for a minute, sort of holding my breath, and then says to myself:
>
> "All right, then, I'll go to hell"—and tore it up.
>
> It was awful thoughts and awful words, but they was said. And I let them stay said; and never thought no more about reforming.

It was a triumph over the sacred tribal law of conformity—the assertion of the individual will in opposition to society—and it reveals the heart of Mark Twain's philosophy. The rebel Huck is no other than the rebel Mark Twain whose wrath was quick to flame up against the unrighteous customs and laws of caste. If men were only honest realists—that is, if they were men and not credulous fools—how quickly the stables might be cleansed and life become decent and humane. If only the good brains could be segregated and trained in a real "man-factory," the history of civilization might become something the angels need not weep over as they read it. It all comes back to an honest realism that in accepting fact will clear away the superstitious fogs in which men have floundered and suffered hitherto. The one sacred duty laid on every rational being is the duty of rebellion against sham—to deny the divinity of clothes, to thrust out quack kings and priests and lords, to refuse a witless loyalty to things. /95/

QUESTIONS FOR DISCUSSION AND WRITING

1. With the aid of Parrington and other critics, elaborate on Parrington's statement that *Huckleberry Finn* is "a drama of the struggle between the individual and the village *mores.*"
2. What does Parrington mean when he says that the novel exemplifies "the familiar thesis that the stuff of life springs strong and wholesome from the great human stock"?
3. What have critics made of the "little pagan soul" of Huck? Would they all agree to the application of this label to Huck? What labels would some of the critics prefer, and why would they so prefer?
4. What is terrifying about the conflict between the clash of the village code and the natural code in *Huckleberry Finn?*
5. Parrington thinks that conformity is a central problem in *Huckleberry Finn.* In what ways is that problem important in the novel?
6. Do most critics agree with Parrington's statement of the theme of *Huckleberry Finn?* What disagreement has there been?

MARK TWAIN'S AMERICA

by Bernard DeVoto

The kernel of "Huckleberry Finn" is in a speech of Huck's toward the end of "Tom Sawyer." At the foot of the dead-limb tree t'other side of Still-House branch, he doubts the value of finding buried treasure. 'Pap would come back to thish yer /310/ town some day and get his claws on it if I didn't hurry up, and I tell you he'd clean it out pretty quick." "Old Times on the Mississippi", contains a

Reprinted from *Mark Twain's America* by Bernard DeVoto. Published by Little, Brown and Company, Boston, 1932. Reprinted by permission of the present copyright holder and publisher, Houghton Mifflin Company.

passage as integral with Huck's journey as anything in his book, and "Life on the Mississippi", written over the period when Huck was gestated, has many incidents on their way to fruition.[1] The Darnell-Watson feud is the Grangerford-Shepherdson trouble in chrysalis, a desultory tale told by a passenger as the *Gold Dust* passes through the chute of Island Number 8. On the upstream voyage as yet anonymous strollers forecast David Garrick the younger and Edmund Keen the elder. John A. Murrell's inheritors hint at revenge in the staterooms of a wrecked steamboat and other creatures of midnight presage the turmoil of search and escape through underbrush. Nor are these volumes the only ones in which pupal stages of incidents in "Huckleberry Finn" may be observed: most of the books that precede have passages of premonition. Why not? It was a book he was fore-ordained to write: it brought harmoniously to a focus everything that had a basic reality in his mind.

The opening is just "Tom Sawyer" and pretty poor "Tom Sawyer" at that. Huck's report of his emotions while ghosts are talking to him in the wind is a promise of what is to come, but Tom Sawyer's gang commenting on "Don Quixote" lacks the fineness of its predecessor. Discussions of ransom and Tom's exposition of Aladdin's lamp are feeble; such finish as they have comes from Huck's tolerant but obstinate common sense, here making its first experiments. But no flavor of the real Odyssey appears until Miss Watson forbids him to avert by magic the bad luck made inevitable by spilled salt, thus precipitating his trouble, and he immediately finds in the snow the impression of a boot heel in which nails make a cross to keep off the devil. . . . It is expedient to list here the book's obvious faults. After a first half in which, following the appearance of old man Finn, /311/ no touch is unsure, Mark's intuition begins to falter occasionally. When the Duke has Louis XVII learn a Shakespearian speech compounded out of Sol Smith and George Ealer, high and poetic reality lapses into farce. (Predictably. The humorist's necessity to write burlesque had frequently ruined fine things in the earlier books.) The King's conversion is weakened by his use of pirates instead of the neighborhood church which his predecessor Simon Suggs had more persuasively employed. (Predictably. The necessity to carry a joke into cosmic reaches had betrayed him often enough before.) Huck's discourse on the domestic manners of royalty is a blemish. (Extravaganza had diluted satire in many earlier contexts.) Huck's confusion

[1] Critics who enjoy dealing with the unconscious mind as the womb of art are offered such passages for amusement. I reluctantly confess, however, my fear that they will not indicate a father fixation, Mark's incestuous love of his sister, a forgotten reading of Nathaniel Wanley, or zoöphily.

when he tries to lie to the harelipped girl is perfunctory. (Improvisation had substituted for structure sufficiently often in Mark's previous fiction.) The concluding episodes of the attempted fraud on the Wilks family are weak in their technical devices—the manipulation required to postpone the detection of imposture, for instance, is annoying. Thereafter the narrative runs downhill through a steadily growing incredibility. The use of ghosts, the deceptions practiced on Aunt Sally and Uncle Silas, the whole episode built around the delivery of Jim from prison—all these are far below the accomplishment of what has gone before. Mark was once more betrayed. He intended a further chapter in his tireless attack on romanticism, especially Southern romanticism, and nothing in his mind or training enabled him to understand that this extemporized burlesque was a defacement of his purer work. His boundless gusto expended itself equally on the true and the false. . . . Predictably. It has been observed that he was incapable of sustained and disciplined imagination. One could expect it no more reasonably here than in "The Innocents Abroad."

So, though I regard comparisons as worthless in æsthetics, the obligation of a critic of Mark Twain rests on me to point out these selfsame faults in the only American novel which even enthusiasm can offer to dispute the preëminence of "The Adventures of Huckleberry Finn." Much more identity than has ever been noticed in print exists in the careers of Mark Twain and Herman Melville, whose minds were as antipathetic as religion /312/ and reality or the subjective and the objective worlds can be. Similarly, Jonathan Edwards's successor, when he came to write his masterpiece, plentifully anticipated the errors of Mark Twain and went beyond them. "Moby Dick" has, as fiction, no structure whatever. Its lines of force mercilessly intercept one another. Its improvisations are commoner and falser than those in Huck Finn. It does not suffer from burlesque (exuberant vitality had no place in Melville's nature) but its verbal humor is sometimes more vicariously humiliating than such passages as Huck's discussion of kings—a miracle, no doubt, withheld Mark Twain from the mere jokes habitual to him. And, though Melville could write great prose, his book frequently escapes into a passionately swooning rhetoric that is unconscious burlesque. He was no surer than Mark, he was in fact less sure, of the true object of his book, and much less sure of the technical instruments necessary to achieve it. That much of weakness the two novels have in common. It is convenient to point out, this much having been said, that they are otherwise antipathies. "Moby Dick" opposes metaphysics to the objective reality of "Huckleberry Finn." It is a study in demonology, bound to the world of experience by no more durable threads than a few passages in the lives of mates, harpooners and sailors who are otherwise mostly symbol or mist. They were the book's disregarded possibility of great realism. Melville preferred to sigh through eternity after the infinite. It is a search which has an eternal value for some minds. Other minds, if they look to fiction for values of time instead of eternity and of the finite instead of the infinite, are likely to relinquish the *Pequod's* voyage toward fulfillment of man's destiny and prefer a lumber raft's voyage down inland waters after no more ambitious purpose than to see what the world is like.

The title announces the structure: a picaresque novel concerned with the adventures of Huckleberry Finn. The form is the one most native to Mark Twain and so best adapted to his use. No more than Huck and the river's motion gives continuity to a series of episodes which are in essence only developed anecdotes. They originate in the tradition of newspaper humor, but the once uncomplicated form becomes here the instrument of /313/ great fiction. The lineage goes back to a native art; the novel derives from the folk and embodies their mode of thought more purely and more completely than any other ever written. Toward the beginning of this preface it was asserted that the life of the southwestern frontier was umbilical to the mind of Mark Twain. The blood and tissue of "Huckleberry Finn" have been formed in no other way. That life here finds issue more memorably than it has anywhere else, and since the frontier is a phase through which most of the nation has passed, the book comes nearer than any other to identify with the national life. The gigantic amorphousness of our past makes impossible, or merely idle, any attempt to fix in the form of idea the meaning of nationality. But more truly with "Huckleberry Finn" than with any other book, inquiry may satisfy itself: here is America.

The book has the fecundity, the multiplicity, of genius. It is the story of a wandering—so provocative a symbol that it moved Rudyard Kipling to discover another sagacious boy beneath a cannon and conduct him down an endless road, an enterprise that enormously fell short of its model. It is a passage through the structure of the nation. It is an exploration of the human race, whose adjective needs no explicit recording. It is an adventure of pageantry, horror, loveliness, and the tropisms of the mind. It is a faring-forth with inexhaustible delight through the variety of America. It is the restlessness of the young democracy borne southward on the river—the energy, the lawlessness, the groping ardor of the flux perfectly comprehended in a fragment of lumber raft drifting on the June flood. In a worn phrase—it is God's plenty.

The arrival of Huck's father lifts the narrative from the occupations of boyhood to as mature intelligence as fiction has anywhere. The new interest begins on a major chord, for old man Finn is the perfect portrait of the squatter. Behind him are the observations of hundreds of anonymous or forgotten realists who essayed to present the clay-eaters or piney-woods people, as well as a lifelong interest of Mark Twain's. It is amazing how few pages of type he occupies; the effect is as of a prolonged, minute analysis. There is no analysis; a clear light is focused /314/ on him and the dispassionate, final knowledge of his creator permits him to reveal himself. We learn of him only that he had heard about Huck's money "away down the river", but a complete biography shines through his speech. This rises to the drunken monologue about a government that can't take a-hold of a prowling, thieving, white-shirted free nigger. The old man subsides to an attack of snakes, is heard rowing his skiff in darkness, and then is just a frowsy corpse, shot in the back, which drifts downstream with the flood.

Something exquisite and delicate went into that creation—as into the casuals of the riverside. Mrs. Judith Loftus is employed to start Huck and Jim upon their voyage. She is just a device, but she outtops a hundred-odd patient attempts of fiction to sketch the pioneer wife. In her shrewdness, curiosity, initiative and brusque humanity one reads an entire history. Mere allusions—the ferryboat owner, the oarsmen who flee from smallpox, even raftsmen heard joking in the dark—have an incomparable authenticity. There is also the crowd. The loafers of Brickville whittle under the store fronts. They set a dog upon a sow that has "wholloped" herself right down in the way and "laugh and look grateful for the noise." Presently a bubble rises through this human mire: the drunken Boggs, the best-naturedest old fool in Arkansaw, comes riding into Brickville, on the waw-path. Colonel Sherburn finds it necessary to shoot him; and then, in one of the most blinding flashlights in all fiction, a "long, lanky man, with long hair and a big white fur stovepipe hat on the back of his head" rehearses the murder. "The people that had seen the thing said he done it perfect." So Buck Harkness leads a mob to Sherburn's house for a lynching but the Colonel breaks up the mob with a speech in which contempt effervesces like red nitric.

But in such passages as this, the clearly seen individuals merge into something greater, a social whole, a civilization, seen just as clearly. Pokeville, where the King is converted at the camp-meeting, Brickville, and the town below the P'int where a tanner has died are one with Dawson's Landing and Napoleon—but more concentrated and thereby more final. It seems unneces- /315/ sary to linger in consideration of this society. At the time of its appearance in 1885 a number of other novelists, perhaps fecundated by "The Gilded Age", were considering similar themes. The name of any one of them—Charles Egbert Craddock or Mary E. Wilkins or Edward Eggleston will do—is enough to distinguish honest talent from genius. The impulse weakened under the æstheticism of the Nineties, and it was not till after the World War that the countryside again received consideration in these terms. To set Brickville against Gopher Prairie or Winesburg is to perceive at once the finality of Mark Twain. The long lanky man in a white stovepipe hat who rehearses the death of Boggs has recorded this society with an unemotional certainty beside which either Mr. Lewis's anger or Mr. Anderson's misery seems a transitory hysterics.

The completeness of the society must be insisted upon. One should scrutinize the family of the dead tanner and their friends and neighbors, and orient them by reference to the family of Colonel Grangerford. The Wilkses belong to the industrious respectability of the towns. Their speech and thinking, the objects of their desire, the circumstances of their relationships are the totality of their kind. The funeral of Peter Wilks is, as fiction, many themes blended together; it is, among them, a supreme exhibition of the midcontinental culture of its time—almost an archæological display. When the undertaker tiptoes among the mourners to silence a howling dog and returns to whisper "He had a rat", something final has been said about this life. But Colonel Grangerford is a gentleman. Incidentally to the feud, which is the principal occupation of this episode, Southern gentility is examined. James's Basil Ransom was an embraced tradition; Colonel Grangerford is a reality. His daughter's elopement, a device for the precipitation of the plot, is out of fiction; the feud itself, with all the lovingly studied details of the scene, are from life. Gentility decorates the parlor with Emmaline Grangerford's verse and sketches. Its neurons show in the management of more than a hundred niggers quite as positively as in the parlor, or in the ceremonies of family inter- /316/ course and the simple code of honor, so indistinguishable from that of the Iroquois, which results in mass murder.

The portraiture which begins among the dregs with old man Finn ends with the Grangerfords. Between these strata has come every level of the South. What is the integrity of an artist? It would seem to consist in an intelligence which holds itself to the statement of a perceived truth, refusing to color it with an emotion of the artist's consequent to the truth. . . . These scenes are warm with an originality and a gusto that exist nowhere else in American fiction, and yet they are most notable for Mark Twain's detachment. There is no coloration, no resentment, no comment of any kind. The thing itself is rendered. If repudiation is complete, it exists implicitly in the thing.[2]

The differentiation of the speech these people use is so subtly done that Mark had to defend himself against an accusation of carelessness. He did not want readers to "suppose that all these characters were trying to talk alike and not succeeding." Superlatives are accurate once more: no equal sensitiveness to American speech has ever been brought to fiction. But a triumph in dialect is after all one of the smaller triumphs of novel-writing, and the important thing to be observed about Huckleberry's speech is its achievement in making the vernacular a perfect instrument for all the necessities of fiction. Like Melville, Mark Twain could write empty rhetoric enough when the mood was on him, and the set pieces of description in the travel books are as trying as the McGuffey selections which may have influenced them, while a willingness to let tears flow menaces a good many effects elsewhere. Yet his writing is never mediocre and is mostly, even in the least pretentious efforts, a formidable strength. Beginning with "Life on the Mississippi" it becomes, as Mr. Ford has remarked, one of the great styles of English literature. No analysis /317/ need be made here: its basis is simplicity, adaptability, an intimate liaison with the senses, and fidelity to the idioms of speech. Against the assertions of criticism, it should be remembered that such a style is not developed inattentively, nor are infants born with one by God's providence. Mark's lifelong pleasure in the peculiarities of language, which has distressed commentators, was the interest of any artist in his tools. . . . The successful use of an American vernacular as the sole prose medium of a masterpiece is a triumph in technique. Such attempts have been common in two and a half centuries of English fiction, but no other attempt on the highest level has succeeded. In this respect, too, "Huckleberry Finn" is unique. Patently, American literature has nothing to compare with it. Huck's language is a sensitive, subtle, and versatile instrument—capable of every effect it is called upon to manage. Whether it be the purely descriptive necessity of recording the river's mystery, or the notation of psychological states so minute and transitory as the effect on a boy of ghosts crying in the wind, or the fixation of individuality in dialogue, or the charged finality that may be typified by the King's "Hain't we got all the fools in town on

[2] Criticism has spent some pain on Mark Twain's deletion from "Life on the Mississippi" of a passage which, he was persuaded, might affect sales in the South. Apparently those who were outraged by this pandering to prejudice did not bother to read the suppressed passage. It is considerably less offensive to Southern sensibilities than several passages which remain in "Life on the Mississippi" and beside a good half of "Huckleberry Finn" it is innocuous.

our side? And ain't that a big enough majority in any town?"—the prose fulfills its obligation with the casual competence of genius. The fiction of Mark Twain had brought many innovations to the national literature—themes, lives, and interests of the greatest originality. This superb adaptation of vernacular to the purposes of art is another innovation, one which has only in the last few years begun to have a dim and crude but still perceptible fruition.

A tradition almost as old as prose narrative joins to the novel another tributary of world literature when a purely American wandering brings two further creatures of twilight to the raft. The Duke of Bilgewater and the Lost Dauphin were born of Mark's inexhaustible delight in worthlessness, but are manysided. Pretension of nobility is one of his commonest themes, here wrought into pure comedy. The Duke is akin to characters in the other books; the King embodies a legend widespread and unimaginably glorious on the frontier. The ambiguity surrounding the death of Louis XVII gave to history riots, dynasties and /318/ social comedies that still absorb much reverence in Florence and Paris. It gave mythology a superb legend, which at once accommodated itself to American belief. Up the river from New Orleans, one of the most pious repositories of allegiance, stories of the dethroned Bourbon gratified believers during three generations. The legend must have entertained Mark's boyhood but the circumstances of his Dauphin suggest that he more enjoyed the appearance of Eleazar Williams, who became an international celebrity in 1853. The whole course of his life probably gave him no more satisfying exhibition of the race's folly than the discovery of a Bourbon king in the person of this Mohawk half-breed turned Christian and missionary, who had systematically defrauded his church and his people. The story is one of the occasional ecstasies with which history rewards the patient mind.

The two rogues are formed from the nation's scum. They are products of chance and opportunity, drifters down rivers and across the countryside in the service of themselves. The Duke has sold medicines, among them a preparation to remove tartar from the teeth; he has acted tragedy and can sling a lecture sometimes; he can teach singing-geography school or take a turn to mesmerism or phrenology when there's a chance. The King can tell fortunes and can cure cancer or paralysis by the laying on of hands; but preaching, missionarying, and the temperance revival are his best lines. American universals meet here; once more, this is a whole history, and into these drifters is poured an enormous store of the nation's experience. They have begotten hordes of successors since 1885 but none that joins their immortality. They belong with Colonel Sellers: they are the pure stuff of comedy. Their destiny is guile: to collect the tax which freedom and wit levy on respectability. Their voyage is down a river deep in the American continent; they are born of a purely American scene. Yet the river becomes one of the world's roads and these disreputables join, of right, a select fellowship. They are Diana's foresters: the brotherhood that receives them, approving their passage, is immortal in the assenting dreams of literature. Such freed spirits /319/ as Panurge, Falstaff, Gil Blas and the Abbé Coignard are of that fellowship; no Americans except the Duke and the Dauphin have joined it. None seems likely to.

Yet the fabric on which all this richness is embroidered is the journey of Huck and Jim down the Mississippi on the June rise. There, finally, the book's glamour resides. To discuss that glamour would be futile. In a sense, Huck speaks to the national shrewdness, facing adequately what he meets, succeeding by means of native intelligence whose roots are ours—and ours only. In a sense, he exists for a delight or wonder inseparable from the American race. This passage down the flooded river, through pageantry and spectacle, amidst an infinite variety of life, something of surprise or gratification surely to be met with each new incident—it is the heritage of a nation not unjustly symbolized by the river's flow. Huck sleeping under the stars or wakefully drifting through an immensity dotted only by far lights or scurrying to a cave while the forest bends under a cloudburst satisfies blind gropings of the mind. The margin widens to obscurity. Beyond awareness, a need for freedom, an insatiable hunger for its use, finds in him a kind of satisfaction. At the margin, too, the endless flow speaks for something quite as immediate. It is movement, not quiet. By day or darkness the current is unceasing; its rhythm, at the obscure margin, speaks affirmatively. For life is movement—a down-river voyage amidst strangeness.

Go warily in that obscurity. One does not care to leave Huck in the twilight at such a threshold, among the dim shapes about which no one can speak with authority. Unquestionably something of him is resident there—with something of Tom, the disreputables, Colonel Sellers and some others. But first he is a shrewd boy who takes a raft down the Mississippi, through a world incomparably alive. With him goes a fullness made and shaped wholly of America. It is only because the world he passes through is real and only because it is American that his journey escapes into universals and is immortal. His book is American life formed into great fiction.

Somewhere in the person of Mark Twain, who wrote it, must have been an artist—as American. /320/

QUESTIONS FOR DISCUSSION AND WRITING

1. Beginning with DeVoto, summarize the critical evaluation of the beginning of *Huckleberry Finn*.
2. With the aid of your instructor, work out a full definition of "picaresque" novel. Would such a novel be possible today? Why, or why not?
3. "No more than Huck and the river's motion gives continuity to" the novel (p. 313). Search criticism for opposing views, and take sides.
4. What does DeVoto mean when he says of *Huckleberry Finn*, "here is America"? Is all of America in the novel? Is it not the picture of just one small area of the country?
5. What does DeVoto mean by saying that something "exquisite and delicate" went into the making of Pap?
6. Beginning with DeVoto's comments on Judith Loftus (p. 315), write a careful critique of this minor character.
7. Why does DeVoto call the scene in which the murder of Boggs is reenacted a "blinding flashlight" (p. 315)?
8. Does DeVoto's admiration for the Duke and Dauphin seem just or extravagant?
9. DeVoto says there is a *glamour* to *Huckleberry Finn*. Define the term *glamour* in the context of the novel.

CRUELTY IN THE *Adventures of Huckleberry Finn*

by V. S. Pritchett

When Mark Twain turned upon the religion of his childhood because it was intolerable, he was unaware that it would destroy him by turning him into a money-grubber of the most disastrously Puritan kind. Fortunately the resources of the imagination are endless even when a fanatical philosophy wrecks human life, genius and happiness. Out of the mess which Twain made of his life, amid the awful pile of tripe which he wrote, there does rise one book which has the serenity of a thing of genius. *Huckleberry Finn* takes the breath away. Knowing Mark Twain's life, knowing the hell of vulgarity from which the book has ascended, one dreads as one turns from page to page the seemingly inevitable flop. How can a low comedian, so tortured and so angry, refrain from blackguarding God, Man and Nature for the narrow boredom of his early life, and ruining the perfect comedy and horror of this story? But imaginative writers appear to get at least one lucky break in their careers; for a moment the conflicts are assimilated, the engine ceases to work against itself. *Huckleberry Finn* does not flop. America gets its first truly indigenous masterpiece. The small boyhood of Huck Finn is the small boyhood of a new culture.

The curious thing about *Huckleberry Finn* is that, although it is one of the funniest books in all literature and really astonishing in the variety of its farce and character, we are even more moved than we are amused by it. Why are we moved? Do we feel the sentiment of sympathy only? Are we sighing with some envy and self-pity? "Alas, Huck Finn is just what I would have been in my boyhood if I had had half a chance?" Are we sorry for the vagrant, or are we moved by his rebellion? These minor feelings may play their part; but they are only sighs on the surface of the main stream of our emotion. Mark Twain has brought to his subject far more than this personal longing; he has become the channel of the generic emotion which floods all

From article by V. S. Pritchett in *New Statesman And Nation*, XXII, 545 (2 August 1941), p. 113. Reprinted by permission of *New Statesman And Nation*.

really American literature—the emotion of nostalgia. In that absurd, brilliant, hit-or-miss book, *Studies in Classical American Literature*, which is so often dead right, D. H. Lawrence called this feeling the longing of the rebel for a master. It may be simply the longing for a spiritual home, but it is as strong in Mark Twain as it is implicit in Hemingway. One finds this feeling in Anglo-Irish literature which is also colonial and, in a less lasting way, in the work of Kipling. The peculiar power of American nostalgia is that it is not only harking back to something lost in the past, but suggests also the tragedy of a lost future. As Huck Finn and old Jim drift down the Mississippi from one horrifying little town to the next and hear the voices of men quietly swearing at one another across the water; as they pass the time of day with the scroungers, rogues, murderers, the lonely women, the frothing revivalists, the maundering boatmen and fantastic drunks of the river towns, we see the human wastage that is left in the wake of a great effort of the human will, the hopes frustrated, the idealism which has been whittled down to eccentricity and craft. These people are the price paid for building a new country. It is not, once you have faced it—which Dickens did not do in Martin Chuzzlewit, obsessed as he was with the negative pathos of the immigrant—it is not a disheartening spectacle; for the value of a native humour like Twain's is that it expresses a profound reality in human nature: the ability of man to adjust himself to circumstance and to live somehow.

Movement is one of the great consolers of human woe; movement, a sense of continual migration, is the history of America. This factor gives Twain's wonderful descriptions of the journey down the Mississippi their haunting overtone. His natural sensibility which is shown nowhere else in his writings and which is indeed vulgarly repressed in them is awakened:

> . . . then we set down on the sandy bottom where the water was about knee-deep and watched the daylight come. Not a sound anywhere—perfectly still—just like the whole world was asleep, only sometimes the bullfrogs a-clattering maybe. The first thing to see, looking away over the water, was a kind of dull line—that was the woods on the other side—you couldn't make nothing else out; then a pale place in the sky; then more paleness, spreading around; then the river softened up, away off, and wasn't black any more but grey; you could see little dark spots drifting along, ever so far away—trading scows and such things; and long black streaks—rafts; sometimes you could hear a sweep screaking; or jumbled-up

> voices, it was so still, and sounds come so far; and by-and-by you could see a streak on the water which you know by the look of the streak that there's a snag in the swift current which breaks on it and that makes that streak look that way; and you see the mist curl up off the water, and the east reddens up, and the river, and you make out a log cabin in the edge of the woods, away on the bank t'other side of the river, being a woodyard likely, and piled by them cheats so you can throw a dog through it anywheres . . .

The subject of *Huckleberry Finn* is the comical but also brutal effect of an anarchic rebellion against civilization and especially its traditions:

> I reckon I got to light out for the Territory ahead of the rest, because Aunt Sally she's going to adopt me and sivilize me and I can't stand it. I been there before.

Huck isn't interested in "Moses and the Bulrushers" because Huck "don't take no stock of dead people." He garbles European history when he is discussing Kings with Jim, the negro. Whether Huck is the kind of boy who will grow up to build a new civilization is doubtful; Tom Sawyer obviously would do so because he is imaginative. Huck never imagines anything except fears. Huck is "low-down plain ornery," in trouble because of the way he was brought up with "Pap." He is a natural anarchist and bum. He can live without civilization, depending on simple affections and workaday loyalties. He is the first of those typical American portraits of the underdog, which have culminated in the "poor white" literature and Charlie Chaplin—an underdog who gets along on horse sense, so to speak. Romanticism, ideas, ideals, are repugnant to Huck.

–Mark Twain obliges you to accept the boy as the humorous norm. Without him the violence of the book would be stark reporting of low life. For if this is a great comic book it is also a book of terror and brutality. Think of the scenes: Pap with d.t.'s chasing Huck round the cabin with a knife; Huck sitting up all night with a gun preparing to shoot the old man; Huck's early familiarity with corpses; the pig killing scene; the sight of the frame house (evidently some sort of brothel) floating down the Mississippi with a murdered man in it; the fantastic events at the Southerner's house where two families are shooting each other down in a vendetta; the drunken Boggs who comes into town to pick a quarrel and is eventually coolly shot dead before the eyes of his screaming young daughter by the man he has insulted. The "Duke" and the "King," those cynical rascals whose adventures liven up the second half of the story, are sharpers, twisters and crooks of the lowest kind. Yet a child is relating all this with a child's detachment and with a touch of morbidity. Marvellous as it all is as picaresque episode and as a description of the mess of frontier life, it is strong meat. Sometimes we wonder how Twain's public stomached such illusionless reporting. The sardonic humour and the important fact that in this one book Mark Twain never forced a point nor overwrote—in the Dickens way, for example—are of course the transfiguring and beguiling forces. The corpse and coffin humour is a dry wine which raises his animal spirits. Old Jim not only looked like a dead man after "the King" had painted him blue, but like one "who had been dead a considerable time." Judiciousness is carried to the comic limit.

Is *Huckleberry Finn* one of the great works of picaresque literature? It is, granting the limits of a boy's mind in the hero and the author, a comic masterpiece; but this limitation is important. It is not a book which grows spiritually, if we compare it to *Quixote, Dead Souls* or even *Pickwick;* and it is lacking in that civilized quality which you are bound to lose when you throw over civilization—the quality of pity. One is left with the cruelty of American humour, a cruelty which is softened by the shrewd moralisings of the humorous Wards, the Will Rogers. And once Mark Twain passed this exquisite moment of his maturity, he went to bits in that morass of sentimentality, cynicism, melodrama and vulgarity which have damned him for the adult reader. I advise those who haven't read *Huckleberry Finn* since their school days to read it again. /113/

QUESTIONS FOR DISCUSSION AND WRITING

1. Pritchett says that in *Huckleberry Finn,* Mark Twain "has become the channel of the generic emotion which floods all really American literature—the emotion of nostalgia." What do other critics say which might support or oppose this statement?

2. We would probably all agree with Pritchett that the effect of Huck's rebellion is comical, but do you agree that it—the effect of Huck's rebellion—is also brutal? Discuss the brutality in the novel and its relationship to Huck's rebellion. What do other critics have to say about brutality in *Huckleberry Finn?*

3. "Huck never imagines anything except fear," says Pritchett. Is he right? Describe Huck's imagination as fully as you can.

4. Extend Pritchett's list of the scenes of terror and brutality in *Huckleberry Finn.* Does Pritchett seem to have followed any principle of selection in choosing the ones he did?

5. Is Pritchett right in saying that *Huckleberry Finn* lacks the quality of pity? Do or would other critics in this volume agree with Pritchett on this point?

THE LEAGUE OF FRIGHTENED PHILISTINES

by James T. Farrell

Mark Twain has often been made the sport of critical fashions. During his lifetime he was slow in gaining recognition, except as a humorist. His writing, especially because of his views on the institution of monarchy, disturbed some of the literary democrats of the Eastern seaboard. His masterpiece, *The Adventures of Huckleberry Finn,* was barred from some public libraries. In general, too much of the critical writing on Mark Twain has stressed his failures and his limitations. His views on feudalism and, more generally, on thirteen centuries of Christian civilization have been misinterpreted, and he is sometimes pictured merely as the crass American frontiersman who could not rise to the level of appreciating the glories of European culture. It has been remarked that he might have corrected some of this gaucherié had he only known Henry Adams.[1]

While it is true that he was unhistorical in his approach to European culture, it nonetheless remains that many of his critics have been equally unhistorical. And, at the very least, there was in Twain a

[1]Of the best known writers who misunderstand Mark Twain I would mention particularly Lewis Mumford (in *The Golden Day*) and Van Wyck Brooks. And it is surprising, to say the least, that Parrington lamented the fact that Twain did not know Henry Adams.

healthy sense of democratic feelings: a hatred of oppression and injustice, a deep-seated conviction that men were more important than the rags and cloth of the past, than /25/ the trumpery, the show, the color, the glitter attached to outmoded historic institutions. His attacks on romanticism were literary necessities. In order to gain acceptance for what he wanted to write, he had to attack the unhealthy influence that this tradition exerted in America. As Bernard De Voto has demonstrated in detail in *Mark Twain's America,* Twain's source of inspiration was the frontier. He is the literary summation of pioneer America. And in *The Adventures of Huckleberry Finn,* he distilled and transmuted his material in terms of great writing.

Mark Twain was both a genuine democrat and a cynic. As a democrat he defended the Jacobins. Democratic ideas seemed to be part of his very blood and flesh. His individualism, and consequently his sense of the worth of human beings, is a direct product of democratic ideas. And he expressed these magnificently when he made an unschooled boy and a runaway slave the heroes of what is truly an American odyssey. His cynicism is related to the many disillusioning observations of the failure of democratic ideas. In his most buoyant and productive periods, this cynicism is not sharply contradictory to his democratic feelings. Rather, it suggests something of the healthy cynicism of the *sansculottés.* In his latter days he witnessed the triumph of industrialism and the rapid expansion of American capitalism. His conscience was disturbed, as were the consciences of many writers and thinking people in both Europe and America. Then he became a bleak determinist somewhat on the order of the late Clarence Darrow. His cynicism concerning "the damned human race" became corrosive. He visioned the individual man alone in a dreary waste of empty space. But his two boys, Tom and Huck, rise above his discouragement, they are his strongest expression of democratic hopes. Most particularly, Huck Finn is an ideal expression of the positive side of Mark Twain.

It is significant that Tom and Huck are boys rather than men, and therefore the more easily surrounded with an aura of optimism. Whereas the adults in their Mississippi village look /26/ down on Negro slaves as if they were not human beings, Tom and Huck tend even to envy them. Less influenced by the village standards, they can associate more freely with Negroes than can adults. And consequently, Huck is able to come to grips with the moral problems posed by the very existence of the institution of chattel slavery. Huck lives like a pioneer, like a squatter in miniature. His respect for property rights is almost nil. To filch watermelons and other food, to "borrow" someone else's canoe, to ignore conventions and moral standards—none of this troubles his conscience. But when it so happens that property rights involve another human being, then he faces a moral problem. This problem cuts into the heart of pre-Civil War America. And Huck resolves the problem by deciding he will have to help the Negro, Jim, even at the risk of eternal damnation. To help a Negro slave escape is a "low-down thing to do." A person "don't want to take no consequence of it." The more this problem troubles Huck, "the more my conscience kept grinding me, and the more wicked and low-down and ornery I got to feeling." He tries to soften his conscience by convincing himself that he was brought up "wicked." He tries to pray, "but one can't pray a lie." He plans to write Jim's owner a letter and thereby save himself from this evil. He can't. The humanity of Jim outweighs the moral code of Huck's environment. Huck makes a moral choice: he helps Jim to escape. He is in it for good, so he will go "the whole hog." Here we see Huck affirming the value of a living human being of the present as against the claims justified in an institution of the past. And this affirmation is the very core of Mark Twain's own sense of the worth of human beings. To continue: Tom and Huck are shrewd, daring, ingenious. These are traits that Mark Twain admired. Tom Sawyer is the type of boy who could grow up to be a Pudd'nhead Wilson. The resourcefulness of Huck parallels that of the Connecticut Yankee. Thus, when Tom and Huck outwit adults, we must not interpret these passages merely as humor. Through his two unspoiled boys Twain forcefully emphasized his own attitudes and values.

The Adventures of Tom Sawyer is a boy's book. Its sequel, /27/ *The Adventures of Huckleberry Finn*, is an adult's novel. However, the two books should not be considered separately, for Tom and Huck are contrasts. Tom is a romantic; Huck, a realist. At first this temperamental difference seems paradoxical when we think of the circumstances of their lives. Tom lives a regular life. Cared for by his Aunt Polly, he is an accepted member of the community. He is sent to school, is taken to church and Sunday school, and he goes on picnics with other children whose parents also live orderly lives. He becomes the boyhood sweetheart of Becky Thatcher, whose father is one of the leading figures in the village. Tom seeks to escape from regularity by romanticism. He feeds on detective and adventure stories (in fact, the very characterization of Tom constitutes a satire on this form of writing), and he strives to translate what he reads into the real world around him. Huck, on the contrary, is a realist living under romantic circumstances. There is no order in his life. He is a child of whim and impulse, heedless of authority and convention. The other boys are warned by their parents and their teacher not to associate with him. But Huck represents common sense as opposed to romanticism. Since his problems are of a life-and-death character, he must be a realist in order to survive. Tom's real problems are settled for him, so that he is more concerned with those of his imagination. Huck, equally adventurous, cannot afford the luxury of romanticism.

As a result of these differences, Huck appears to be more mature than Tom, although they are of the same age. At the conclusion of *The Adventures of Huckleberry Finn,* Tom seems to be the same charming boy he was when we first met him, while Huck has developed and grown in character, having acquired a clearer and purer sense of moral values. It is this fact that explains the difference between the two books—revealed also in the humor, which is much more pointed in the second novel. There was usually a devastating attack behind the playfulness and humor of Mark Twain. The extravaganza, the burlesque included in the saga of Huck Finn is pointed at the old South and cuts to the heart of a whole society. The sharpest /28/ humor in *The Adventures of Tom Sawyer* strikes less deeply; it is directed at adventure writing and at the school system of the period. But, taken together, both boys stand in contrast to "the damned human race."

The institution of chattel slavery always forms the background against which these boys live. It forces itself into the very content of consciousness, not only of Tom and Huck, but of all the members of their village. As Bernard De Voto has pointed out, the existence of slavery explains the role that superstition plays in the minds of Tom and Huck. Here Mark Twain made a neat social comment. He told us, in effect, that if we preserve the institution of slavery it will permeate our entire culture and become a formidable barrier to progress. Just as slavery produces meanness and brutality, so does it perpetuate magic. Briefly, the backwardness of the slaves, treated as property rather than as human beings, will blunt the moral and intellectual development of the masters. Twain's penetrating revelation of the moral and social consequences of slavery is focused in the relationship between Huck and Jim, the runaway slave, for it is through intimate association with him that Huck's moral landscape is broadened. Huck must even learn that a Negro can love his family as tenderly as white folks do. Jim shines through the novel as a man with dignity, loyalty, and courage. Drifting along the Mississippi, he assumes heroic proportions, demonstrating by contrast that many of the white men surrounding him are cruel or foolish. This is most clearly drawn in the case of the King and the Duke, who are rascals, but who are also symbolic figures, representing the dead institutions of the past. And Huck makes the symbolism explicit when he tells Jim that they are not at all bad when one considers what real kings and dukes have done in history.

It need not be stressed that Mark Twain re-created almost a full sense of life on the Mississippi. This is undisputed. He wrote with ease and buoyancy: there is humor, sensibility, and beauty in his style. But there is real penetration, too. He evokes an entire epoch, by giving it form, solidity, depth.

Generations of Americans have read of these two boys. They /29/ have become part of the consciousness of most literate people in this country, and one feels, on rereading their stories, as if one is meeting old and imperishable friends. But they do not represent merely the idyllic times of boyhood. The world in which they lived was full of its own cruelties. One reason they are so charming is that we see their unspoiled images flashed against the mirror of that world. Tom and Huck are symbols of the possibilities in human beings. Today they stand as a test not only of ourselves but of the whole of American society. They are, with all their charm, like two accusing figures, with their fingers pointing down the decades of American history. Their very characters seem to ask why—why has this promise not been realized? Why is it so rarely that the man becomes what the boy gave promise of becoming? This is part of their significance as enduring characters in American literature. /30/

QUESTIONS FOR DISCUSSION AND WRITING

1. Explain in detail why Huck tends to envy the Negroes in his Mississippi village. Are critics of the novel in general agreement on the attitudes of Huck toward Negroes?
2. With reference to the novel, to Farrell, and to other critics, explain the meaning of the word *consequently* in the second full sentence of page 27.
3. Comment on Farrell's statements about Huck's "conventions and moral standards" on page 27.
4. Discuss Farrell's statement that Huck's "respect for property rights is almost nil."
5. Explain the role of "institutions" in *The Adventures of Huckleberry Finn*. What do other critics say about them?
6. In what ways is Huck a realist? How is this related to the theme of the novel?

7. Farrell calls Huck a realist. Using evidence from other critics, make a case for Huck as a romantic.
8. Is Huck, as Farrell says, "heedless of authority and convention" (p. 28)? Has this been the usual opinion of Huck?
9. Why does Farrell say that Huck "cannot afford the luxury of romanticism" (p. 28)?
10. In what ways is Huck "symbol of the possibilities in human beings" (p. 30)?

[AN INTRODUCTION TO HUCKLEBERRY FINN]

by Lionel Trilling

In 1876 Mark Twain published *The Adventures of Tom Sawyer* and in the same year he began what he called "another boys' book." He set little store by the new venture and said that he had undertaken it "more to be at work than anything else." His heart was not in it—"I like it only tolerably well as far as I have got," he said, "and may possibly pigeonhole or burn the MS when it is done." He pigeonholed it long before it was done and for as much as four years. In 1880 he took it out and carried it forward a little, only to abandon it again. He had a theory of unconscious composition and believed that a book must write itself; the book which he referred to as "Huck Finn's Autobiography" refused to do the job of its own creation and he would not coerce it.

But then in the summer of 1882 Mark Twain was possessed by a charge of literary energy which, as he wrote to a friend, was more intense than any he had experienced for many years. He worked all day and every day, and periodically he so fatigued himself that he had to recruit his strength by a day or two of smoking and reading in bed. It is impossible not to suppose that this great creative drive was connected with—was perhaps the direct result of—the visit to the Mississippi he had made earlier in the year, the trip which forms the matter of the second part of *Life on the Mississippi*. His boyhood and youth on the river he so profoundly loved had been at once the happiest and most significant part of Mark Twain's life; his return to it in middle age stirred vital memories which revived and refreshed the idea of *Huckleberry Finn*. Now at last the book was not only ready but eager to write itself. But it was not to receive much conscious help from its author. He was always full of second-rate literary schemes and now, in the early weeks of the summer, with *Huckleberry Finn* waiting to complete itself, he turned his hot energy upon several of these sorry projects, the completion of which gave him as /v/ much sense of satisfying productivity as did his eventual absorption in *Huckleberry Finn*.

When at last *Huckleberry Finn* was completed and published and widely loved, Mark Twain became somewhat aware of what he had accomplished with this book that had been begun as journeywork and depreciated, postponed, threatened with destruction. It is his masterpiece, and perhaps he learned to know that. But he could scarcely have estimated it for what it is, one of the world's great books and one of the central documents of American culture.

2

Wherein does its greatness lie? Primarily in its power of telling the truth. An awareness of this quality as it exists in *Tom Sawyer* once led Mark Twain to say of the earlier work that "it is *not* a boys' book at all. It will be read only by adults. It is written only for adults." But this was only a manner of speaking, Mark Twain's way of asserting, with a discernible touch of irritation, the degree of truth he had achieved. It does not represent his usual view either of boys' books or of boys. No one, as he well knew, sets a higher value on truth than a boy. Truth is the whole of a boy's conscious demand upon the world of adults. He is likely to believe that the adult world is in a conspiracy to lie to him, and it is this belief, by no means unfounded, that arouses Tom and Huck and all boys to their moral sensitivity, their everlasting concern with justice, which they call fairness. At the same time it often makes them skillful and profound liars in their own defense, yet they do not tell the ultimate lie of adults: they do not lie to themselves. That is why Mark Twain felt that it was impossible to carry Tom Sawyer beyond boyhood—in maturity "he would lie just like all the other one-horse men of literature and the reader would conceive a hearty contempt for him."

Certainly one element in the greatness of *Huckleberry Finn*—as also in the lesser greatness of *Tom Sawyer*—is that it succeeds first as a boys' book. One can read it at ten and then annually ever after, and each year find that it is as fresh as /vi/ the year before, that it has changed only in becoming somewhat larger. To read it young is like planting a tree young—each year adds a new growth-ring of meaning, and the book is as little likely as the tree to become dull. So, we may imagine, an Athenian boy grew up together with the *Odyssey*. There are few other books which we can know so young and love so long.

The truth of *Huckleberry Finn* is of a different kind from that of *Tom Sawyer*. It is a more intense truth, fiercer and more complex. *Tom Sawyer* has the truth of honesty—what it says about things and feelings is never false and always both adequate and beautiful. *Huckleberry Finn* has this kind of truth, too, but it has also the truth of moral passion; it deals directly with the virtue and depravity of man's heart.

Perhaps the best clue to the greatness of *Huckleberry Finn* has been given to us by a writer who is as different from Mark Twain as it is possible for one Missourian to be from another. T. S. Eliot's poem, "The Dry Salvages," the third of his *Four Quartets*, begins with a meditation on the Mississippi, which Mr. Eliot knew in his St. Louis boyhood. These are the opening lines:

> I do not know much about gods; but I think that the river
> Is a strong brown god . . .

And the meditation goes on to speak of the god as

> almost forgotten
> By the dwellers in cities—ever, however, implacable,
> Keeping his seasons and rages, destroyer, reminder
> Of what men choose to forget. Unhonoured, unpropitiated
> By worshippers of the machine, but waiting, watching and waiting.[1]

Huckleberry Finn is a great book because it is about a god—about, that is, a power which seems to have a mind and will of its own, and which, to men of moral imagination, appears to embody a great moral idea. /vii/

Huck himself is the servant of the river-god, and he comes very close to being aware of the divine nature of the being he serves. The world

[1] Copyright, 1943, by T. S. Eliot, reprinted by permission of Harcourt, Brace and Company.

he inhabits is perfectly equipped to accommodate a deity, for it is full of presences and meanings which it conveys by natural signs and also by preternatural omens and taboos: to look at the moon over the left shoulder, to shake the tablecloth after sundown, to handle a snakeskin, are ways of offending the obscure and prevalent spirits. Huck is at odds, on moral and æsthetic grounds, with the only form of Christianity he knows, and his very intense moral life may be said to derive from his love of the river. He lives in a perpetual adoration of the Mississippi's power and charm. Huck, of course, always expresses himself better than he can know, but nothing draws upon his gift of speech like his response to his deity. After every sally into the social life of the shore, he returns to the river with relief and thanksgiving; and at each return, regular and explicit as a chorus in a Greek tragedy, there is a hymn of praise to the god's beauty, mystery, and strength, and to his noble grandeur in contrast with the pettiness of men.

Generally the god is benign, a being of long sunny days and spacious nights. But, like any god, he is also dangerous and deceptive. He generates fogs which bewilder, and he contrives echoes and false distances which confuse. His sandbars can ground and his hidden snags can mortally wound a great steamboat. He can cut away the solid earth from under a man's feet and take his house with it. The sense of the danger of the river is what saves the book from any touch of the sentimentality and moral ineptitude of most works of the imagination which contrast the life of nature with the life of society.

The river itself is only divine; it is not ethical and good. But its nature seems to foster the goodness of those who love it and try to fit themselves to its ways. And we must observe that we cannot make—that Mark Twain does not make—an absolute opposition between the river and human society. To Huck much of the charm of the river life is human: it is the /viii/ raft and the wigwam and Jim. He has not run away from Miss Watson and the Widow Douglas and his brutal father to a completely individualistic liberty, for in Jim he finds his true father, very much as Stephen Dedalus in James Joyce's *Ulysses* finds his true father in Leopold Bloom.[2] The boy and the Negro slave form a family, a primitive community—and it is a community of saints.

Huck's intense and even complex moral quality may possibly not appear on a first reading, for one may be caught and convinced by his

[2] In Joyce's *Finnegans Wake* both Mark Twain and Huckleberry Finn appear frequently. The theme of rivers is, of course, dominant in the book; and Huck's name suits Joyce's purpose, as so many names do, for Finn is one of the many names of his hero. Mark Twain's love of and gift for the spoken language makes another reason for Joyce's interest in him.

own estimate of himself, by his brags about his lazy hedonism, his avowed preference for being alone, his dislike of civilization. The fact is, of course, that he is involved in civilization up to his ears. His escape from society is but his way of reaching what society ideally dreams of for itself. Responsibility is the very essence of his character, and it is perhaps to the point that the original of Huck, a boyhood companion of Mark Twain's named Tom Blankenship, did, like Huck, "light out for the Territory," only to become a justice of the peace in Montana, "a good citizen and greatly respected."

Huck does indeed have all the capacities for simple happiness he says he has, but circumstances and his own moral nature make him the least carefree of boys—he is always "in a sweat" over the predicament of someone else. He has a great sense of the sadness of human life, and although he likes to be alone, the words "lonely" and "loneliness" are frequent with him. The note of his special sensibility is struck early in the story: "Well, when Tom and me got to the edge of the hilltop we looked away down into the village and could see three or four lights twinkling where there were sick folks, maybe; and the stars over us was sparkling ever so fine; and down by the village was the river, a whole mile broad, and /ix/ awful still and grand." The identification of those three or four lonely lights as the lamps of sick-watches defines Huck's character.

His sympathy is quick and immediate. When the circus audience laughs at the supposedly drunken man who tries to ride the horse, Huck is only miserable: "It wasn't funny to me . . . ; I was all of a tremble to see his danger." When he imprisons the intending murderers on the wrecked steamboat, his first thought is of how to get someone to rescue them, for he considers "how dreadful it was, even for murderers, to be in such a fix. I says to myself, there ain't no telling but I might come to be a murderer myself yet, and then how would I like it?" But his sympathy is never sentimental. When at last he knows that the murderers are beyond help, he has no inclination to false pathos. "I felt a little bit heavy-hearted about the gang, but not much, for I reckoned that if they could stand it I could." His will is genuinely good and therefore he has no need to torture himself with guilty second thoughts.

Not the least remarkable thing about Huck's feeling for people is that his tenderness goes along with the assumption that his fellow men are likely to be dangerous and wicked. He travels incognito, never telling the truth about himself and never twice telling the same lie, for he trusts no one and the lie comforts him even when it is not necessary. He instinctively knows that the best way to keep a party of men away from Jim on the raft is to beg them to come aboard to help his family stricken with smallpox. And if he had not already had the knowledge of human weakness and stupidity and cowardice, he would soon have acquired it, for all his encounters forcibly teach it to him—the insensate feud of the Grangerfords and Shepherdsons, the invasion of the raft by the Duke and the King, the murder of Boggs, the lynching party, and the speech of Colonel Sherburn. Yet his profound and bitter knowledge of human depravity never prevents him from being a friend to man.

No personal pride interferes with his well-being. He knows what status is and on the whole he respects it—he is really a /x/ very *respectable* person and inclines to like "quality folks"—but he himself is unaffected by it. He himself has never had status, he has always been the lowest of the low, and the considerable fortune he had acquired in *The Adventures of Tom Sawyer* is never real to him. When the Duke suggests that Huck and Jim render him the personal service that accords with his rank, Huck's only comment is, "Well, that was easy so we done it." He is injured in every possible way by the Duke and the King, used and exploited and manipulated, yet when he hears that they are in danger from a mob, his natural impulse is to warn them. And when he fails of his purpose and the two men are tarred and feathered and ridden on a rail, his only thought is, "Well, it made me sick to see it; and I was sorry for them poor pitiful rascals, it seemed like I couldn't ever feel any hardness against them any more in the world."

And if Huck and Jim on the raft do indeed make a community of saints, it is because they do not have an ounce of pride between them. Yet this is not perfectly true, for the one disagreement they ever have is over a matter of pride. It is on the occasion when Jim and Huck have been separated by the fog. Jim has mourned Huck as dead, and then, exhausted, has fallen asleep. When he awakes and finds that Huck has returned, he is overjoyed; but Huck convinces him that he has only dreamed the incident, that there has been no fog, no separation, no chase, no reunion, and then allows him to make an elaborate "interpretation" of the dream he now believes he has had. Then the joke is sprung, and in the growing light of the dawn Huck points to the debris of leaves on the raft and the broken oar.

> Jim looked at the trash, and then looked at me, and back at the trash again. He had got the dream fixed so strong in his head that he couldn't seem to shake it loose and get the facts back into its place again right away. But when he did get the thing straightened around he looked at me steady without ever smiling, and says: /xi/

"What do dey stan' for? I'se gwyne to tell you. When I got all wore out wid work, en wid de callin' for you, en went to sleep, my heart wuz mos' broke bekase you wuz los', en I didn' k'yer no mo' what became er me en de raf'. En when I wake up en fine you back agin, all safe en soun', de tears come, en I could a got down on my knees en kiss yo' foot, I's so thankful. En all you wuz thinkin' 'bout wuz how you could make a fool uv ole Jim wid a lie. Dat truck dah is *trash;* en trash is what people is dat puts dirt on de head er dey fren's en makes 'em ashamed."

Then he got up slow and walked to the wigwam, and went in there without saying anything but that.

The pride of human affection has been touched, one of the few prides that has any true dignity. And at its utterance, Huck's one last dim vestige of pride of status, his sense of his position as a white man, wholly vanishes: "It was fifteen minutes before I could work myself up to go and humble myself to a nigger; but I done it, and I warn't sorry for it afterward, neither."

This incident is the beginning of the moral testing and development which a character so morally sensitive as Huck's must inevitably undergo. And it becomes an heroic character when, on the urging of affection, Huck discards the moral code he has always taken for granted and resolves to help Jim in his escape from slavery. The intensity of his struggle over the act suggests how deeply he is involved in the society which he rejects. The satiric brilliance of the episode lies, of course, in Huck's solving his problem not by doing "right" but by doing "wrong." He has only to consult his conscience, the conscience of a Southern boy in the middle of the last century, to know that he ought to return Jim to slavery. And as soon as he makes the decision according to conscience and decides to inform on Jim, he has all the warmly gratifying emotions of conscious virtue. "Why, it was astonishing, the way I felt as light as a feather right straight off, and my troubles all gone . . . I felt good and all washed clean of sin for the first time I had ever felt so in my life, and I knowed I could pray /xii/ now." And when at last he finds that he cannot endure his decision but must change it and help Jim in his escape, it is not because he has acquired any new ideas about slavery—he believes that he detests Abolitionists; he himself answers when he is asked if the explosion of a steamboat boiler had hurt anyone, "No'm, killed a nigger," and of course he finds nothing wrong in the responsive comment, "Well, it's lucky because sometimes people do get hurt." Ideas and ideals can be of no help to him in his moral crisis. He no more condemns slavery than Tristram and Lancelot condemn marriage; he is as consciously *wicked* as any illicit lover of romance and he consents to be damned for a personal devotion, never questioning the justice of the punishment he has incurred.

Huckleberry Finn was once barred from certain libraries and schools for its alleged subversion of morality. The authorities had in mind the book's endemic lying, the petty thefts, the denigrations of respectability and religion, the bad language and the bad grammar. We smile at that excessive care, yet in point of fact *Huckleberry Finn* is indeed a subversive book—no one who reads thoughtfully the dialectic of Huck's great moral crisis will ever again be wholly able to accept without some question and some irony the assumptions of the respectable morality by which he lives, nor will ever again be certain that what he considers the clear dictates of moral reason are not merely the engrained customary beliefs of his time and place.

3

We are not likely to miss in *Huckleberry Finn* the subtle, implicit moral meaning of the great river. But we are likely to understand these moral implications as having to do only with personal and individual conduct. And since the sum of individual pettiness is on the whole pretty constant, we are likely to think of the book as applicable to mankind in general and at all times and in all places, and we praise it by calling it "universal." And so it is; but like many books to which that large adjective applies, it is also local and particular. It has a /xiii/ particular moral reference to the United States in the period after the Civil War. It was then when, in Mr. Eliot's phrase, the river was forgotten, and precisely by the "dwellers in cities," by the "worshippers of the machine."

The Civil War and the development of the railroads ended the great days when the river was the central artery of the nation. No contrast could be more moving than that between the hot, turbulent energy of the river life of the first part of *Life on the Mississippi* and the melancholy reminiscence of the second part. And the war that brought the end of the rich Mississippi days also marked a change in the quality of life in America which, to many men, consisted of a deterioration of American moral values. It is of course a human habit to look back on the past and to find it a better and more innocent time than the present. Yet in this instance there seems to be an objective basis for the judgment. We cannot disregard the testimony of men so diverse as Henry Adams, Walt Whitman, William Dean Howells, and Mark Twain himself, to mention but a few of the many who were in agreement on this point. All spoke of something that had gone out of American life after the war, some simplicity, some innocence, some peace. None of them was under any illusion about the amount of ordinary human wickedness that existed in the old days, and Mark Twain certainly was not. The difference was in the public attitude, in the things that were now accepted and made respectable in the national ideal. It was, they all felt, connected with new emotions about money. As Mark Twain said, where formerly "the people had desired money," now they "fall down and worship it." The new gospel was, "Get money. Get it quickly. Get it in abundance. Get it in prodigious abundance. Get it dishonestly if you can, honestly if you must." [3]

With the end of the Civil War capitalism had established itself. The relaxing influence of the frontier was coming to an end. Americans increasingly became "dwellers in cities" and "worshippers of /xiv/ the machine." Mark Twain himself became a notable part of this new dispensation. No one worshipped the machine more than he did, or thought he did—he ruined himself by his devotion to the Paige typesetting machine by which he hoped to make a fortune even greater than he had made by his writing, and he sang the praises of the machine age in *A Connecticut Yankee in King Arthur's Court.* He associated intimately with the dominant figures of American business enterprise. Yet at the same time he hated the new way of life and kept bitter memoranda of his scorn, commenting on the low morality or the bad taste or the smugness and dullness of the men who were shaping the national ideal and directing the destiny of the nation.

Mark Twain said of *Tom Sawyer* that it "is simply a hymn, put into prose form to give it a worldly air." He might have said the same, and with even more reason, of *Huckleberry Finn,* which is a hymn to an older America forever gone, an America which had its great national faults, which was full of violence and even of cruelty, but which still maintained its sense of reality, for it was not yet enthralled by money, the father of ultimate illusion and lies. Against the money-god stands the river-god, whose comments are silent—sunlight, space, uncrowded time, stillness and danger. It was quickly forgotten once its practical usefulness had passed, but, as Mr. Eliot's poem says, "The river is within us. . . ."

4

In form and style *Huckleberry Finn* is an almost perfect work. Only one mistake has ever been charged against it, that it concludes with Tom Sawyer's elaborate, too elaborate, game of Jim's escape. Cer-

[3] *Mark Twain in Eruption,* edited by Bernard DeVoto, p. 77.

tainly this episode is too long—in the original draft it was much longer—and certainly it is a falling-off, as almost anything would have to be, from the incidents of the river. Yet it has a certain formal aptness—like, say, that of the Turkish initiation which brings Molière's *Le Bourgeois Gentilhomme* to its close. It is a rather mechanical development of an idea, and yet some device is needed to permit Huck to return to his anonymity, to give up the role of hero, to fall into /xv/ the background which he prefers, for he is modest in all things and could not well endure the attention and glamour which attend a hero at a book's end. For this purpose nothing could serve better than the mind of Tom Sawyer with its literary furnishings, its conscious romantic desire for experience and the hero's part, and its ingenious schematization of life to achieve that aim.

The form of the book is based on the simplest of all novel-forms, the so-called picaresque novel, or novel of the road, which strings its incidents on the line of the hero's travels. But, as Pascal says, "rivers are roads that move," and the movement of the road in its own mysterious life transmutes the primitive simplicity of the form: the road itself is the greatest character in this novel of the road, and the hero's departures from the river and his returns to it compose a subtle and significant pattern. The linear simplicity of the picaresque novel is further modified by the story's having a clear dramatic organization: it has a beginning, a middle and an end, and a mounting suspense of interest.

As for the style of the book, it is not less than definitive in American literature. The prose of *Huckleberry Finn* established for written prose the virtues of American colloquial speech. This has nothing to do with pronunciation or grammar. It has something to do with ease and freedom in the use of language. Most of all it has to do with the structure of the sentence, which is simple, direct, and fluent, maintaining the rhythm of the word-groups of speech and the intonations of the speaking voice.

In the matter of language, American literature had a special problem. The young nation was inclined to think that the mark of the truly literary product was a grandiosity and elegance not to be found in the common speech. It therefore encouraged a greater breach between its vernacular and its literary language than, say, English literature of the same period ever allowed. This accounts for the hollow ring one now and then hears even in the work of our best writers in the first half of the last century. English writers of equal stature would /xvi/ never have made the lapses into rhetorical excess that are common in Cooper and Poe and that are to be found even in Melville and Hawthorne.

Yet at the same time that the language of ambitious literature was high and thus always in danger of falseness, the American reader was keenly interested in the actualities of daily speech. No literature, indeed, was ever so taken up with matters of speech as ours was. "Dialect," which attracted even our serious writers, was the accepted common ground of our popular humorous writing. Nothing in social life seemed so remarkable as the different forms which speech could take—the brogue of the immigrant Irish or the mispronunciation of the German, the "affectation" of the English, the reputed precision of the Bostonian, the legendary twang of the Yankee farmer, and the drawl of the Pike County man. Mark Twain, of course, was in the tradition of humor that exploited this interest, and no one could play with it nearly so well. Although today the carefully spelled-out dialects of nineteenth-century American humor are likely to seem dull enough, the subtle variations of speech of *Huckleberry Finn*, of which Mark Twain was justly proud, are still part of the liveliness and flavor of the book.

Out of his knowledge of the actual speech of America Mark Twain forged a classic prose. The adjective may seem a strange one, yet it is apt. Forget the misspellings and the faults of grammar, and the prose will be seen to move with the greatest simplicity, directness, lucidity, and grace. These qualities are by no means accidental. Mark Twain, who read widely, was passionately interested in the problems of style; the mark of the strictest literary sensibility is everywhere to be found in the prose of *Huckleberry Finn*.

It is this prose that Ernest Hemingway had chiefly in mind when he said that "all modern American literature comes from one book by Mark Twain called *Huckleberry Finn*." Hemingway's own prose stems from it directly and consciously; so does the prose of the two modern writers who most influenced Hemingway's early style, Gertrude Stein and Sher- /xvii/ wood Anderson (although neither of them could maintain the robust purity of their model); so, too, does the best of William Faulkner's prose, which, like Mark Twain's own, reinforces the colloquial tradition with the literary tradition. Indeed, it may be said that almost every contemporary writer who deals conscientiously with the problems and possibility of prose must feel, directly or indirectly, the influence of Mark Twain. He is the master of the style that escapes the fixity of the printed page, that sounds in our ears with the immediacy of the heard voice, the very voice of unpretentious truth. /xviii/

QUESTIONS FOR DISCUSSION AND WRITING

1. What do you think makes *The Adventures of Huckleberry Finn* "one of the central documents of American culture"?
2. Explain Huck's views of religion and his struggle with it.
3. Discuss the Mississippi as a god in this novel.
4. Explain in detail Trilling's assertion that the river "is only divine." What has been the critical opinion of the role of the Mississippi in *The Adventures of Huckleberry Finn?*
5. Make a full case for Jim as Huck's "true father."
6. Why does Trilling say that Huck and Jim form a "community of saints"?
7. How is loneliness related to the theme of the novel? How is pride related to the theme?
8. What, if anything, keeps this novel from being sentimental?
9. What is Huck's major weakness, his major strength?
10. Discuss *The Adventures of Huckleberry Finn* as a "subversive" book.
11. Do you agree with Trilling's defense of the novel's ending? Why or why not? Can you make a better defense?
12. Analyze in detail the prose style of a small part of the novel.

MARK TWAIN AS A LITERARY ARTIST

by Gladys Carmen Bellamy

Tom and Huck may themselves be viewed as symbols of the two aspects of life. Tom Sawyer has a home and a loving, overwatchful aunt who doses him with painkiller; he swipes doughnuts and plays hooky and goes in swimming; he is stirred by an ambition to appear as a hero in Sunday school; he is thrilled by his imaginary adventures. On the whole, Tom's is mostly an idyllic existence. In contrast appears Huck Finn. Huck fears his father and apparently never knew his mother; a homeless waif, he sleeps on doorsteps or in hogsheads; he is troubled by no ambition and steers clear of Sunday school; his life is as aimless as a bit of drift on the Mississippi. And yet Mark Twain finds Huck and Huck's life infinitely worth while. Huck himself nowhere suggests that his life is not satisfactory.

But Huck Finn wears a moral garment definitely tinged with gray. In the book which he relates, he lies to everybody who threatens Jim's safety or his own. Life is precious to him; freedom is precious to him. And it is no wonder that he lies. Young as he is, he has known a deal of violence. He escapes his drunken father by staging a mock murder—his own; he notes that the Grangerfords carry their guns to church and watches their feud end in the murder of boys; he sees the drunken, blackguarding Boggs and is at hand when /336/ the blackguarding is ended by Sherburn's bullet; he associates daily with the king and the duke, two creatures who emerge from the slime of the river, as amoral as gnomes. But Huck has a code of his own and sticks to it in defiance of hell itself. He is frequently troubled by his conscience. Huck's conscience appears at times to be much keener than that of the romantic Tom Sawyer.[1] Tom makes a great show of

[1] Still, I cannot agree with Mr. DeVoto's statement (*Mark Twain at Work*, 21) that Mark Twain denies us "the entire struggle of fear, pity, and horror" which precedes Tom's testifying for Muff Potter, "in order to give us the simple melodrama of the revelation." Although not so detailed as is Huck's

From *Mark Twain As a Literary Artist*, by Gladys Carmen Bellamy, copyright 1950 by the University of Oklahoma Press, Norman.

adhering to the letter of the law, while Huck cuts through to the essentials of the spirit.

Although Huck's adventures were popular with readers from the first, contemporary critics preferred *The Prince and the Pauper*, as did Mark Twain's own family. There was, however, as Mr. DeVoto has noted, an occasional recognition. Barrett Wendell of Harvard, in *A Literary History of America* (1900), devoted only a few lines to Mark Twain in a book of five hundred pages; but he mentioned "a book which . . . one is disposed for all its eccentricity to call the most admirable work of literary art as yet produced on this continent . . . that Odyssean story . . . to which Mark Twain gave the grotesque name of 'Huckleberry Finn.' "[2]

Out of the countless lines praising the book, I have selected this passage because the "eccentricity" which Wendell noted is an element important for the understanding of the story. Huck Finn is not a "normal" boy; he has not had a normal bringing up, and his life has prepared him to be surprised at nothing. Commenting upon Mark Twain's technique in making use of the eccentricity of Huck, John Erskine said that Mark Twain skilfully "manipulated his material . . . so that the most outrageous melodrama could present itself as matter of fact, through the medium of Huckleberry's temperament, and even while we are rearranging the values and discerning what the boy was blind to, we . . . concede that he is true to life"—/337/ for the sort of life his has been. The romanticist, narrator of the unusual adventures of Huck and Jim; the realist, portrayer of the daily round of life in small towns along the river; and the satirist, critic of the narrowness and meanness of human nature—in this story Mark Twain is "all three kinds of storyteller at once"; and the way he blends the realistic, the satiric, and the romantic elements has produced a thing that is art—a book, in John Erskine's phrase, "so close to the life of the people that it can hold any reader, and yet so subtle in its art that the craftsman tries to find out how it was done."

It is no secret that Mark Twain had difficulty in writing *Huckleberry Finn*. He wrote about half of it and then put the manuscript

later battle with his conscience, an analysis of Tom's struggle appears. Tom wakes the morning after the murder, "gloomy and sad"; when Potter is accused, "Tom's fearful secret and gnawing conscience disturbed his sleep" for a week; he carried small offerings to Potter in the jail and thus "helped to ease his conscience"; during his vacation the secret of the murder was "a very cancer for permanency and pain"; he hung about the jail and when he found Potter hopeless and resigned, he "went home miserable, and his dreams that night were full of horrors"; finally his "harassed conscience" hounded him to the lawyer's house, where he told his story.

[2] DeVoto, *Mark Twain's America*, 300.

away to gather dust for almost seven years; yet the finished whole seems easy, simple, natural. Huck, the unifying thread that ties everything together, gains in stature by having no taller rivals near him—only the river tramps who impose themselves on his generosity and the hunted Negro whom he befriends.

In spite of its episodic nature, the book falls naturally into three thematic units. In the first sixteen chapters the theme has to do with what is of and from St. Petersburg: Huck, Tom, Nigger Jim, and Pap. The second thematic unit includes the most strongly satiric, the most powerful part of the book, bringing Huck and Jim into contact with the outside world. In the cross-section of the South through which they journey, Huck witnesses the Grangerford-Shepherdson feud, the chicanery of the king and the duke, the killing of Boggs, Colonel Sherburn's quelling of the mob, and finally the village funeral. The characters of the king and the duke add to the thematic unity of this section. The third thematic unit is short, a sort of coda to the rest, covering the period at the Phelps farm in which Tom re-enters the story. This section repeats the romanticized motif of the first part and thus brings the book around full-circle, before its close.

The art of characterization is the one most important to a novelist, and Mark Twain's characters are his greatest literary achievement. Something of his method in characterization may be learned from a passage he wrote in 1907:

> Every man is in his own person the whole human race, with not a detail lacking. I am the whole human race without a detail lacking; I have studied the human race with diligence and strong interest all these years /338/ in my own person; in myself I find in big or little proportion every quality and every defect that is findable in the mass of the race.

This suggests that when he had need of a certain trait, his habit was to dig for it within himself, to isolate and study it, then to enlarge it to the proportion proper to the character in question. This suggestion is borne out by a marginal note in one of his books: "If Byron—if any man—draws 50 characters, they are all himself—50 shades, 50 moods, of his own character, And when the man draws them well, why do they stir my admiration? Because they are me—I recognize myself."

A careful study of *Huckleberry Finn* shows that it is the characters and their interrelationship which determine the arrangement and structure of the book. The three thematic sections subdivide into little units notable for the contrast they offer each other. The first three chapters continue, naturally enough, the vein of *Tom Sawyer*, to which this book becomes a sort of sequel. Everything is colored by the excitement of Tom's imaginary adventures; he insists on doing all things according to the books he has read, from having his Gang sign in blood their oaths of allegiance to capturing and holding people for ransom. Ben Rogers, a Gang member, wants to know what being "ransomed" means, and Tom replies:

> "I don't know. But that's what they do. I've seen it in books; and of course that's what we've got to do."
>
> "But how can we do it if we don't know what it is?"
>
> "Why, blame it all, we've *got* to do it. Don't I tell you it's in the books? Do you want to go to doing different from what's in the books and get things all muddled up?"

And here, in a simple argument among boys, Mark Twain sets the pattern for this, his greatest story, as a satire on institutionalism. The three figures, Tom, Huck, and Jim, represent three gradations of thought and three levels of civilization. Tom, pretending so intensely that it becomes so, says we can't do it except as in the books. Is this what civilization really is—merely a pretense according to a set pattern? Tom is on the highest level, in the sense of being most civilized; but he represents a mawkish, romantic, artificial civilization. Compared with him, Nigger Jim and Huck are primitives; and the closer Mark Twain gets to primitivism, the better his writing /339/ becomes. He shows us the African in Jim, imbuing him with a dark knowledge that lies in his blood and his nerve ends. Huck Finn stands between these two; he is the "natural man," suggesting Walt Whitman's dream of the great American who should be simple and free. Both Tom and Jim are in bondage to institutionalism.[3] Tom can't do anything against the rules of his books; Jim can't do anything against the rules of his taboos, his voodoo fears and charms and superstitions. Only Huck is free of institutions. Tom and Jim are always sure they are right, since each has his institution to consult and to follow; but Huck is tormented by doubts. When he is with Tom, he is willing to join Tom in following the books; when he is with Jim, he is careful not to break Jim's taboos, especially after the incident of the rattlesnake skin. But when Huck is alone, because he has no rules to go by he is guided by the voice within himself. He listens to what goes on inside him. He is free to probe within his own heart,

[3] I am indebted to Professor Floyd Stovall, formerly of North Texas State Teachers College and now of the University of North Carolina, for the suggestion that *Huckleberry Finn* is a satire on institutionalism, as well as for some suggestions pertaining to the structure of the book.

where is to be found whatever bit of divinity man has—what we know as his soul.

If *Tom Sawyer* is accepted as a satire against the moralizing Sunday school tales, *Huckleberry Finn* has a much broader field as a satire against institutionalism in general. The institution of slavery is basic in this book, just as it is in *Pudd'nhead Wilson*. In *A Connecticut Yankee*, Mark Twain fulminates against church and state. In *Joan of Arc* he attacks the oppressions of formal religion and formal law. In *Hadleyburg* he frowns upon the institutionalism by which young people are trained in hypocrisy and the forms of empty "honor." Indeed, he sees the village itself as an institution—the tight little institution of the mores of the folk, which dictates the condemnation of all outlanders and innovators.

Within each of the thematic units in *Huckleberry Finn* there is a subtle variation of character and atmosphere. After the idyllic, romantic atmosphere which permeates the first three chapters, in the next four the story veers sharply from the mood of *Tom Sawyer*, and Pap takes the stage, drunken and disreputable, feeling himself the victim of sundry social ills. Into this satiric portrait went Mark Twain's years of observation of mountain whites, piney-woods people, and river rats. Pap is completely revealed through his oration on /340/ the "guv'ment." This unit ends when Huck flees because he fears his father will kill him in a fit of delirium tremens.

After so much violence, Jackson's Island gives him a feeling of peace. He explores the island, and just as he begins to feel lonely he discovers Jim, a Negro who has run away from home because his owner is planning to sell him "down to Orleans"—the Negro's equivalent of hell. Thereafter the runaway slave and the outcast waif share the island and comfort each other. This small unit of four chapters, the interlude on Jackson's Island, ends once more in the threat of violence and fear. Men are approaching the island to search for Jim.

Mark Twain's prefatory note warns the reader that seven different dialects are used in the book; the shadings among them are so fine that not every reader can perceive them, and he does not want readers to think that "all these characters were trying to talk alike and not succeeding." His sensitivity to speech enabled him to say, "The shadings have not been done in haphazard fashion, or by guesswork, but painstakingly." But the artistry of such shadings in dialect fades before his skill in employing the vernacular of Huck Finn for a book-length narrative. Huck has a strong, vivid, natural imagination—not an artificial one, such as Tom's, or a superstitious one, such as Jim's. He describes, with memorable effect, a summer storm which he and Jim watched from the security of their cave on the island:

> . . . it looked all blue-black outside, and lovely; and the rain would thrash along by so thick that the trees off a little ways looked dim and spider-webby; and here would come a blast of wind that would bend the trees down and turn up the pale underside of the leaves; and then a perfect ripper of a gust would follow along and set the branches to tossing their arms as if they was just wild; and next, when it was just about the bluest and blackest—*fst!* it was as bright as glory, and you'd have a little glimpse of tree-tops a-plunging about a way off yonder in the storm, hundreds of yards further than you could see before; dark as sin again in a second, and now you'd hear the thunder let go with an awful crash, and then go rumbling, grumbling, tumbling, down the sky towards the under side of the world, like rolling empty barrels down stairs—where it's long stairs and they bounce a good deal, you know.

Mark Twain's elemental imagination lends vigor and freshness to many passages. As Huck and Jim lie on their backs at night looking up at the stars, while the raft slips silently down the river, they argue /341/ about whether the stars "was made or only just happened": "Jim said the moon could 'a' *laid* them; well, that looked kind of reasonable . . . because I've seen a frog lay most as many." Huck describes Pap as having hair that was "long and tangled and greasy, and hung down, and you could see his eyes shining through like he was behind vines," while his face was white—"not like another man's white, but a white to make a body sick . . . a fish-belly white." At the parlor funeral of Peter Wilks, "the undertaker he slid around in his black gloves with his softy soothering ways, . . . making no more sound than a cat. . . . He was the softest, glidingest, stealthiest man I ever see." When the old king got a sudden shock, he "squashed down like a bluff bank that the river has cut under, it took him so sudden." Huck's language is equal to any effect demanded of it.

Part of the power of this book lies in Mark Twain's drawing of the character of Nigger Jim. From the time Jim first appears, a "big nigger" silhouetted in the kitchen door with the light behind him, he is a figure of dignity. In the famous syllogism in which Jim argues that since a Frenchman is a man, he should talk like a man, Mark Twain shows Jim's slow, purposeful reasoning. But in other moods Jim's spirit opens out to a wider horizon. Like Huck, he senses the beauty of the river. In his interpretation of a dream, Jim lets "the big, clear river" symbolize "the free States"—in other words, freedom. If "The Enchanted Village" might serve as a subtitle for *Tom Sawyer*, so "The Road to Freedom" might serve the same purpose for *Huckleberry Finn*. Jim has two big scenes in the book. One occurs when he relates the tragic moment of his discovery that his little girl was "plumb deef en dumb, Huck, plumb deef en dumb." His second big scene comes when he risks capture to help the doctor care for the wounded Tom Sawyer.

Whatever may be said of Tom Sawyer, Huck Finn is a developing character. Much of his development is due to his association with Jim and his increasing respect for the black man. In *Tom Sawyer*, Huck apologized to Tom for eating with a Negro, the Rogers' Uncle Jake, who had given him food: "A body's got to do things when he's awful hungry he wouldn't . . . as a steady thing." When he first finds Jim on the island, he is glad simply because he wants companionship; but as the two share the peace of the place, Huck comes to regard Jim as a human being rather than a faithful dog. When he hears there is a reward for Jim, the money offers no temptation to /342/ him; but under attack by his conscience, he fears he may have done wrong in helping a slave to escape. His traditions and environment pull him one way; what he feels in his heart pulls him the other way. Finally, he goes so far as to write a note to Miss Watson, Jim's owner, telling her where Jim is to be found. At first, he feels better for writing the note:

> . . . thinking how near I come to being lost and going to hell. . . . [Then I] got to thinking over our trip down the river; and I see Jim before me all the time: in the day and in the night-time, . . . and we a-floating along, talking and singing and laughing. But somehow I couldn't seem to strike no places to harden me against him, but only the other kind . . . and then I happened to look around and see that paper.
>
> It was a close place. I took it up and held it in my hand. I was a-trembling, because I'd got to decide, forever, betwixt two things, and I knowed it. I studied a minute, sort of holding my breath, and then says to myself:
>
> "All right, then, "I'll *go* to hell"—and tore it up.

A part of Huck's development came when he apologized to Jim for fooling him about a dream. Jim very properly resented Huck's deceit, and Huck was abashed before Jim's stately indignation. When Huck waked in the night to find Jim mourning for his children—'Po' little 'Lizabeth! po' little Johnny!"—a new realization was borne in upon the boy: "I do believe he cared just as much for his people as white folks does for their'n. It don't seem natural, but I reckon it's so." Although the doctor and others seemed amazed at Jim's risking capture to aid the wounded Tom, Huck felt no surprise at all: "I knowed he was white inside."

The beautiful stretches of the river had power over Huck's spirit, as is shown in his own words: "It was kind of solemn, drifting down the big, still river . . . looking up at the stars, and we didn't ever feel like talking loud, and it warn't often we laughed." He has learned to read early in the story, and he reads at the Grangerford home; of *Pilgrim's Progress*, his verdict is, "The statements was interesting, but tough." He feels that somebody should write a poetical tribute to the dead Emmeline Grangerford, "so I tried to sweat out a verse or two myself, but I couldn't seem to make it go somehow." Such a sentiment would have seemed out of character for Huck in the beginning, but not now. He describes Colonel Granger- /343/ ford as an aristocrat, and his own sensitive nature responds to the Colonel's fine-wire temperament: "everybody was always good-mannered where he was."

The first thematic unit ends with the smashing of the raft by a steamboat. This incident also ended the writing of *Huckleberry Finn* for almost seven years.[4] Mark Twain had written thus far in the summer of 1876; he apparently had no further plan, and when the raft was smashed, he stopped the book. Two years after he had shelved *Huckleberry Finn*, he wrote the 1878 letter to Howells, explaining that he felt himself unable to write successful satire because to do so calls for "a calm, judicial good humor." His trip down the river in 1882 to get material for *Life on the Mississippi* naturally recalled the river story to his mind. He must have then arrived at the design which made the book a masterpiece. All the meannesses of Mark Twain's "damned human race" are seen through the eyes and presented through the lips of Huck Finn. And thus Mark Twain was enabled, at last, to attain the calm detachment with which satire should be presented.

The second thematic unit begins when Huck stops at the Grangerford mansion after the wreck of the raft. The Grangerford-Shepherdson feud is one of the most tragic things in the book, but nothing is told with greater restraint. This restraint is art; but Mark Twain, as John Erskine observed, makes it seem the work of nature. Beginning his account of the climax of the feud, Huck says, "I don't want to talk much about the next day." All that blood and dying was nauseating to the boy, and "it would make him sick again" if he should tell about the killings. He tries not to remember the details, because those memories spoil his sleep at night. To measure Mark Twain's growth in artistry, one has only to compare this restraint with the early sketches in which the reformer purposefully emphasized blood and

[4] DeVoto, *Mark Twain at Work*, 53, 62.

violence for their shock value in directing attention to situations he deplored. Now, to get back to the raft and to Jim is, for Huck, like going home; and his soul expands in the healing peace of the quiet river: "We said there warn't no home like a raft. . . . Other places do seem so cramped up and smothery."

After the episode of the feud, the king and the duke board the raft and begin to dominate the lives of Huck and Jim. The loafers of Bricksville, Arkansas, lean and whittle; around noon, they all /344/ laugh and look glad, for old man Boggs comes riding into town drunk and begins to blackguard Colonel Sherburn. Finally Sherburn's outraged honor demands that he stop this blackguarding with a bullet, and Boggs dies in a little drugstore, with a heavy Bible on his chest.

All these wrongs are condemned through the mere fact of their presentation. With the exception of one scene, Mark Twain is invisible, inaudible, lost in the artistry of Huck's particular kind of communication. In that scene Colonel Sherburn appears on his veranda to pour his withering scorn down upon the mob and send them scurrying like whipped curs. "I know you clear through. I was born and raised in the South, and I've lived in the North." It is Mark Twain speaking:

> So I know the average all around. The average man's a coward. . . . Your mistake is that you didn't bring a man with you; that's one mistake, and the other is that you didn't come in the dark and fetch your masks. . . . The pitifulest thing out is a mob. . . . But a mob without any *man* at the head of it is *beneath* pitifulness. Now the thing for *you* to do is to droop your tails and go home and crawl in a hole.

Mark Twain's voice rings out, clear and unmistakable, in the hit at militarism: "an army is—a mob; they don't fight with courage that's born in them, but with courage that's borrowed from their mass." If a "Colonel" had talked like that, would Huck have reported him like that? No matter; the force of the book is so strong at this point that the illusion is not shattered; but the utter objectivity of the scene immediately preceding ranks it far above this one.

There, we see the innate cruelty of the dead-alive loafers. "There couldn't anything wake them up all over, and make them happy all over, like . . . putting turpentine on a stray dog and setting fire to him, or tying a tin pan to his tail and see him run himself to death." Then old Boggs rides in "on the waw-path," a pitiful figure who "throwed his hat down in the mud and rode over it, and . . . went a-raging down the street again, with his gray hair a-flying" while the loafers, at first "listening and laughing and going on," are quickly sobered by the ultimatum of Colonel Sherburn. "Everybody that seen the shooting was telling how it happened," and one "long, lanky man, with long hair and a big white fur stovepipe hat" enacted the scene in its entirety. Huck's comment is, "The people that had seen the thing said he done it perfect." And Mr. DeVoto /345/ adds that the long lanky man records this society "with an unemotional certainty beside which either Mr. Lewis's anger or Mr. Anderson's misery" seem merely hysterical. Those who understand Mark Twain can only guess how much of that calm detachment, that "unemotional certainty," was sheer artistry, a triumph of technique.

With each of these scenes, Huck's character develops as his experience is widened. He perceives the manly qualities of Jim and scales correctly the duke and the king; he knows that the duke is not so low as the king, and yet he is tolerant of the "poor old king" when he sees him in "a little low doggery, very tight, and a lot of loafers bullyragging him for sport." When Huck finds himself stranded on the *Walter Scott* with some murderers, his sympathy, broad and beautiful, makes him realize "how dreadful it was, even for murderers, to be in such a fix. I says to myself, there ain't no telling but I might come to be a murderer myself yet, and then how would I like it?" In his last glimpse of the king and the duke, tarred and feathered so that they "just looked like a couple of monstrous big soldier-plumes," he was "sorry for them poor pitiful rascals," and it made him sick to see it: "Human beings *can* be awful cruel to one another."

There is an occasional hint of determinism in *Huckleberry Finn*. Early in the story Huck backslides under the power of environment while living with Pap: ". . . I was used to being where I was, and liked it." If fear of his drunken father had not driven him forth, Mark Twain seems to say, Huck might have become another Pap. When his conscience troubles him over not giving up the runaway slave, he excuses himself on the ground of early environment and its effects:

> . . . I knowed very well I had done wrong, and I see it warn't no use for me to try to learn to do right; a body that don't get *started* right when he's little ain't got no show—when the pinch comes there ain't nothing to back him up. . . . Then I . . . says to myself, hold on; s'pose you'd a done right and give Jim up, would you felt better than what you do now? No, I says, I'd feel bad—I'd feel just the same way I do now. Well, then, says I, what's the use you learning to do right when it's troublesome to do right and ain't no trouble to do wrong, and the wages is the same?

Huck's questioning of himself recalls Ernest Hemingway's defini- /346/ tion of morality, which appears early in *Death in the Afternoon*: "I know only that what is moral is what you feel good after." Unquestionably, Mark Twain and Hemingway are akin in their preoccupation with death and in the care and skill with which they write the idiom of their people; but it seems to me that Hemingway's nearest approach to the earlier writer lies in the moral tests his characters apply inwardly. Having no moral code to go by, they test an action by the way they feel after it.[5]

Huck usually looks into his own heart for guidance. He "goes to studying things out" whenever he feels himself "in a tight place." He learns from experience, but his environment determines him only as his experiences develop what is within. Moral intuition is the basis on which his character rests. But if a man is not responsible to God or to society, and Mark Twain's determinism holds that he is not, why should he be responsible to himself? The inner voice of conscience, the voice of God, always holds him morally responsible. In this way *Huckleberry Finn* is a wise book, as all great books are wise.

In the final thematic unit, the story lags for most readers. Tom re-enters the plot to free Jim according to all the time-worn devices of literature, thus resuming his perpetual game of make-believe. Tom's imagined adventures are merely cheap after the real ones which Huck and Jim have experienced together. Is this anticlimax altogether accidental? Was Mark Twain perhaps comparing the genuine experience of life with the fanciful, secondhand one? If the book is viewed as a satire on institutionalism, Tom's silly insistence on "going by the books" has more point. Or, remembering Jim's use of the "big, clear river" to symbolize freedom, is there an even deeper symbolism here? the fact that, living in a civilization, we can keep our freedom only by conforming to its patterns? /347/

QUESTIONS FOR DISCUSSION AND WRITING

1. Develop and support the assertion that "Tom and Huck [are] symbols of two aspects of life." (p. 336)

2. Find evidence in *Huckleberry Finn* for each of the "three kinds of storyteller" which Erskine and Miss Bellamy find there.

[5] Joseph Warren Beach said, "In certain ways, contemporary American fiction opens with Ernest Hemingway." In the first chapter of *The Green Hills of Africa*, Hemingway himself said: "All modern American literature comes from one book by Mark Twain called *Huckleberry Finn*. . . . it's the best book we've had. All American writing comes from that. There was nothing before. There has been nothing as good since."

3. Comment on the "three thematic units" Miss Bellamy finds in *Huckleberry Finn;* what have other critics said about the sections of *Huckleberry Finn?*

4. Do you recognize yourself in Huckleberry Finn? If so, suggest what there is about him that helps you to see yourself mirrored in him; if not, find those qualities in his character that keep you from seeing yourself in him.

5. Present a study of two or more units in any of Miss Bellamy's "thematic sections" which contrast significantly with each other.

6. Do other critics find Huck "free of institutions"? (p. 340) Do you?

7. In what ways does Mark Twain show us "the African in Jim"? (p. 340)

8. Attack or offer further support to the idea that Jim is a victim of institutionalism. (p. 340)

9. Miss Bellamy admires Huck's imagination and expression; select passages which illustrate these qualities, and analyze them.

10. Evaluate "The Road to Freedom" as a subtitle for *Huckleberry Finn;* what have other critics said which can help you here?

11. Why should a man be in a "calm, judicial good humor" in order to write successful satire? (p. 344) Use the novel to illustrate your answer.

12. What is determinism? How much of it, beyond what Miss Bellamy presents, do you find in *Huckleberry Finn?*

MR. ELIOT, MR. TRILLING, AND *HUCKLEBERRY FINN*

by Leo Marx

In the losing battle that the plot fights with the characters, it often takes a cowardly revenge. Nearly all novels are feeble at the end. This is because the plot requires to be wound up. Why is this necessary? Why is there not a convention which allows a novelist to stop as soon as he feels muddled or bored? Alas, he has to round things off, and usually the characters go dead while he is at work, and our final impression of them is through deadness.

E. M FORSTER

The Adventures of Huckleberry Finn has not always occupied its present high place in the canon of American literature. When it was first published in 1885, the book disturbed and offended many reviewers, particularly spokesmen for the genteel tradition.[1] In fact, a fairly accurate inventory of the narrow standards of such critics might be made simply by listing epithets they applied to Clemens' novel. They called it vulgar, rough, inelegant, irreverent, coarse, semi-obscene, trashy and vicious.[2] So much for them. Today (we like to think) we know the true worth of the book. Everyone now agrees that *Huckle-*

[1] I use the term "genteel tradition" as George Santayana characterized it in his famous address "The Genteel Tradition in American Philosophy," first delivered in 1911 and published the following year in his *Winds of Doctrine*. Santayana described the genteel tradition as an "old mentality" inherited from Europe. It consists of the various dilutions of Christian theology and morality, as in transcendentalism—a fastidious and stale philosophy of life no longer relevant to the thought and activities of the United States. "America," he said, "is a young country with an old mentality." (Later references to Santayana also refer to this essay.)

[2] For an account of the first reviews, see A. L. Vogelback, "The Publication and Reception of *Huckleberry Finn* in America," *American Literature*, XI (November, 1939), 260–272.

berry Finn is a masterpiece: it is probably the one book in our literature about which highbrows and lowbrows can agree. Our most serious critics praise it. Never- /423/ theless, a close look at what two of the best among them have recently written will likewise reveal, I believe, serious weaknesses in current criticism. Today the problem of evaluating the book is as much obscured by unqualified praise as it once was by parochial hostility.

I have in mind essays by Lionel Trilling and T. S. Eliot.[3] Both praise the book, but in praising it both feel obligated to say something in justification of what so many readers have felt to be its great flaw: the disappointing "ending," the episode which begins when Huck arrives at the Phelps place and Tom Sawyer reappears. There are good reasons why Mr. Trilling and Mr. Eliot should feel the need to face this issue. From the point of view of scope alone, more is involved than the mere "ending"; the episode comprises almost one-fifth of the text. The problem, in any case, is unavoidable. I have discussed *Huckleberry Finn* in courses with hundreds of college students, and I have found only a handful who did not confess their dissatisfaction with the extravagant mock rescue of Nigger Jim and the denouement itself. The same question always comes up: "What went wrong with Twain's novel?" Even Bernard DeVoto, whose wholehearted commitment to Clemens' genius is well known, has said of the ending that "in the whole reach of the English novel there is no more abrupt or more chilling descent." [4] Mr. Trilling and Mr. Eliot do not agree. They both attempt, and on similar grounds, to explain and defend the conclusion.

Of the two, Mr. Trilling makes the more moderate claim for Clemens' novel. He does admit that there is a "falling off" at the end; nevertheless he supports the episode as having "a certain formal aptness." Mr. Eliot's approval is without serious qualification. He allows no objections, asserts that "it is right that the mood of the end of the book should bring us back to the beginning." I mean later to discuss their views in some detail, but here /424/ it is only necessary to note that both critics see the problem as one of form. And so it is. Like many questions of form in literature, however, this one is not finally separable from a question of "content," of value, or, if you will, of moral insight. To bring *Huckleberry Finn* to a satisfactory close, Clemens had to do more than find a neat device for ending

[3] Mr. Eliot's essay is the introduction to the edition of *Huckleberry Finn* published by the Cresset Press, London, 1950. Mr. Trilling's is the introduction to an edition of the novel published by Rinehart, New York, 1948, and later reprinted in his *The Liberal Imagination*, Viking, New York, 1950.
[4] *Mark Twain at Work* (Cambridge, 1942), p. 92.

a story. His problem, though it may never have occurred to him, was to invent an action capable of placing in focus the meaning of the journey down the Mississippi.

I believe that the ending of *Huckleberry Finn* makes so many readers uneasy because they rightly sense that it jeopardizes the significance of the entire novel. To take seriously what happens at the Phelps farm is to take lightly the entire downstream journey. What is the meaning of the journey? With this question all discussion of *Huckleberry Finn* must begin. It is true that the voyage down the river has many aspects of a boy's idyl. We owe much of its hold upon our imagination to the enchanting image of the raft's unhurried drift with the current. The leisure, the absence of constraint, the beauty of the river—all these things delight us. "It's lovely to live on a raft." And the multitudinous life of the great valley we see through Huck's eyes has a fascination of its own. Then, of course, there is humor—laughter so spontaneous, so free of bitterness present almost everywhere in American humor that readers often forget how grim a spectacle of human existence Huck contemplates. Humor in this novel flows from a bright joy of life as remote from our world as living on a raft.

Yet along with the idyllic and the epical and the funny in *Huckleberry Finn,* there is a coil of meaning which does for the disparate elements of the novel what a spring does for a watch. The meaning is not in the least obscure. It is made explicit again and again. The very words with which Clemens launches Huck and Jim upon their voyage indicate that theirs is not a boy's lark but a quest for freedom. From the electrifying moment when Huck comes back to Jackson's Island and rouses Jim with the news that a search party is on the way, we are meant to believe that Huck is enlisted in the cause of freedom. "Git up and hump yourself, Jim!" /425/ he cries. "There ain't a minute to lose. They're after us!" What particularly counts here is the *us.* No one is after Huck; no one but Jim knows he is alive. In that small word Clemens compresses the exhilarating power of Huck's instinctive humanity. His unpremeditated identification with Jim's flight from slavery is an unforgettable moment in American experience, and it may be said at once that any culmination of the journey which detracts from the urgency and dignity with which it begins will necessarily be unsatisfactory. Huck realizes this himself, and says so when, much later, he comes back to the raft after discovering that the Duke and the King have sold Jim:

> After all this long journey . . . here it was all come to nothing, everything all busted up and ruined, because they could have the heart to serve Jim such a trick as that, and make him a slave

> again all his life, and amongst strangers, too, for forty dirty dollars.

Huck knows that the journey will have been a failure unless it takes Jim to freedom. It is true that we do discover, in the end, that Jim is free, but we also find out that the journey was not the means by which he finally reached freedom.

The most obvious thing wrong with the ending, then, is the flimsy contrivance by which Clemens frees Jim. In the end we not only discover that Jim has been a free man for two months, but that his freedom has been granted by old Miss Watson. If this were only a mechanical device for terminating the action, it might not call for much comment. But it is more than that: it is a significant clue to the import of the last ten chapters. Remember who Miss Watson is. She is the Widow's sister whom Huck introduces in the first pages of the novel. It is she who keeps "pecking" at Huck, who tries to teach him to spell and to pray and to keep his feet off the furniture. She is an ardent proselytizer for piety and good manners, and her greed provides the occasion for the journey in the first place. She is Jim's owner, and he decides to flee only when he realizes that she is about to break her word (she cannot resist a slave trader's offer of eight hundred dollars) and sell him down the river away from his family. /426/

Miss Watson, in short, is the Enemy. If we except a predilection for physical violence, she exhibits all the outstanding traits of the valley society. She pronounces the polite lies of civilization that suffocate Huck's spirit. The freedom which Jim seeks, and which Huck and Jim temporarily enjoy aboard the raft, is accordingly freedom *from* everything for which Miss Watson stands. Indeed, the very intensity of the novel derives from the discordance between the aspirations of the fugitives and the respectable code for which she is a spokesman. Therefore, her regeneration, of which the deathbed freeing of Jim is the unconvincing sign, hints a resolution of the novel's essential conflict. Perhaps because this device most transparently reveals that shift in point of view which he could not avoid, and which is less easily discerned elsewhere in the concluding chapters, Clemens plays it down. He makes little attempt to account for Miss Watson's change of heart, a change particularly surprising in view of Jim's brazen escape. Had Clemens given this episode dramatic emphasis appropriate to its function, Miss Watson's bestowal of freedom upon Jim would have proclaimed what the rest of the ending actually accomplishes—a vindication of persons and attitudes Huck and Jim had symbolically repudiated when they set forth downstream.

It may be said, and with some justice, that a reading of the ending as a virtual reversal of meanings implicit in the rest of the novel misses the point—that I have taken the final episode too seriously. I agree that Clemens certainly did not intend us to read it so solemnly. The ending, one might contend, is simply a burlesque upon Tom's taste for literary romance. Surely the tone of the episode is familiar to readers of Mark Twain. The preposterous monkey business attendant upon Jim's "rescue," the careless improvisation, the nonchalant disregard for common-sense plausibility—all these things should not surprise readers of Twain or any low comedy in the tradition of "Western humor." However, the trouble is, first, that the ending hardly comes off as burlesque: it is *too* fanciful, *too* extravagant; and it is tedious. For example, to provide a "gaudy" atmosphere for the escape, Huck and Tom catch a couple of dozen snakes. Then the snakes escape. /427/

> No, there warn't no real scarcity of snakes about the house for a considerable spell. You'd see them dripping from the rafters and places every now and then; and they generly landed in your plate, or down the back of your neck. . . .

Even if this were *good* burlesque, which it is not, what is it doing here? It is out of keeping; the slapstick tone jars with the underlying seriousness of the voyage.

Huckleberry Finn is a masterpiece because it brings Western humor to perfection and yet transcends the narrow limits of its conventions. But the ending does not. During the final extravaganza we are forced to put aside many of the mature emotions evoked earlier by the vivid rendering of Jim's fear of capture, the tenderness of Huck's and Jim's regard for each other, and Huck's excruciating moments of wavering between honesty and respectability. None of these emotions are called forth by the anticlimactic final sequence. I do not mean to suggest that the inclusion of low comedy per se is a flaw in *Huckleberry Finn*. One does not object to the shenanigans of the rogues; there is ample precedent for the place of extravagant humor even in works of high seriousness. But here the case differs from most which come to mind: the major characters themselves are forced to play low comedy roles. Moreover, the most serious motive in the novel, Jim's yearning for freedom, is made the object of nonsense. The conclusion, in short, is farce, but the rest of the novel is not.

That Clemens reverts in the end to the conventional manner of Western low comedy is most evident in what happens to the principals. Huck and Jim become comic characters; that is a much more serious ground for dissatisfaction than the unexplained regeneration of Miss Watson. Remember that Huck has grown in stature throughout the journey. By the time he arrives at the Phelps place, he is not the boy who had been playing robbers with Tom's gang in St. Petersburg the summer before. All he has seen and felt since he parted from Tom has deepened his knowledge of human nature and of himself. Clemens makes a point of Huck's development in two scenes which occur just before he meets Tom again. The first describes Huck's final capitulation to his own sense of right and /428/ wrong: "All right, then, I'll *go* to Hell." This is the climactic moment in the ripening of his self-knowledge. Shortly afterward, when he comes upon a mob riding the Duke and the King out of town on a rail, we are given his most memorable insight into the nature of man. Although these rogues had subjected Huck to every indignity, what he sees provokes this celebrated comment:

> Well, it made me sick to see it; and I was sorry for them poor pitiful rascals, it seemed like I couldn't ever feel any hardness against them any more in the world. It was a dreadful thing to see. Human beings can be awful cruel to one another.

The sign of Huck's maturity here is neither the compassion nor the skepticism, for both had been marks of his personality from the first. Rather, the special quality of these reflections is the extraordinary combination of the two, a mature blending of his instinctive suspicion of human motives with his capacity for pity.

But at this point Tom reappears. Soon Huck has fallen almost completely under his sway once more, and we are asked to believe that the boy who felt pity for the rogues is now capable of making Jim's capture the occasion for a game. He becomes Tom's helpless accomplice, submissive and gullible. No wonder that Clemens has Huck remark, when Huck first realizes Aunt Sally has mistaken him for Tom, that "it was like being born again." Exactly. In the end, Huck regresses to the subordinate role in which he had first appeared in *The Adventures of Tom Sawyer*. Most of those traits which made him so appealing a hero now disappear. He had never, for example, found pain or misfortune amusing. At the circus, when a clown disguised as a drunk took a precarious ride on a prancing horse, the crowd loved the excitement and danger; "it warn't funny to me, though," said Huck. But now, in the end, he submits in awe to Tom's notion of what is amusing. To satisfy Tom's hunger for adventure he makes himself a party to sport which aggravates Jim's misery.

It should be added at once that Jim doesn't mind too much. The fact is that he has undergone a similar transformation. On the raft he was an individual, man enough to denounce Huck when Huck made him the victim of a practical joke. In the closing epi- /429/ sode, however, we lose sight of Jim in the maze of farcical invention. He ceases to be a man. He allows Huck and "Mars Tom" to fill his hut with rats and snakes, "and every time a rat bit Jim he would get up and write a line in his journal whilst the ink was fresh." This creature who bleeds ink and feels no pain is something less than human. He has been made over in the image of a flat stereotype: the submissive stage-Negro. These antics divest Jim, as well as Huck, of much of his dignity and individuality.[5]

What I have been saying is that the flimsy devices of plot, the discordant farcical tone, and the disintegration of the major characters all betray the failure of the ending. These are not aspects merely of form in a technical sense, but of meaning. For that matter, I would maintain that this book has little or no formal unity independent of the joint purpose of Huck and Jim. What components of the novel, we may ask, provide the continuity which links one adventure with another? The most important is the unifying consciousness of Huck, the narrator, and the fact that we follow the same principals through the entire string of adventures. Events, moreover, occur in a temporal sequence. Then there is the river; after each adventure Huck and Jim return to the raft and the river. Both Mr. Trilling and Mr. Eliot speak eloquently of the river as a source of unity, and they refer to the river as a god. Mr. Trilling says that Huck is "the servant of the river-god." Mr. Eliot puts it this way: "The River gives the book its form. But for the River, the book might be only a sequence of adventures with a happy ending." This seems to me an extravagant view of the function of the neutral agency of the river. Clemens had a knowledgeable respect for the Mississippi and, without sanctifying it, was able to provide excellent reasons for Huck's and Jim's intense relation with it. It is a source of food and beauty and terror and serenity of mind. But above all, it provides motion; it is the means by which Huck and Jim move away from a menacing civilization. They return to the river to continue their journey. The river cannot, does not, supply purpose. That purpose is a facet of their conscious- /430/ ness, and without the motive of escape from society, *Huckleberry Finn* would indeed "be only a sequence of adventures." Mr. Eliot's remark indicates how lightly he takes the quest for freedom. His somewhat fanciful exaggeration of the river's role is of a piece with his neglect of the theme at the novel's center.

That theme is heightened by the juxtaposition of sharp images of

[5] For these observations on the transformation of Jim in the closing episodes, I am indebted to the excellent unpublished essay by Mr. Chadwick Hansen on the subject of Clemens and Western humor.

contrasting social orders: the microcosmic community Huck and Jim establish aboard the raft and the actual society which exists along the Mississippi's banks. The two are separated by the river, the road to freedom upon which Huck and Jim must travel. Huck tells us what the river means to them when, after the Wilks episode, he and Jim once again shove their raft into the current: "It *did* seem so good to be free again and all by ourselves on the big river, and nobody to bother us." The river is indifferent. But its sphere is relatively uncontaminated by the civilization they flee, and so the river allows Huck and Jim some measure of freedom at once, the moment they set foot on Jackson's Island or the raft. Only on the island and the raft do they have a chance to practice that idea of brotherhood to which they are devoted. "Other places do seem so cramped and smothery," Huck explains, "but a raft don't. You feel mighty free and easy and comfortable on a raft." The main thing is freedom.

On the raft the escaped slave and the white boy try to practice their code: "What you want, above all things, on a raft, is for everybody to be satisfied, and feel right and kind towards the others." This human credo constitutes the paramount affirmation of *The Adventures of Huckleberry Finn,* and it obliquely aims a devastating criticism at the existing social order. It is a creed which Huck and Jim bring to the river. It neither emanates from nature nor is it addressed to nature. Therefore I do not see that it means much to talk about the river as a god in this novel. The river's connection with this high aspiration for man is that it provides a means of escape, a place where the code can be tested. The truly profound meanings of the novel are generated by the impingement of the actual world of slavery, feuds, lynching, murder, and a spurious Christian morality upon the ideal of the raft. The result is a tension which somehow demands release in the novel's ending. /431/

But Clemens was unable to effect this release and at the same time control the central theme. The unhappy truth about the ending of *Huckleberry Finn* is that the author, having revealed the tawdry nature of the culture of the great valley, yielded to its essential complacency. The general tenor of the closing scenes, to which the token regeneration of Miss Watson is merely one superficial clue, amounts to just that. In fact, this entire reading of *Huckleberry Finn* merely confirms the brilliant insight of George Santayana, who many years ago spoke of American humorists, of whom he considered Mark Twain an outstanding representative, as having only "half escaped" the genteel tradition. Santayana meant that men like Clemens were able to "point to what contradicts it in the facts; but not in order to abandon the genteel tradition, for they have nothing solid to put in its place."

This seems to me the real key to the failure of *Huckleberry Finn.* Clemens had presented the contrast between the two social orders but could not, or would not, accept the tragic fact that the one he had rejected was an image of solid reality and the other an ecstatic dream. Instead he gives us the cozy reunion with Aunt Polly in a scene fairly bursting with approbation of the entire family, the Phelpses included.

Like Miss Watson, the Phelpses are almost perfect specimens of the dominant culture. They are kind to their friends and relatives; they have no taste for violence; they are people capable of devoting themselves to their spectacular dinners while they keep Jim locked in the little hut down by the ash hopper, with its lone window boarded up. (Of course Aunt Sally visits Jim to see if he is "comfortable," and Uncle Silas comes in "to pray with him.") These people, with their comfortable Sunday-dinner conviviality and the runaway slave padlocked nearby, are reminiscent of those solid German citizens we have heard about in our time who tried to maintain a similarly *gemütlich* way of life within virtual earshot of Buchenwald. I do not mean to imply that Clemens was unaware of the shabby morality of such people. After the abortive escape of Jim, when Tom asks about him, Aunt Sally replies: "Him? . . . the runaway nigger? . . . They've got him back, safe and sound, and /432/ he's in the cabin again, on bread and water, and loaded down with chains, till he's claimed or sold!" Clemens understood people like the Phelpses, but nevertheless he was forced to rely upon them to provide his happy ending. The satisfactory outcome of Jim's quest for freedom must be attributed to the benevolence of the very people whose inhumanity first made it necessary.

But to return to the contention of Mr. Trilling and Mr. Eliot that the ending is more or less satisfactory after all. As I have said, Mr. Trilling approves of the "formal aptness" of the conclusion. He says that "some device is needed to permit Huck to return to his anonymity, to give up the role of hero," and that therefore "nothing could serve better than the mind of Tom Sawyer with its literary furnishings, its conscious romantic desire for experience and the hero's part, and its ingenious schematization of life. . . ." Though more detailed, this is essentially akin to Mr. Eliot's blunt assertion that "it is right that the mood at the end of the book should bring us back to that of the beginning." I submit that it is wrong for the end of the book to bring us back to that mood. The mood of the beginning of *Huckleberry Finn* is the mood of Huck's attempt to accommodate himself to the ways of St. Petersburg. It is the mood of the end of *The Adventures of Tom Sawyer,* when the boys had been acclaimed heroes, and when Huck was accepted as a candidate for respectability. That is the state in which we find him at the beginning of *Huckleberry Finn.* But Huck cannot stand the new way of life, and his mood gradually shifts to the mood of rebellion which dominates the novel until he meets Tom again. At first, in the second chapter, we see him still eager to be accepted by the nice boys of the town. Tom leads the gang in reenacting adventures he has culled from books, but gradually Huck's pragmatic turn of mind gets him in trouble. He has little tolerance for Tom's brand of make-believe. He irritates Tom. Tom calls him a "numbskull," and finally Huck throws up the whole business:

> So then I judged that all that stuff was only just one of Tom Sawyer's lies. I reckoned he believed in the A-rabs and the elephants, but as for me I think different. It had all the marks of a Sunday school. /433/

With this statement, which ends the third chapter, Huck parts company with Tom. The fact is that Huck has rejected Tom's romanticizing of experience; moreover, he has rejected it as part of the larger pattern of society's make-believe, typified by Sunday school. But if he cannot accept Tom's harmless fantasies about the A-rabs, how are we to believe that a year later Huck is capable of awe-struck submission to the far more extravagant fantasies with which Tom invests the mock rescue of Jim?

After Huck's escape from his "pap," the drift of the action, like that of the Mississippi's current, is *away* from St. Petersburg. Huck leaves Tom and the A-rabs behind, along with the Widow, Miss Watson, and all the pseudo-religious ritual in which nice boy's must partake. The return, in the end, to the mood of the beginning therefore means defeat—Huck's defeat; to return to that mood *joyously* is to portray defeat in the guise of victory.

Mr. Eliot and Mr. Trilling deny this. The overriding consideration for them is form—form which seems largely to mean symmetry of structure. It is fitting, Mr. Eliot maintains, that the book should come full circle and bring Huck once more under Tom's sway. Why? Because it begins that way. But it seems to me that such structural unity is *imposed* upon the novel, and therefore is meretricious. It is a jerry-built structure, achieved only by sacrifice of characters and theme. Here the controlling principle of form apparently is unity, but unfortunately a unity much too superficially conceived. Structure, after all, is only one element—indeed, one of the more mechanical elements—of unity. A unified work must surely manifest coherence of meaning and clear development of theme, yet the ending of *Huckle-*

berry Finn blurs both. The eagerness of Mr. Eliot and Mr. Trilling to justify the ending is symptomatic of that absolutist impulse of our critics to find reasons, once a work has been admitted to the highest canon of literary reputability, for admiring every bit of it.

What is perhaps most striking about these judgments of Mr. Eliot's and Mr. Trilling's is that they are so patently out of harmony with the basic standards of both critics. For one thing, both men hold far more complex ideas of the nature of literary unity than /434/ their comments upon *Huckleberry Finn* would suggest. For another, both critics are essentially moralists, yet here we find them turning away from a moral issue in order to praise a dubious structural unity. Their efforts to explain away the flaw in Clemens' novel suffer from a certain narrowness surprising to anyone who knows their work. These facts suggest that we may be in the presence of a tendency in contemporary criticism which the critics themselves do not fully recognize.

Is there an explanation? How does it happen that two of our most respected critics should seem to treat so lightly the glaring lapse of moral imagination in *Huckleberry Finn?* Perhaps—and I stress the conjectural nature of what I am saying—perhaps the kind of moral issue raised by *Huckleberry Finn* is not the kind of moral issue to which today's criticism readily addresses itself. Today our critics, no less than our novelists and poets, are most sensitively attuned to moral problems which arise in the sphere of individual behavior. They are deeply aware of sin, of individual infractions of our culture's Christian ethic. But my impression is that they are, possibly because of the strength of the reaction against the mechanical sociological criticism of the thirties, less sensitive to questions of what might be called social or political morality.

By social or political morality I refer to the values implicit in a social system, values which may be quite distinct from the personal morality of any given individual within the society. Now *The Adventures of Huckleberry Finn,* like all novels, deals with the behavior of individuals. But one mark of Clemens' greatness is his deft presentation of the disparity between what people do when they behave as individuals and what they do when forced into roles imposed upon them by society. Take, for example, Aunt Sally and Uncle Silas Phelps, who consider themselves Christians, who are by impulse generous and humane, but who happen also to be staunch upholders of certain degrading and inhuman social institutions. When they are confronted with an escaped slave, the imperatives of social morality outweigh all pious professions.

The conflict between what people think they stand for and what social pressure forces them to do is central to the novel. It is present

/435/ to the mind of Huck and, indeed, accounts for his most serious inner conflicts. He knows how he feels about Jim, but he also knows what he is expected to do about Jim. This division within his mind corresponds to the division of the novel's moral terrain into the areas represented by the raft on the one hand and society on the other. His victory over his "yaller dog" conscience therefore assumes heroic size: it is a victory over the prevailing morality. But the last fifth of the novel has the effect of diminishing the importance and uniqueness of Huck's victory. We are asked to assume that somehow freedom can be achieved in spite of the crippling power of what I have called the social morality. Consequently the less importance we attach to that force as it operates in the novel, the more acceptable the ending becomes.

Moreover, the idea of freedom, which Mr. Eliot and Mr. Trilling seem to slight, takes on its full significance only when we acknowledge the power which society exerts over the minds of men in the world of *Huckleberry Finn*. For freedom in this book specifically means freedom from society and its imperatives. This is not the traditional Christian conception of freedom. Huck and Jim seek freedom not from a burden of individual guilt and sin, but from social constraint. That is to say, evil in *Huckleberry Finn* is the product of civilization, and if this is indicative of Clemens' rather too simple view of human nature, nevertheless the fact is that Huck, when he can divest himself of the taint of social conditioning (as in the incantatory account of sunrise on the river), is entirely free of anxiety and guilt. The only guilt he actually knows arises from infractions of a social code. (The guilt he feels after playing the prank on Jim stems from his betrayal of the law of the raft.) Huck's and Jim's creed is secular. Its object is harmony among men, and so Huck is not much concerned with his own salvation. He repeatedly renounces prayer in favor of pragmatic solutions to his problems. In other words, the central insights of the novel belong to the tradition of the Enlightenment. The meaning of the quest itself is hardly reconcilable with that conception of human nature embodied in the myth of original sin. In view of the current fashion of reaffirming man's innate depravity, it is perhaps not surprising /436/ to find the virtues of *Huckleberry Finn* attributed not to its meaning but to its form.

But "if this was not the right ending for the book," Mr. Eliot asks, "what ending would have been right?" Although this question places the critic in an awkward position (he is not always equipped to rewrite what he criticizes), there are some things which may justifiably be said about the "right" ending of *Huckleberry Finn*. It may be legitimate, even if presumptuous, to indicate certain conditions which a hypothetical ending would have to satisfy if it were to be congruent with the rest of the novel. If the conclusion is not to be something merely tacked on to close the action, then its broad outline must be immanent in the body of the work.

It is surely reasonable to ask that the conclusion provide a plausible outcome to the quest. Yet freedom, in the ecstatic sense that Huck and Jim knew it aboard the raft, was hardly to be had in the Mississippi Valley in the 1840's, or, for that matter, in any other known human society. A satisfactory ending would inevitably cause the reader some frustration. That Clemens felt such disappointment to be inevitable is borne out by an examination of the novel's clear, if unconscious, symbolic pattern. Consider, for instance, the inferences to be drawn from the book's geography. The river, to whose current Huck and Jim entrust themselves, actually carries them to the heart of slave territory. Once the raft passes Cairo, the quest is virtually doomed. Until the steamboat smashes the raft, we are kept in a state of anxiety about Jim's escape. (It may be significant that at this point Clemens found himself unable to continue work on the manuscript, and put it aside for several years.) Beyond Cairo, Clemens allows the intensity of that anxiety to diminish, and it is probably no accident that the fainter it becomes, the more he falls back upon the devices of low comedy. Huck and Jim make no serious effort to turn north, and there are times (during the Wilks episode) when Clemens allows Huck to forget all about Jim. It is as if the author, anticipating the dilemma he had finally to face, instinctively dissipated the power of his major theme./437/

Consider, too, the circumscribed nature of the raft as a means of moving toward freedom. The raft lacks power and maneuverability. It can only move easily with the current—southward into slave country. Nor can it evade the mechanized power of the steamboat. These impotencies of the raft correspond to the innocent helplessness of its occupants. Unresisted, the rogues invade and take over the raft. Though it is the symbolic locus of the novel's central affirmations, the raft provides an uncertain and indeed precarious mode of traveling toward freedom. This seems another confirmation of Santayana's perception. To say that Clemens only half escaped the genteel tradition is not to say that he failed to note any of the creed's inadequacies, but rather that he had "nothing solid" to put in its place. The raft patently was not capable of carrying the burden of hope Clemens placed on it.[6] (Whether this is to be attributed to the nature of his

[6] Gladys Bellamy (*Mark Twain as a Literary Artist*, Norman, Oklahoma, 1950, p. 221) has noted the insubstantial, dream-like quality of the image of the raft. Clemens thus discusses travel by raft in *A Tramp Abroad*: "the motion

vision or to the actual state of American society in the nineteenth century is another interesting question.) In any case, the geography of the novel, the raft's powerlessness, the goodness and vulnerability of Huck and Jim, all prefigure a conclusion quite different in tone from that which Clemens gave us. These facts constitute what Hart Crane might have called the novel's "logic of metaphor," and this logic—probably inadvertent—actually takes us to the underlying meaning of *The Adventures of Huckleberry Finn*. Through the symbols we reach a truth which the ending obscures: the quest cannot succeed.

Fortunately, Clemens broke through to this truth in the novel's last sentences:

> But I reckon I got to light out for the territory ahead of the rest, because Aunt Sally she's going to adopt me and sivilize me, and I can't stand it. I been there before.

Mr. Eliot properly praises this as "the only possible concluding /438/ sentence." But one sentence can hardly be advanced, as Mr. Eliot advances this one, to support the rightness of ten chapters. Moreover, if this sentence is right, then the rest of the conclusion is wrong, for its meaning clashes with that of the final burlesque. Huck's decision to go west ahead of the inescapable advance of civilization is a confession of defeat. It means that the raft is to be abandoned. On the other hand, the jubilation of the family reunion and the proclaiming of Jim's freedom create a quite different mood. The tone, except for these last words, is one of unclouded success. I believe this is the source of the almost universal dissatisfaction with the conclusion. One can hardly forget that a bloody civil war did not resolve the issue.

Should Clemens have made Huck a tragic hero? Both Mr. Eliot and Mr. Trilling argue that that would have been a mistake, and they are very probably correct. But between the ending as we have it and tragedy in the fullest sense, there was vast room for invention. Clemens might have contrived an action which left Jim's fate as much in doubt as Huck's. Such an ending would have allowed us to assume that the principals were defeated but alive, and the quest unsuccessful but not abandoned. This, after all, would have been consonant with the symbols, the characters, and the theme as Clemens had created them—and with history.

Clemens did not acknowledge the truth his novel contained. He

---

of the raft is . . . gentle, and gliding, and smooth, and noiseless; it calms down all feverish activities, it soothes to sleep all nervous . . . impatience; under its restful influence all the troubles and vexations and sorrows that harass the mind vanish away, and existence becomes a dream . . . a deep and tranquil ecstasy."

had taken hold of a situation in which a partial defeat was inevitable, but he was unable to—or unaware of the need to—give imaginative substance to that fact. If an illusion of success was indispensable, where was it to come from? Obviously Huck and Jim could not succeed by their own efforts. At this point Clemens, having only half escaped the genteel tradition, one of whose pre-eminent characteristics was an optimism undaunted by disheartening truth, returned to it. *Why* he did so is another story, having to do with his parents and his boyhood, with his own personality and his wife's and especially with the character of his audience. But whatever the explanation, the faint-hearted ending of *The Adventures of Huckleberry Finn* remains an important datum in the record of American thought and imagination. It has been noted before, both by critics /439/ and nonprofessional readers. It should not be forgotten now.

To minimize the seriousness of what must be accounted a major flaw in so great a work is, in a sense, to repeat Clemens' failure of nerve. This is a disservice to criticism. Today we particularly need a criticism alert to lapses of moral vision. A measured appraisal of the failures and successes of our writers, past and present, can show us a great deal about literature and about ourselves. That is the critic's function. But he cannot perform that function if he substitutes considerations of technique for considerations of truth. Not only will such methods lead to errors of literary judgment, but beyond that, they may well encourage comparable evasions in other areas. It seems not unlikely, for instance, that the current preoccupation with matters of form is bound up with a tendency, by no means confined to literary quarters, to shy away from painful answers to complex questions of political morality. The conclusion to *The Adventures of Huckleberry Finn* shielded both Clemens and his audience from such an answer. But we ought not to be as tender-minded. For Huck Finn's besetting problem, the disparity between his best impulses and the behavior the community attempted to impose upon him, is as surely ours as it was Twain's. /440/

QUESTIONS FOR DISCUSSION AND WRITING

1. In Clemens' day *The Adventures of Huckleberry Finn* was called "vulgar, rough, inelegant, irreverent, coarse, semi-obscene, trashy and vicious," says Marx (p. 423). In the older criticism, these qualities were considered weaknesses of the novel. What about the novel might have brought forth such criticism?

2. What weaknesses does Marx find in modern criticism of this novel? Do you agree? What weaknesses do you find that Marx does not mention?
3. Do you agree with Marx's statements about the ending of *Huckleberry Finn?* Do you think the critics who dislike the ending are correct?
4. How important does Marx think humor is in *Huckleberry Finn?* What does he think the humor is used for?
5. Using Marx, other critics, and the novel itself, explain the role of Miss Watson.
6. Is Jim different at the end from the way he was at the beginning? Why do the critics think he is?
7. What does Marx mean when he says, "Like Miss Watson, the Phelpses are almost perfect specimens of the dominant culture"?
8. Explain in detail what Marx means by calling the raft "the symbolic locus of the novel's central affirmations."
9. What does Marx think is the theme of *Huckleberry Finn?*

THE RISE OF THE AMERICAN NOVEL

by Alexander Cowie

Huckleberry Finn is of sterner stuff than *Tom Sawyer,* possibly because Huck himself was based largely on an actual boy, Tom Blanken- /612/ ship, who was several degrees more shady in background and more rugged in character than the Samuel Clemens who had drawn on himself so largely for Tom Sawyer's portrait. The boys' club atmosphere which hovers occasionally over *Tom Sawyer* is largely

Reprinted from Alexander Cowie's *The Rise Of The American Novel,* American Book Company, 1948, by permission of the publisher.

banished in *Huckleberry Finn* and is indeed most noticeable in Tom's insistence on "regularly" freeing Jim after he is already legally freed. The river flows deeper through *Huckleberry Finn*, too. If, as has been suggested, critics have exaggerated the extent of the river's influence in Mark Twain, this book is a poor place to hatch a rebuttal to their argument. The river evokes the deepest romance and the most eerie moments in the book besides affording much-needed mooring for the somewhat scattered episodes of the story. The raft on the river is one of the most important pieces of machinery in American fiction and its freight, part black and part white, one of the most cherished loadings. The river, too, is the best place to look at the stars from:

> It's lovely to live on a raft. We had the sky up there, all speckled with stars, and we used to lay on our backs and look up at them, and discuss about whether they was made or only just happened. Jim he allowed they was made, but I allowed they happened; I judged it would have took too long to *make* so many. Jim said the moon could a *laid* them; well, that looked kind of reasonable, so I didn't say nothing against it, because I've seen a frog lay most as many, so of course it could be done. We used to watch the stars that fell, too, and see them streak down. Jim allowed they'd got spoiled and was hove out of the nest.

Here we are not far from the centre of the epic quality of *Huckleberry Finn*—a derelict boy and a runaway slave on a makeshift raft floating perilously down the centre of the continent with the passengers giving voice to crude symbolism to express their feeling about the birth of the infinite heavens.

This tone, which is shattered elsewhere in the book, gives *Huckleberry Finn* permanent value as art, but could not make it a popular classic. There must be exciting, original narrative. The action here is perhaps better unified than in *Tom Sawyer*, but the most that can be said is that its parts are basted together. The reader is warned against looking for a plot on pain of death administered by the author. The fortunes of Huck and of Jim do run through the book and the fate of Jim does provide a focal problem. But focus is lost when the reader's interest is switched to prolonged episodic treatment of the Grangerford-Shepherdson feud and (despite Jim's frequent reappearance) the picaresque plundering engaged in by "the Duke of Bridgewater" and "the /613/ late Dauphin." Jim is dumped out of the story when it is convenient to talk of other matters, that is all. Yet he is a character drawn (albeit in simple strokes) with great sympathy and understanding: he is a reminder of the fact, often lost sight of, that Mark Twain was first of all a Southerner. The rogues who steal the show for so long—the Duke and the Dauphin—represent types of sharpers and fakers who actually operated up and down the Mississippi in Mark Twain's youth. Mark Twain undoubtedly had some first-hand acquaintance with their kind in his piloting days, but there is discernible in *Huckleberry Finn* also a literary strain derived from one of the few kinds of narrative Mark Twain enjoyed reading, the picaresque. The cony-catching tricks and dodges employed by Mark Twain's bogus gentry are far older than the towns of Hannibal or Cairo. Even Huck exhibits a dexterity that at times casts a literary suspicion upon him—as for example when he is discovered for a boy when he closes his legs to catch an object instead of letting the apron catch it. Yet Huck's character is not seriously flawed by literary inheritance, and his mischiefmaking like that of Tom's is comparatively mild:

> Huck . . . is a rogue with limitations. Although ready in lies, deceits, and disguises, and a petty thief, he is sound at heart. He scruples at helping to steal a "nigger;" [*sic*] he cannot bring himself to join with professional rogues in a swindle of moment; he protects the weak, and is loyal to his friends. To the Don Quixote of the imaginative Tom Sawyer he plays a delightful Sancho.

But Huck is essentially an American boy, atypical perhaps in his scabrous background but fully representative of his general species in his interest in dead cats, indigenous superstitions, raft-life, petty pilfering, playing pirate, and various oddments growing out of juvenile conception of the life of chivalry and adventure. He is native too in his contempt for the alleged advantages of clean clothes and domestic security. He speaks an uncouth but serviceable vernacular. He has a wholesome resistance to surface polish and the softening effects of culture and intramural religion. He is more real in this respect than his father. For when the father discovers Huck's temporary "improvement" under the hand of Miss Watson, his remarks are carried beyond the point of such a father's natural protest. Here, as often, Mark Twain allows himself to push his fun-making beyond realistic limits:

> "Don't you give me none o' your lip," says he. "You've put on considerable many frills since I been away. I'll take you down a peg before I get done with you. You're educated, too, they say /614/—can read and write. You think you're better 'n your father, now, don't you, because he can't? *I'll* take it out of you. Who told you you might meddle with such hifalut'n foolishness, hey?—who told you you could?"

> "The widow. She told me."
>
> "The widow, hey?—and who told the widow she could put in her shovel about a thing that ain't none of her business?"
>
> "Nobody never told her."
>
> "Well, I'll learn her how to meddle. And looky here—you drop that school, you hear? I'll learn people to bring up a boy to put on airs over his own father and let on to be better'n what *he* is. You lemme catch you fooling around that school again, you hear? Your mother couldn't read, and she couldn't write, nuther, before she died. None of the family couldn't before *they* died. *I* can't; and here you're a-swelling yourself up like this. I ain't the man to stand it--you hear? Say, lemme hear you read."
>
> I took up a book and begun something about General Washington and the wars. When I'd read about a half a minute, he fetched the book a whack with his hand and knocked it across the house. He says:
>
> "It's so. You can do it. I had my doubts when you told me. Now looky here; you stop that putting on frills. I won't have it. I'll lay for you, my smarty; and if I catch you about that school I'll tan you good. First you know you'll get religion, too. I never see such a son."

The character of Huck, like that of most of Mark Twain's people, is of course finally revealed in action not in "analysis." Besides those traits already mentioned Huck displayed a superb resourcefulness in the face of difficulty, and it is this as much as anything else which makes him a hero. Mark Twain showed it in various episodes, of which the near-capture of Nigger Jim may serve as an example not only of Huck's skill in meeting an emergency but also of Mark Twain's incomparable skill in investing exciting incident with a maximum of suspense. If he was unequal to sustaining a plot, Mark Twain had few equals in the management of incident. In this case, as often, he brings his hero to within an ace of defeat only to let him recover. The process is then repeated, the tension constantly increasing, a second and sometimes a third time. Finally the reader sees no possible means of escape, but by an ingenious reversal Mark Twain saves the situation through stratagem. The situation in point is created when two men, hunting runaway Negroes, suspect that Huck (at the moment in a canoe) is harboring one on the raft. He admits that there is a man on board the raft but when asked if the man is black or white he is so clumsy and hesitating with /615/ his lie (saying the occupant of the raft is white) that the men decide they will go and see for themselves.

This move Huck tries cannily to forestall by telling them that the man is his "pap" and that he is sick. But the men, though tempted not to waste the time, reckon they'll have to go help Huck tow the raft ashore. From such dangerous co-operation Huck must now rescue the situation by devising a new stratagem. The men have actually rowed a stroke or two toward the raft when Huck attempts to dissuade them:

> "Pap'll be mighty much obleeged to you, I can tell you. Everybody goes away when I want them to help me tow the raft ashore, and I can't do it by myself."
>
> "Well, that's infernal mean. Odd, too. Say, boy, what's the matter with your father?"
>
> "It's the—a—the—well, it ain't anything much."
>
> They stopped pulling. It warn't but a mighty little ways to the raft now. One says:
>
> "Boy, that's a lie. What *is* the matter with your pap? Answer up square now, and it'll be the better for you."
>
> "I will, sir, I will, honest—but don't leave us, please. It's the—the—Gentlemen, if you'll only pull ahead, and let me heave you the headline, you won't have to come a-near the raft —please do."
>
> "Set her back, John, set her back!" says one. They backed water. "Keep away, boy—keep to looard. Confound it, I just expect the wind has blowed it to us. Your pap's got the small-pox, and you know it precious well. Why didn't you come out and say so? Do you want to spread it all over?"
>
> "Well," says I, a-blubbering, "I've told everybody before, and they just went away and left us."

The fear of smallpox effectually stops the slave-hunters, who now prepare to compromise with their consciences by giving Huck elaborate directions for a rescue at a point considerably lower on the river, advising him not to "let on" again about the smallpox. The episode is now virtually ended, a perfect example of the creation and maintenance of suspense. But Mark Twain cannot resist the temptation to gild the story by having the men feel so sorry for Huck and his poor father that each of them puts a twenty-dollar gold piece on a board for Huck to pick up when it floats to him. Here in one incident is the method of Mark Twain at its best—followed by a tail-piece which almost ruins the effect by a touch of farce. Of many similar units the narratives of Mark Twain are composed. They refuse to coalesce into one whole, but each is in its way superb. Their effectiveness like that of the whole book comes from the skilful ratio Mark Twain maintains between realism and /616/ romance. His faithful attention to certain minutiae forces the reader to endorse Mark Twain as a realist, but at the same time the book is stepped up imaginatively by a subtle process which divests it of that bleak prosaicness which is just as true a part of childhood as romantic zest. In the last analysis the realism is predominant, and this is only natural, for the whole story is conveyed to the reader in that virile, colloquial idiom, frequently taking the form of authentic dialect, which was one of Mark Twain's chief contributions to the novel. /617/

QUESTIONS FOR DISCUSSION AND WRITING

1. Discuss Cowie's term "epic quality" in its relevance to *Huckleberry Finn.*
2. Take Cowie's statement that in *Huckleberry Finn* the Mississippi River "evokes the deepest romance and the most eerie moments in the book" as the central idea for a paper and develop that idea by specific references to the novel. What have other critics had to say about the quality imparted to the novel by the river?
3. Agree or disagree with Cowie's remark that Huck is "fully representative of his general species"—the American boy.
4. Would the majority of the critics represented in this volume agree with Cowie that the episodic units of the novel "refuse to coalesce into one whole, but each is in its way superb"?
5. Does it seem to you that Cowie is correct in saying the realism in *Huckleberry Finn* is predominant over the romance? What does Cowie appear to mean by the terms "realism" and "romance"? Can you give examples of each from the novel?

THE STRUCTURE OF *HUCKLEBERRY FINN*

by Frank Baldanza

The much-vexed question of the structure of *Huckleberry Finn* has received both distinguished and penetrating attention; T. S. Eliot and Lionel Trilling have defended the plot as a whole in their introductions to editions of the novel, and Leo Marx has ably replied to both.[1] James Cox and Philip Young have attempted symbolic and psychological interpretations which make passing comments on structure: [2] I should like to suggest, however, that both groups of critics, although they have made valuable exploratory searches, have neglected the one aspect of the structure which is perhaps the most rewarding to investigate.

In the first place, as Edgar Goold points out in regard to Twain's theory of the novel:

> Concerning plot construction and related matters Clemens's contribution is of somewhat lesser significance for the writer of fiction than the uninitiated might expect. . . . His own temperament and training did not tend to develop in him the ability to plan carefully and practice the sustained concentration necessary for tight and well-developed plots.[3]

That this failure in planning out his plots had a temperamental basis is corroborated, perhaps, by Twain's virulent antipathy to the total work of such a careful planner as Jane Austen. But many other critics, of whom I choose James Cox as representative, argue that the structure

[1] Leo Marx, "Mr. Eliot, Mr. Trilling, and *Huckleberry Finn*," *American Scholar*, XXII, 423–440 (Autumn, 1953).

[2] James M. Cox, "Remarks on the Sad Initiation of Huckleberry Finn," *Sewanee Review*, LXII, 389–405 (Summer, 1954); Philip Young, *Ernest Hemingway* (New York, 1952), pp. 181–212.

[3] "Mark Twain on the Writing of Fiction," *American Literature*, XXVI, 148–149 (May, 1954).

Reprinted from *American Literature*, XXVII (November 1955). By permission of Duke University Press and Frank Baldanza.

of *Huckleberry Finn* is determined by the interplay of sets of symbols —civilization and the frontier, gentility and barbarism, freedom and bondage, and the like. These ideas certainly play a major part in the development of the book because they are, in a certain sense, what the book is about; but the ques- /347/ tion ought to be in what way Twain uses these ideas. Bernard De Voto, who assures us that "Mark Twain was not a systematic thinker," finds him "as feeble a novice as ever ventured into [metaphysics].[4] He goes on to say that

> . . . there is a type of mind, and the lovers of *Huckleberry Finn* belong to it, which prefers experience to metaphysical abstractions and the thing to its symbol. Such minds think of *Huckleberry Finn* as the greatest work of nineteenth century fiction in America precisely because it is not a voyage in pursuit of a white whale but a voyage among feudists, mobbers, thieves, rogues, nigger-hunters, and murderers, precisely because Huck never encounters a symbol but always some actual human being working out an actual destiny.[5]

But even if we overlook Twain's antisymbolic cast of mind (in which we should hardly be justified), we find that his own ambivalence blurs the neatness of whatever categories we set up. Even though we interpret the book as a "sad initiation" into society, we are baffled by the final sentence in which Huck lights out for the territory; if he has adamantly resisted the culture of the towns, then he is not in any sense "initiated." And if we try to see the book as a progression toward Jim's liberation, we must ask why the Boggs episode, the Shepherdson-Grangerford feud, and the Wilks interlude, which compose the bulk of the central portion, are so remarkably irrelevant to the thesis. Even toward the close of the book, Huck is scandalized by Tom's easy acquiescence in the escape plot, and invokes the wrath of society on such behavior. The resolution of these dilemmas is perhaps to be found in Twain's own ambivalences, but an analysis of these leads us into biography or psychology and inevitably away from *Huckleberry Finn*. Nevertheless, if we hold to any aesthetic standards at all, we hardly have the right to make extravagant claims for a book which we must admit in the same breath is negligible as a work of art.

Let us for a moment abandon the search for any plotted or symbolic or psychological unity in the novel and return to what we know about Mark Twain's temperament and about his habits of composition; in this way we can more easily make an inductive study of the kind of structure he put into the novel, rather than /348/ impose from

[4] *Mark Twain at Work* (Cambridge, Mass., 1942), p. 99.
[5] *Ibid.*, p. 100.

the outside some preconceived pattern. Bernard De Voto, who gave an entire book to Twain's work habits, tells us that

> He wrote on impulse, and when impulse was in circuit with the deeper levels of his phantasy things went well, but when the circuit was broken he could only improvise. Improvisation was responsible for the worst and commonest blemishes in his books —and, because he could not long sustain it, for the breaking-off of many manuscripts. He had little ability to impose structure on his material; he could not think and feel it through to its own implicit form. He got "ideas" for books, stories, or sketches and jotted them down in his notebooks where they survive by the hundred, promising or feeble but almost always undeveloped. He caught fire easily and when an "idea" inflamed him, he attacked it with verve and enthusiasm, trusting to luck, providence, or his demon to make it good.[6]

We might say, as many have said, that the picaresque form would certainly be the ideal genre for such a talent, and that in the kind of episodic, spurting movement of such tales Twain would find his best vehicle; however, at the best, such an "explanation" of the structure of the book consists simply in the substitution of one word for another.

Let us rather try to see whether the very *élan* of his improvisation did not often carry him forward through a form which is implicit in his method. In Chapter VIII of his suggestive *Aspects of the Novel*, E. M. Forster remarks the same method as the fundamental source for the structure of Marcel Proust's *A la Recherche du Temps Perdu*. Like Twain's great river novel, "the book is chaotic, ill constructed, it has and will have no external shape. . . ." But Forster finds that "it hangs together because it is stitched internally, because it contains rhythms."[7] The parallel is enforced by what Forster tells us of Proust's work habits, because he attributes the quality of rhythm in the novel to a type of temperament that accords precisely with what we have already found in Goold's and De Voto's descriptions of Mark Twain: "I doubt that it can be achieved by the writers who plan their books beforehand, it has to depend on a local impulse when the right interval is reached."[8] Local impulse and lack of planning, the two

[6] *Ibid.*, p. 52.

[7] (New York, 1927), p. 236.

[8] *Ibid.*, p. 240. Forster precedes this analysis by one of James's *The Ambassadors* as an example of "Pattern." Although he never states it overtly, Forster is simply demonstrating, in his contrast between James and Proust (Pattern and Rhythm), the difference between conscious and unconscious intention.

prime /349/ characteristics of Twain's genius, then, ought to produce in his novel effects parallel to those rhythmic stitchings that Forster finds so exquisite in the work of the great French novelist.

But before we turn to *Huckleberry Finn* itself, we ought to have a clearer idea of what Forster means by rhythm in the French novel. He selects as his example the "little phrase" from the sonata by Vinteuil, later incorporated into a sextet: Proust employs this musical phrase, which recurs innumerable times in the course of his narrative, in such a manner, says Forster, that in itself it has a "musical" function in the novel. Although most critics are rightly chary about any such metaphorical applications of music to literature, we can see that Forster has a clear definition of what he means by a "musical" function. The use of "repetition plus variation" is the key to this kind of rhythm.[9] Simple repetition of a theme, such as Forster finds in Meredith, is dead patterning; but repetition with variation and development, and especially with varying degrees of emphasis, is rhythm:

> . . . the little phrase has a life of its own, unconnected with the lives of its auditors, as with the life of the man who composed it. It is almost an actor, but not quite, and that "not quite" means that its power has gone towards stitching Proust's book together from the inside, and towards the establishment of beauty and the ravishing of the reader's memory. There are times when the little phrase—from its gloomy inception, through the sonata into the sextet—means everything to the reader. There are times when it means nothing and is forgotten, and this seems to me the function of rhythm in fiction; not to be there all the time like a pattern, but by its lovely waxing and waning to fill us with surprise and freshness and hope.[10]

I propose to show that without advanced planning, and spurred by momentary impulses, Mark Twain—in all probability unconsciously—constructed whole passages of *Huckleberry Finn* on an aesthetic principle of repetition and variation. Because the process was unconscious, it does not attain the regularity of Proust's employment of the Vinteuil theme, and we must also remember that /350/ Twain was working on a much smaller scale than the seemingly inexhaustible French analyst. But to take one simple example, we remember how Huck early in the book saws his way out of his father's cabin undetected because he works behind a blanket that is stretched over the wall; toward the end of the book, Jim's escape is managed through a

[9] Mr. Cox uses these very terms in referring to *Tom Sawyer;* he does not indicate, however, whether or not he draws them from Forster.

[10] Forster, *op. cit.*, p. 239.

hole dug beneath the cabin, again disguised by a hanging blanket. Regardless of how we justify the correspondence on other grounds, it remains as a repetition of an earlier incident with a variation: it is, as Forster remarks, the variation which gives a sense of freshness and surprise, but it is the repetition that ravishes the memory, and, in its implicit assumption of order, it perhaps gives hope too.[11]

If we survey the total bulk of such correspondences in the novel, we find that they bear out our earlier assumption that they occur as unplanned, impulsive repetitions, sometimes seemingly enforcing a moral lesson, and other times existing simply as abstract aesthetic flourishes. An example of the latter is Tom's gratuitous insistence on having a rattlesnake to keep Jim company in the Phelpses' cabin, which recalls, solely for the aesthetic pleasure involved, the great to-do earlier in the book over the rattlesnake skin and over Jim's being bitten in the heel.

The largest group of repetitions centers about the situations in which Huck encounters rogues on his side trips. Here we might distinguish several themes, all of which are involved with the self-defeating nature of evil, as exemplified in Chaucer's "Pardoner's Tale." We need not assume that Twain chose such material for its profound moral significance, however; probably it was simply what came to hand and what he knew would please his readers. For the first of these themes, we might use one of Twain's chapter headings, "Better let blame' well alone": if Huck and Jim had not boarded the *Walter Scott* they would have been better off. In the same way, Bill and Packard would have made a clean getaway if they had not returned for Turner's share of the money, thus giving Huck and Jim the chance to take their boat, and consequently abandoning them ironically to the fate they had reserved /351/ for Turner. This greedy lingering at the scene of the crime in order to squeeze out every last cent is repeated subtly, and with a variation, when the Duke and the Dauphin, not content with the huge sum of gold, remain at the Wilks home in order to auction the goods and clean up the small change; it is repeated even more subtly, and with even wider variation, when Tom refuses to free Jim the easy way, but lingers in order to fulfil all the conditions of his rigorous code, and suffers a bullet wound because of his greed for glory. This last example, too, shows how the aesthetic requirements of the novel dovetail with the meaning: most critics

[11] We can see the same principle at work in the material that Twain decided not to use in the novel itself. Chapter III of *Life on the Mississippi*, for example, uses the device of Huck's overhearing conversations while hidden on a raft in the same way that he overhears the discussion of Bill and Packard on the *Walter Scott*.

have been content with explaining the final passages of the novel solely in terms of Tom's romanticism, but with the need for rhythm in mind, we can see that Twain chose—again, probably unconsciously—to manage the incident so that it echoed the previous patterns of "better let blame' well alone."

A second major repetitive theme is that of desertion. Just as Bill and Packard lack even the honor of thieves in their plan to abandon Turner, so, on the third night of the "Royal Nonesuch" performance, Huck and the Duke flee the theater before the performance; Huck thinks that they are abandoning the Dauphin to an angry crowd, but to his immense surprise, he finds the Dauphin asleep in the wigwam on the raft. Later in the book, when another angry mob has the three of them in tow in the graveyard at the end of the Wilks episode, Huck flees when he has the chance, and when the Duke and the Dauphin catch up with him at the opening of Chapter XXX, they make the same accusation that Turner might have made to his companions, and that the Dauphin might have made to Huck and the Duke after the Nonesuch flight. "Tryin' to give us the slip, was ye, you pup! Tired of our company, hey?" The elaborate argument on who has a right to desert whom is a kind of climactic repetition of the whole theme in the book, although Twain reserves one more repetition, as a kind of coda, for the splitting up of Tom and Jim and Huck after their flight from the Phelpses.

To these two themes of lingering for spoils and abandoning companions we might add a third, which perhaps approaches patterning more nearly than any of the others—that of the crowd. But again, I think we can see that each individual treatment of a crowd /352/ incident was impulsive on Twain's part, and that any pattern we find in the repetitions is either unconsciously or accidentally ordained. The first large crowd is that on the boat searching for Huck's body, a "good" crowd of friends (with the exception of Pap) bent on a mission of mercy: "Pap, and Judge Thatcher, and Bessie Thatcher, and Joe Harper, and Tom Sawyer, and his old Aunt Polly, and Sid and Mary, and plenty more." Then the first nuance of possibly evil motivations on the part of a crowd is indicated in Mr. Loftus's proposed search of the island to get the reward for Jim's capture. Later we descend to the cowardly violence of the Sherburn lynching manqué, of the odoriferous Nonesuch mob, and of the stupid avengers of the Wilks family; after the tarring and feathering of the royal impostors, we return to the "good" crowd in the final chapters where the farmers and their garrulous wives congregate to help Mr. Phelps. The variation in this employment of crowds is rich and inexhaustible; they are all foiled, regardless of the quality of their motives, except the mob that metes out justice to the Duke and the Dauphin; they are all impressionable and stupid, and their little ruses, like the plan of the first Nonesuch crowd, are all pitifully inadequate. The two "good" crowds which appear at the opening and the closing of the book, do attain their ends, but in so indirect a fashion that they are rendered ridiculous: in the first case, Huck muses that the bread filled with quicksilver *did* reach him, and that the widow's and the parson's prayers *were* answered after a fashion; and in the latter case the crowd *did* finally solve the mystery, but only by pure accident. At the center of the problem, though, is the example of the Shepherdson-Grangerford "crowd"; whether Twain intended it or not, this central incident in the book embodies all the paradoxes of motivation that impelled the other crowds, because it is by a code of honor that these two groups defeat themselves, even as the rogues defeated themselves by lack of a code.

And, in speaking of the gullibility of the crowd and the roguery of the tricksters, we are reminded that before any of these examples of man's baseness occur in the book, Huck, in Chapter XV, gulls Jim himself, and in Huck's conscience-stricken reaction to Jim's eloquent rebuke, Twain sets the pattern for our reaction to the complicated roguery of the vagabonds. /353/

These examples are perhaps sufficient to suggest the kind of rhythm that pulses through the novel by repetition and variation; it remains to indicate that just as such repetitions were conceived unconsciously or accidentally on the author's part, so their influence on the reader may be largely without his conscious attention to the means by which he is beguiled into finding the book somehow ordered within his recollection, but by an order he cannot explain very clearly in terms of conventional plotting or symbols.

Thus it is unnecessary to survey in detail the abundantly burgeoning variations on change of identity, on superstition and prophecy, and on lying which stitch one chapter to another in the reader's memory. One could nearly make a parlor game of searching out minor correspondences like Huck's dressing as a girl when he visits Mrs. Loftus, and Tom's later insistence on Huck's assumption of the "yaller wench's frock" when he delivers the note to the Phelpses. The very proliferation of such repetitions, in fact, proves that Twain had no control over them and that they simply flowed from his pen as exuberant impulse. What is more, it seems to me that this principle of repetition, as in the preceding example, gives some dignity and power to what had heretofore been excused as the blemishes of a feverishly melodramatic imagination.

It remains to note that in at least one case the principle of repetition rays out to include unconscious recollection of culture tales as well as incidents treated earlier in the novel; this should not surprise us, because Blair and De Voto have shown how the Royal Nonesuch incident was derived from an obscene frontier tale.[12] In the present case, we remember that the critics who emphasize the symbolic structure of the book are quick to point out that Huck is "dead" throughout the book as far as the rest of his friends know. When Jim sees him for the first time, he falls to his knees and entreats the ghost to leave him. The same reaction, with a significant variation, occurs to Tom when he sees Huck toward the end of the book in Chapter XXXIII:

> I says:
> "I hain't come back—I hain't been *gone*."
> When he heard my voice it righted him up some, but he warn't quite satisfied yet. He says: /354/
> "Don't you play nothing on me, because I wouldn't on you. Honest injun, you ain't a ghost?"
> "Honest injun, I ain't," I says: [13]
> "Well—I—I—well, that ought to settle it, of course; but I can't somehow seem to understand it no way. Looky here, warn't you ever murdered *at all?*"
> "No. I warn't ever murdered at all—I played it on them. You come in here and feel of me if you don't believe me."
> So he done it; and it satisfied him; and he was that glad to see me again he didn't know what to do.

Tom's doubts on the corporeality of Huck, besides recalling those of Jim, obviously parallel those of his biblical namesake, and this Doubting Thomas satisfies himself in the same way as his predecessor, by feeling of his body. This is, too, an oblique recall of the previous references to Moses and Solomon and the biblical kings. There is no real need to see Huck as a Christ figure, especially since he is Tom's disciple, rather than the reverse; we need only note the fact of Twain's repeating a situation already familiar to his readers simply out of the exuberance of his aesthetic faculty.

If this explanation of the structure of *Huckleberry Finn* has any further recommendation, it is that in accepting it we completely exonerate ourselves—as few other critics can claim to do—from the ominous threats that open the novel:

[12] DeVoto, *op. cit.*, pp. 67–68.
[13] It may be significant that the phrase "honest injun" occurs immediately following Jim's first interview with Huck too.

"Persons attempting to find a motive in this narrative will be prosecuted; persons attempting to find a moral in it will be banished; persons attempting to find a plot in it will be shot." /355/

QUESTIONS FOR DISCUSSION AND WRITING

1. Baldanza points out that three repetitive themes re-occur with variation and development. Select one of these re-occurring themes and add to his list of its varying occurrences.
2. Identify a re-occurring theme that Baldanza does not mention and, by citing examples, show how Twain varied and developed it. What does this re-occurring theme add to the meaning of the novel?
3. How cogent is Baldanza's argument "that Twain had no control over" the re-occurring themes in *Huckleberry Finn?*
4. Survey the discussion, among the selections included in this volume, of the structure of *Huckleberry Finn,* and then assess the contribution Baldanza makes to our understanding of the novel.

WHY *HUCKLEBERRY FINN* IS NOT THE GREAT AMERICAN NOVEL

by William Van O'Connor

From the late nineteenth century to World War I, and even after, there was much discussion of the great American novel. Eventually the idea died, apparently of its own inanity. But in recent years the idea, though not the phrase, has returned to life, for we are informed, from a variety of critical positions, that *The Adventures of Huckleberry Finn* is the truly American novel.

Reprinted from *College English,* XVII (October, 1955) by permission of the publisher and William Van O'Connor.

A novel wants to be circumscribed to live in its own terms, to fulfill itself imaginatively. On the other hand, it speaks to a people and to their beliefs about themselves. Huck is said to live for us somewhat as Roland lives for France or Arthur for England. If Huck is firmly enshrined in myth it would be futile to try to dislodge him. But his place in an American myth would not of itself be assurance that *Huckleberry Finn* is a great novel.

The following observations maintain that the book owes much of its eminence to our mythologizing of the West and, further, that the claim made for it as a source book for all later "American" fiction is not a valid claim. In making such observations it is helpful to refer to the introductions of *Huckleberry Finn* written by T. S. Eliot and Lionel Trilling. It is also necessary, on occasion, to disagree with them. Mr. Eliot reads it—Twain's only masterpiece he says—as the story of the Boy and the River, the former being the unconscious or all but unconscious critic of civilization, its pursuits, wickedness, and vagaries, and the latter the symbol of time that is timeless and of human affairs carried downstream, often capriciously. Lionel Trilling also writes of the unblinking honesty of the boy Huck, and of the river as a god. He finds it a central American document and one of the world's great books.

Both Eliot and Trilling suggest that there is only one flaw, and this not a very serious one, to be charged against the structure of the book: the overly elaborate scheme for Jim's escape engineered by Tom Sawyer in the closing section of the story. Trilling does say the episode is far too long but, like Eliot, he justifies it as a way of returning the reader to civilization, and of freeing Huck, allowing him to disappear. The Tom Sawyer episode is certainly *a* method for bringing off the dénouement, but involved with it is a serious anticlimax. Miss Watson's will had already freed Jim, and all the high-jinks and genuine danger have been merely to satisfy Tom's desire to keep things hopping. Tom is the Practical Joker of American literature and Twain as a streak of it himself, which interferes with his true sense of comedy.

The critical acumen of Eliot and Trilling notwithstanding, there are a number of flaws in *Huckleberry Finn*, some of them attributable to Twain's refusal to respect the "work of art" and others attributable to his imperfect sense of tone. The downstream movement of the story (theme as well as action) runs counter to Jim's effort to escape. Life on the raft may indeed be read as implied criticism of civilization —but it doesn't get Jim any closer to freedom. One may also ask (it has been asked before) why it never occurred to Jim, or to Huck, to strike out for the Illinois shore and freedom. It is possible that

Twain felt Tom's highjinks were necessary not merely to prepare for the disappearance of Huck but to shift attention away from his conflicting themes.

For the downward movement of the novel, of course, the picaresque form /6/ serves the subject very well, allowing for innumerable and rapid adventures, afloat and ashore, and for the sort of ponderings that are peculiar to Huck. The picaresque form is also a clue to the kind of unity the book does have, a melodramatic mixture of reality and unreality and of comedy and horror. It is frequently theatrical in a good sense of the word. But the unity depends on Huck's mind, and too often there are bits of action, dialogue, and observation which are not appropriate to him. There are two sorts of theatricality in the novel, melodrama and claptrap.

Huck's relationship with his father is melodrama. So is the shooting of Boggs, or the tar and feathering of the Duke and King. A proof of their being melodrama is the ease with which one moves from a scene of violence to a humorous dialogue. For example, the encounter of Huck and Jim with the thieves and murderers aboard the *Walter Scott* is followed by the minstrel show, end-men sort of humor of "Was Solomon Wise?" Verisimilitude offers no problem when reality merges with unreality or horror dissolves innocently into comedy, but sometimes Twain's sense of proper distance, the degree and nature of the stylization he is employing, fails him and the action becomes gruesomely real. An instance of this is Huck's telling of the murders in "Why Harney Rode Away for His Hat." The starkness is too unrelieved. The scene does not respect the premises nor the general tone of the novel, and, even though it might work in another novel, it does not work here.

A good deal is made, quite justly, of Huck's affection for Jim, and the example commonly given is Huck's apology to Jim after having tormented him with a lie about there having been no storm. "It was fifteen minutes," Huck says, "before I could work myself up to go and humble myself to a nigger, but I done it, and I warn't sorry for it afterwards neither." But Twain sometimes loses sight of Huck's moral sensitivity. An instance is in Chapters XVII and XVIII.

Near the close of Chapter XVI the raft is run over by an upstream steamboat. In the darkness, after he and Jim have dived into the water, Huck cannot see Jim and his calls go unanswered. Huck then strikes out for shore. The following chapter, "The Grangerfords Take Me In," is a humorous introduction to the Grangerford family. Huck stays with the Grangerfords for many days, perhaps weeks, getting involved in their affairs, notably as courier between the lovers Miss Sophia Grangerford and Harney Shepherdson. No thought about Jim enters Huck's head! It doesn't occur to him to search for the old Negro. Jack, Huck's "nigger servant," finally invites him to see a "stack o' water-moccasins" in a swamp, a trick for leading him to the spot where Jim is hiding. "I poked into the place a ways and come to a little open patch as big as a bedroom all hung round with vines, and found a man lying there asleep—and, by jings, it was my old Jim!" There is not much indication that Huck is greatly relieved or moved at finding Jim alive: "I waked him up, and I reckoned it was going to be a grand surprise to him to see me again. . . . He nearly cried he was so glad. . . ." Huck says nothing about being glad himself. Perhaps we are to read this passage ironically, as an instance of a boy's self-centeredness and believe that true affection lies beneath it. This might be so, but it doesn't explain away Huck's absence of grief over Jim's "death," or his failure to search for him if alive, or his general indifference to Jim's fate.

Technically, too, the device for getting rid of Jim so that Huck can move into the Grangerford-Shepherdson world is awkward and unconvincing. Jim tells Huck he had heard him call for him when they were swimming toward shore but hadn't answered for fear of being detected. Presumably one reply would have quieted Huck and made detection much less likely. And if Huck had been allowed to help Jim hide, or even to maintain some awareness of him, he would be the Huck known to us in "Fooling Old Jim." /7/

Huck's parody (Chapter XVII) of the activities of Emmeline Grangerford, poetess, is extremely amusing, but the "voice" is more nearly Twain's than Huck's. Many other things are put into the mouth of the twelve- or thirteen-year-old Huck that, sometimes only weakly humorous themselves, are Twain himself speaking. This, for example, from a boy with almost no schooling:

> Look at Henry the Eight; this 'n' 's a Sunday-school Superintendent to *him*. And look at Charles Second, and Louis Fourteen, and Louis Fifteen, and James Second, and Edward Second, and Richard Third, and forty more; besides all them Saxon heptarchies that used to rip around so in old times and raise Cain. . . .

There are other witticisms about kings, a theme appropriate enough to *Huckleberry Finn*, but Twain might have found some other way of introducing them. In "An Arkansas Difficulty," where Twain is giving a sense of life in a small river-town, he makes Huck relate an observation on "chawing tobacker" that one would expect to find as "filler" in a nineteenth-century newspaper or magazine. Most incongruous of all, perhaps, is Huck's account of the Duke's rendition of Hamlet's soliloquy.

A more self-conscious artist would not have allowed such discrepancies to mar the tone of his novel. The truth is that Twain, however gifted a raconteur, however much genius he had as an improviser, was not, even in *Huckleberry Finn*, a great novelist.

A glance at Twain's biography reveals attitudes that, if they were related about another "major" writer, would appear highly damaging. In *My Mark Twain* William Dean Howells reported: "He once said to me, I suppose after he had been reading some of my unsparing praise of [Jane Austen]: '*You* seem to think that woman could write,' and he forbore withering me with his scorn. . . ." Howells also wrote: "I fancy his pleasure in poetry was not great, and I do not believe he cared much for the conventionally accepted masterpieces of literature." And of Henry James, whose *The Bostonians* was serialized in the same magazine with *Huckleberry Finn*, Twain said, "I would rather be damned to John Bunyan's heaven than read that." /8/

QUESTIONS FOR DISCUSSION AND WRITING

1. O'Connor charges that *Huckleberry Finn* is in part melodramatic. Support his charge by extending his list of melodramatic events or refute his charge by showing the high seriousness and complex view of life embodied in the events he lists.

2. Is Huck's failure to grieve for the supposedly drowned Jim really a flaw, as O'Connor says it is? Does Twain commit any other artistic sins of omission in the novel?

3. "Most incongruous of all," writes O'Connor, ". . . is Huck's account of the Duke's rendition of Hamlet's soliloquy." What do you suppose O'Connor finds incongruous about it? Is it incongruous? Whether it is incongruous or not, what does the account add to *Huckleberry Finn?*

4. Having finished his list of flaws, O'Connor concludes that Mark Twain "was not, even in *Huckleberry Finn*, a great novelist." Is his list sufficient to call in question the greatness of the novel?

5. If you agree with O'Connor that *Huckleberry Finn* is a greatly flawed novel, develop further support for his position.

6. Do other critics agree with O'Connor in regarding as flaws the elements he points out?

THE UNITY AND COHERENCE OF *HUCKLEBERRY FINN*

by *Richard P. Adams*

Huckleberry Finn received very little critical attention of any kind before 1948. Students up to then were more interested in the life of Samuel Clemens than in the esthetic qualities of his work. It was generally felt that he was not an artist, and that any esthetic consideration of his writing would be a waste of time.

In 1948, however, Lionel Trilling published his brilliant introduction to the Rinehart edition.[1] His defense of the ending of the book, which had always been deplored, led to a controversy. T. S. Eliot, in another brilliant introduction, published in 1950, agreed with Trilling.[2] In 1953 Leo Marx dissented, attacking Trilling, Eliot, and the book.[3] Others, such as E. M. Branch, Gladys Bellamy, J. M. Cox, Lewis Leary, and Frank Baldanza, have approached the story from various esthetic points of view and offered various critical opinions.[4] Several theories and suggestions emerge concerning theme and structure, style and technique, and the esthetic value of the work. But no discussion has yet presented a formula that fully or systematically accounts for the greatness of *Huckleberry Finn* as a work of literary art.

Tom Sawyer has been more fortunate. In 1939 Walter Blair made an analysis of it which shows clearly and fairly completely the prin-

[1] Reprinted in *The Liberal Imagination* (New York, 1950), pp. 104–117.

[2] *The Adventures of Huckleberry Finn* (London, 1950), pp. vii-xvi.

[3] Leo Marx, "Mr. Eliot, Mr. Trilling, and *Huckleberry Finn*," *Am. Schol.*, XXII (Autumn, 1953), 423–440.

[4] Edgar M. Branch, *The Literary Apprenticeship of Mark Twain* (Urbana, 1950), pp. 199–216; Gladys C. Bellamy, *Mark Twain as a Literary Artist* (Norman, 1950), pp. 340–347; James M. Cox, "Remarks on the Sad Initiation of Huckleberry Finn," *SR*, LXII (Summer, 1954), 389–405; Lewis Leary, "Tom and Huck: Innocence on Trial," *VQR*, XXX (Summer, 1954), 417–430; and Frank Baldanza, "The Structure of *Huckleberry Finn*," *AL*, XXVII (Nov. 1955), 347–355. All of these, except the last, more or less strongly disagree with Trilling and Eliot about the ending.

Reprinted from *Tulane Studies in English*, VI (1956) by permission of the publisher.

ciples of construction and of unity that Clemens used in /87/ his better fiction. There are, Blair says, four "lines of action" in *Tom Sawyer*, all concerned with the boy's development toward manhood and moral maturity.

> Each one of these is initiated by a characteristic and typically boyish action. The love story begins with Tom's childishly fickle desertion of his fiancée, Amy Lawrence; the Potter narrative with the superstitious trip to the graveyard; the Jackson's Island episode with the adolescent revolt of the boy against Aunt Polly, and Tom's youthful ambition to be a pirate; the Injun Joe story with the juvenile search for buried treasure. Three of these narrative strands, however, are climaxed by a characteristic and mature sort of action, a sort of action, moreover, directly opposed to the initial action. Tom chivalrously takes Becky's punishment and faithfully helps her in the cave; he defies boyish superstition and courageously testifies for Muff Potter; he forgets a childish antipathy and shows mature concern for his aunt's uneasiness about him. The Injun Joe story, though it is the least useful of the four so far as showing Tom's maturing is concerned, by showing Huck conquering fear to rescue the widow, has a value as a repetition—with variations—of the motif of the book.[5]

The interweaving of these four lines of developing action, Blair feels, gives "reason for believing that the theme, the main action, and the character portrayal in the novel are one—the developing of Tom's character in a series of crucial situations."[6] That is to say, quite correctly I think, that *Tom Sawyer*, for all its apparent casualness of construction, has a high degree of organic unity. Blair does not say that it has a coherent plot, nor would I, but the clear implication is that it does not need one. Its unity and coherence are thematic and symbolic—imaginative in the Coleridgean sense. Its elements are not related by the logic of cause and effect. Instead, they are fused in an organization of imagery that transcends any concept of plot or story line as a series of causally related events.

Huck Finn has a somewhat different structure, but the principle is the same or very similar. It has a symbolic pattern or organization of imagery, not a plot in the traditional sense. Critics who ignore Clemens's warning and come to it looking for a plot are likely to go

[5] Walter Blair, "On the Structure of *Tom Sawyer*," *MP*, XXXVII (Aug. 1939), 84–85.

[6] *Ibid.*, p. 86. Leary, pp. 419–423, in his discussion of *Tom Sawyer*, confirms Blair's theory, but he does not apply it to *Huck Finn*.

astray, fall foul of Trilling and Eliot, and bog down in a fruitless effort to prove that the ending, or the whole book, is a failure. When a critic gets that far out on a limb it is not necessary to shoot him. /88/

The most obvious element of structure in *Huck Finn,* and the one most often noticed, is the picaresque journey down the river, full of inconsequently interspersed and apparently aimless adventures. But it is dangerous to say that much and stop, for the inconsequence does not preclude a plan, and the aimlessness is only apparent. Trilling, in discussing the special qualities of the river as a road, points out some profitable directions for further inquiry. The important thing, he says, is that the river is a moving road,

> . . . and the movement of the road in its own mysterious life transmutes the primitive simplicity of the form: the road itself is the greatest character in this novel of the road, and the hero's departures from the river and his returns to it compose a subtle and significant pattern. The linear simplicity of the picaresque novel is further modified by the story's having a clear dramatic organization: it has a beginning, a middle, and an end, and a mounting suspense of interest.[7]

Trilling perhaps oversimplifies the linear quality of the picaresque novel as Clemens knew it, but he does not overestimate the complexity of *Huck Finn,* and his observations on the "living" quality of the river and on the alternation of Huck's river and shore experiences are valuable clues.

Another clue, of perhaps even greater value, is furnished by James M. Cox's discussion of Huck's "initiation." According to Cox, the "fake murder" that Huck stages in order to get away from his father "is probably the most vital and crucial incident of the entire novel,"[8] and Cox's observations on this event come close to defining the basic structure of the novel. The basic structure, which expresses the theme of the boy's growth and which carries the weight of the incidents and the imagery throughout, is a pattern of symbolic death and rebirth. As Cox points out, the central action on the river begins with Huck's pretended death. It ends with his mistaken recognition as Tom by Aunt Sally Phelps, when he feels that "it was like being born again, I was so glad to find out who I was." This pattern is kept in the focus of the reader's attention, as Cox also observes, by repeated deaths and escapes occurring between, before, and after the main events.

[7] Trilling, p. 115.
[8] Cox, p. 395.

The pattern of death and rebirth is reinforced by the pattern Trilling observes in Huck's departures from and returns to the river; only we need to reverse Trilling's terms, for it is Huck's de- /89/ partures from and returns to shore which are cognate and parallel to the pattern of death and rebirth. The same pattern provides the framework for the "clear dramatic organization" which Trilling notices, and it roughly determines the kind of beginning, middle, and end that the story has. Putting Cox and Trilling together, and oversimplifying for the sake of initial clarity, we can state a more nearly complete definition of the structure of *Huckleberry Finn*. The beginning is Huck's life on shore in and around the village of St. Petersburg with the Widow Douglas and Pap. The middle, initiated by Huck's fake death, is his withdrawal from the life of society and civilization to the river; this withdrawal is repeated after each of his adventures on land. The end is his equivocal rebirth, his qualified return, under a false identity and with many reservations, to civilized life at the Phelps plantation.

The pattern of death and rebirth is also intimately concerned in the "mounting suspense of interest" which Trilling notes. The theme of the book, as we have hinted, is the same as that of *Tom Sawyer:* the growth of a boy to manhood, and his final acceptance of adult moral responsibilities. In this connection the pattern of death and rebirth is more than a technical device. In the tradition of romantic literature, to which *Huck Finn* belongs, it is a form with a meaning. The growth of a boy to manhood is perhaps the most popular of all themes for romantic fiction, and the structure which best expresses it is that of the death-and-rebirth pattern. The reason for this association is based in romantic philosophy, according to which the individual human personality is conceived as an organism which cannot undergo a fundamental change of any kind without being totally reconstituted. Its old self "dies" and its new self, an unpredictably different organism, is "born." Huck's initiation, his transformation from boy to man, is such a change. It is a radical reconstitution of his moral attitude toward the society in which he lives. He grows, therefore, during the time of crucial change, by "dying" out of society, withdrawing into nature on the river, and then returning or being "reborn" into society with a new and different attitude toward it.

It should not have to be said that this return is by no means an uncritical acceptance of conventional social values. The process of Huck's moral growth is, in fact, most emphatically indicated by his decision, made on three separate but closely related occasions, to free Jim from slavery, which is an act of rebellion against society. In a superficial sense the three decisions are the same, but each /90/

means more than the one before, because Huck knows more about the society he is deciding to oppose and because he sees more fully and clearly the implications of the decision and its probable consequences.

The context, which becomes increasingly solid and massive as Huck's knowledge increases, is a complex interrelationship of social, cultural, political, and economic forces. We might skeletonize it by making three simple statements, which we can then elaborate. First, slavery is evil. Second, the pseudo-aristocratic society of the ante-bellum South which fosters and depends on slavery is also evil. Third, the sentimental culture veneer with which that society conceals its evil from itself, if not from others, is evil as well. These propositions apply with increasing cogency to Huck's three decisions, as he learns more about the character and workings, the concrete personal meanings and moral values, of Southern slave-holding aristocracy. The relations among these three intertwined thematic strands in *Huck Finn* are so complex and pervasive that a thorough explication of them would be longer than the book. I shall not try to exhaust them here, but rather to indicate their general character and, by exploring a few of them in some detail, to show how they work.

Huck's first decision to help Jim escape is made casually enough in the process of his own flight from civilization and from the domination of his father. When he comes across his fellow runaway on Jackson's Island, he is so glad to have his lonesomeness relieved by any sort of company that he hardly thinks of difficulties. "People would call me a low-down Abolitionist and despise me for keeping mum," he admits to Jim, "—but that don't make no difference. I ain't a-going to tell, and I ain't a-going back there, anyways." But even this first and easiest decision is preceded by a fairly substantial development of motives and of symbolic motifs. Huck has been introduced to respectable society at the Widow's, where gentility is manifested painfully to him in regular hours, formal meals, and stiff clothing. When Miss Watson tells him about the bad place, he says he wishes he were there. "She got mad then, but I didn't mean no harm. All I wanted was to go somewheres. . . ." Later the same night, in harmony with the fake murder which is to come, he says, "I felt so lonesome I most wished I was dead." Then, in the planning and organization of Tom Sawyer's gang, we see Huck's indirect exposure to the culture of popular books and the sentimental proprieties of "high-toned" robbery and exploitation. Tom and the gang, of course, /91/ are completely unrealistic about the crimes they propose to commit, and blissfully unaware that crime, as gilded by the popular romances, is morally wrong. Farther on, Huck is regaled with Pap's reverse snobbishness on the subject of education and with his poor-white's groundless assertion of superiority over the much better educated "free nigger."

These lights and others like them are placed so as to reveal what Clemens considered to be the characteristic weaknesses, follies, and injustices of prewar Southern society. The essentially false and hypocritical gentility of the would-be aristocracy, the febrile and morally confusing sentimentalism of its favorite literature, and the crime of slavery which was the real basis of its economic and social system are continually brought home to Huck and the reader, in all kinds of dramatic, representative, and symbolic ways. The incidents are not haphazardly chosen or arranged. Each has its revealing gleam to contribute to Huck's unconsciously dawning awareness of the true values of the civilization to which he is being asked to belong. The result is that he runs away and, without any great misgivings at first, agrees to help Jim do the same.

The second decision is made necessary by a qualm of conscience. The fugitives are approaching Cairo, or think they are, and they both believe that Jim is almost free. Says Huck, "It hadn't ever come home to me before, what this thing was that I was doing. But now it did; and it stayed with me, and scorched me more and more." The point of difficulty is that freeing Jim involves robbing his owner, Miss Watson, of the eight hundred dollars he is worth on the market; and Jim makes the difficulty greater by threatening to have his children stolen, if necessary, by an Abolitionist. Huck is immediately and properly horrified. "It most froze me to hear such talk. . . . Here was this nigger, which I had as good as helped to run away, coming right out flat-footed and saying he would steal his children—children that belonged to a man I didn't even know; a man that hadn't ever done me no harm." The juxtaposition of "his" and "belonged" in this sentence, so carefully calculated to drive home the shocking injustice of property rights in human flesh, should not obscure the fact that there is a real moral issue. The great wrong of slavery does not make the lesser wrong of robbery right; a point which most pre-Civil War anti-slavery propagandists preferred to overlook. The issue is resolved by the fact that Huck finds himself unable to turn Jim in, for reasons which he does not fully understand but which the reader can surmise. To put it most simply, his human feelings are /92/ stronger than the commercial morality with which they are in conflict—as of course they should be. Unable to do entirely right, he chooses the lesser evil and goes on helping Jim.

When he repudiates his own conscience in this way, Huck takes a long step farther in his repudiation of Southern society, which has formed his conscience. He says to himself, in his usual innocent way, "what's the use you learning to do right when it's troublesome to do right and ain't no trouble to do wrong, and the wages is just the same? . . . So I reckoned I wouldn't bother no more about it, but after this always do whichever come handiest at the time." The innocence is of Huck, not Clemens, and it represents a remarkably keen penetration into the difficult question of personal or individual morality in relation to social conventions. Huck realizes in practice, though never in conscious theory, that the question is not one of a simple conflict between the individual and the mass, or the social institution, but that the two interpenetrate, and that the individual conscience is usually an ally of the social pressure for conformity.

Thoreau, in "Civil Disobedience," feels himself on solid ground when his conscience tells him to oppose the extension of slavery and the government that sanctions and promotes it. "If," he says, "the injustice . . . is of such a nature that it requires you to be the agent of injustice to another, then, I say, break the law." That seems comparatively easy; all that is needed is the courage to stand up against the government, which Southerners have always had in abundance. But, when the ante-bellum conscience is formed in Missouri instead of Massachusetts, the battle becomes intensely complicated. Its lines are drawn mostly inside the personality, which is then divided against itself. As Trilling remarks, it is the paradox in Huck's own thinking, by the terms of which he does right by doing what he thoroughly believes, in his conscious mind, to be wrong, that makes his character heroic and Clemens's satire brilliant.[9] His battle is desperate, his victory sublime. If it is fine to follow as Thoreau does the dictates of conscience over law, it is finer and much more difficult to follow those of the right over conscience and law combined.

It is fair to say, as it is for the first decision, that everything leading up to this second one contributes to Huck's preparation for making it as he does. We can examine the process most efficiently, perhaps, by focussing on one incident, and tracing its relations to see how they bear on the larger meanings of the action. Let us take, /93/ for example, the adventure of Huck and Jim with the murderers on the wrecked steamboat *Walter Scott*.

This event has a number of bearings, mostly ironic, on the related themes of aristocracy and sentimental literature. One of the antipa-

[9] Trilling, pp. 111–112.

thies which Clemens cherished most warmly and flourished most often was his detestation of Sir Walter Scott and all or almost all his works. In *Life on the Mississippi* Scott is blamed for having checked the "wave of progress" in the South with his propaganda for medieval feudalism, which, according to Clemens, "sets the world in love with dreams and phantoms; with decayed and swinish forms of religion; with decayed and degraded systems of government; with the sillinesses and emptinesses, sham grandeurs, sham gauds, and sham chivalries of a brainless and worthless long-vanished society." The reality behind these shams was, Clemens felt, a sordid and quite common crime. He remarked in a notebook entry, probably made in 1888, that the establishment of a monarchy "is the same sort of crime that surprise and seizure of a weak community's property by a robber gang, and the conversion of the community itself into slaves, is. . . . A monarchy is perpetuated piracy. In its escutcheon should always be the skull and crossbones." [10]

In these terms, the presence of three murderous robbers on a wrecked steamboat named *Walter Scott* is neatly satirical. It echoes, on a note of considerably greater seriousness, the earlier activities of Tom's gang, one of which is a seizure of doughnuts and jam from "a Sunday-school picnic, and only a primer class at that," which Tom insists is a rich caravan—as if that would make the act less shamefully cruel. The American function of Scott and others like him, Clemens implies, is to excuse and gloss over the exploitation of slaves and poor whites, and to glamorize the exploiters as Southern chivalry. The actual behavior of the slave-owning class, according to Clemens's double-edged suggestion, is on the one hand as evil as that of a gang of thieves and murderers, and on the other as silly as that of Tom's infatuated band.

Part of the loot of the *Walter Scott*, which the robbers unknowingly bequeath to Huck and Jim, is a number of appropriate books "about kings and dukes and earls and such, and how gaudy they dressed, and how much style they put on, and called each other your majesty, and your grace, and your lordship, and so on, 'stead of mister. . . ." Huck's reading to Jim from these books leads to /94/ a good deal of talk about Solomon and his wisdom, which Jim rather shrewdly questions, and about Louis XVI and "the dolphin," which prepares for the later advent of the bogus king and duke. The whole incident, in all its ramifications, contributes to the satirical exploration in Huck's experience of the various meanings, pretended and real, false and true, of the aristocratic idea in the South.

[10] *Mark Twain's Notebook*, ed. A. B. Paine (New York and London, 1935), p. 197.

This incident is balanced as well as followed by the much more important one of Huck's separation from Jim in the fog and his practical joke in making Jim think that it was a dream. In this event Huck is made to realize that Jim is a proud and sensitive human being, not livestock or chattel goods, and that the joke has been a cruel and humiliating betrayal of a friend's feelings. Corrupted by his life in a slave society and by the propaganda with which that society tries to justify the crime of slavery, Huck has never before considered that a slave might have feelings as worthy of respect as anyone else's. The speech in which Jim shows him his error, full of simple dignity and a pathos that beautifully consists with its righteous indignation, opens Huck's eyes in a way that is likely to stay in his memory. His reaction is worthy. "It was fifteen minutes," he says, "before I could work myself up to go and humble myself to a nigger; but I done it, and I warn't ever sorry for it afterward, neither. I didn't do him no more mean tricks, and I wouldn't done that one if I'd 'a' knowed it would make him feel that way." This realization, occurring shortly before the second decision to help Jim escape, makes any other decision practically impossible. With his indirect, unconscious realization of the falseness of aristocracy to balance his new awareness of the humanity of the slave, Huck would find it the meanest trick of all to betray Jim and send him back into the status of a piece of property to be exploited by the robber gang which is the reality behind the sham front of Southern aristocracy.

The third and final decision is led up to by a more personal and extensive experience of upperclass Southerners than before. Shortly after the second crisis, Huck and Jim realize that they have passed Cairo in the fog, but before they can do anything to get back, the raft is wrecked by a steamboat and they are separated again. Huck finds himself ashore, beginning a new phase of the story and of his education. His shore adventures alternate, from this point on, with repeated escapes to the river, until he comes to the Phelps plantation. These adventures bring him more dramatically than before into contact, and more often into conflict, with aristocrats of various kinds. The increase of experience, knowledge, and understand- /95/ ing which he gains in this phase leads convincingly to his ultimate decision to repudiate aristocratic society by freeing its victim Jim.

The first aristocrats he meets in person, leaving aside the Widow, Miss Watson, and Judge Thatcher, are the Grangerfords, by whom he is strongly impressed and who are genuinely impressive in many ways. They have the typical aristocratic virtues: they are dignified, hospitable, proud, handsome, cultured (after a fashion), courteous, devout, and kind to strangers and dependents. But the more

Huck learns of them, the more uneasy he becomes about their character and behavior. Clemens, through Huck's observations and comments, gradually undercuts the value of their culture. The description of the house, which is parallel to the account of "The House Beautiful" in *Life on the Mississippi*, is a skillful piece of irony. Huck admires the place immensely, while Clemens mercilessly exposes the queer mixture of arrogant show and pathetic provincialism that it presents to even a moderately sophisticated eye. The description leads up to and is ludicrously topped off by Huck's account of Emmeline Grangerford's esthetic misdeeds in crayon and verse, of the graveyard school run wild and gone to seed. The cultural pretensions of the aristocracy are, by this report, sufficiently harmless in themselves but crude, anachronistic, and highly absurd from any civilized modern point of view.

The feud which is going on between the Grangerfords and the Shepherdsons is a much more serious matter, and it does not depend on the same kind of irony for its effect. It is as deeply horrifying to Huck as it could possibly be to Clemens. The brutal killing of the two boys makes Huck so sick that he cannot even tell about it in detail without getting sick again; and his admiration for the better qualities of the aristocrats is more than canceled by this result of their violence.

The incident is a direct expression of feeling on the part of its author. In *Life on the Mississippi* Clemens goes somewhat out of his way to comment on a published opinion that the South had "the highest type of civilization this continent has seen. . . ." He demonstrates the hollowness of the brag in a footnote with "Illustrations of it thoughtlessly omitted by the advertiser," consisting of newspaper accounts of four fights in which five Southern gentlemen were killed and one injured, with the usual incidental damage to bystanders, reference also being made to four other murders and one nonfatal stabbing in previous engagements involving some of the same gentlemen. The people concerned were of the highest class that /96/ Southern civilization had produced, including a general and his son, a bank president, a college professor, and "two 'highly connected' young Virginians" who fought a duel with butcher knives. It is from this kind of violence that Huck escapes to the river again, wishing that he "hadn't ever come ashore that night to see such things. I ain't ever going to get shut of them—lots of times I dream about them." Clemens had often dreamed about some violent episodes he witnessed as a boy.

Huck's reaction leads to one of his most lyric descriptions of the freedom, comfort, and beauty of the river, and the loveliness of life on a raft. But evil comes into this world also, in the shape of the two confidence men who palm themselves off as "the rightful Duke of Bridgewater" and "the late Dauphin. . . . Looy the Seventeen, son of Looy the Sixteen and Marry Antonette," and who take over in the true aristocratic robber-gang fashion. The cream of the jest is that the duke's claim is accepted by the other rogue so that he may in turn make his higher claim. The cream of the cream is that the duke then has to admit the king's superior status and rights in order that both may exploit the plebeian members of the little commonwealth. But the richest layer of all is Huck's good-naturedly cynical accommodation to the whole arrangement. He sees immediately what frauds these are, but he is pleased when the duke knuckles under; "for what you want, above all things, on a raft, is for everybody to be satisfied, and feel right and kind towards the others."

Clemens's feeling about the kind of imposition practiced—or at least attempted—here is given in another notebook entry: "There are shams and shams; there are frauds and frauds, but the transparentest of all is the sceptered one. We see monarchs meet and go through solemn ceremonies, farces, with straight countenances; but it is not possible to imagine them meeting in private and not laughing in each other's faces." [11] The fraud practiced by the bogus king and duke is no different from the frauds put over by real kings and dukes, except that the latter are bigger. As Huck explains to Jim, after the confidence men have worked over their first town together, they are lucky not to have Henry VIII on their hands, for he was a really accomplished crook; "If we'd 'a' had him along 'stead of our kings he'd 'a' fooled that town a heap worse than ourn done. I don't say that ourn is lambs, because they ain't, when you come right down to the cold facts; but they ain't nothing to *that* old ram, /97/ anyway." This observation reinforces the point already made, implicitly, that the Grangerfords and Shepherdsons, by their more serious imitation of aristocratic ways, are only presenting a more pernicious version of something which at best is a sham and a fraud.

Perhaps the most emphatic impression of the ugly side of Southern chivalry is given by the incident in which Huck witnesses the cold-blooded murder of old Boggs by Colonel Sherburn. Boggs is a noisy but harmless fool, Sherburn a fine example of aristocratic pride—brave and intelligent in his own way, but narrow, selfish, inconsiderate, harsh, and brutal. It is, again, a sickening scene, and it is based on a murder that Clemens witnessed as a boy. But it may be that the importance of the incident for the satirical aspect of the book lies mainly in the character of the townspeople, who are by and large a

[11] *Ibid.*, p. 196. Clemens neglected this view when he later met some royal persons himself.

degraded lot. "There couldn't anything wake them up all over," says Huck, "and make them happy all over, like a dog-fight—unless it might be putting turpentine on a stray dog and setting fire to him, or tying a tin pan to his tail and see him run himself to death." They try half-heartedly to get Boggs to stop his offensive yelling and go home, but they also perversely enjoy the shooting and the old man's death, the view of the body in the drug store window, and the re-enactment of the murder by one of the onlookers. When they go to Sherburn's house with the announced intention of lynching him, he lectures them contemptuously and drives them off with a shotgun, which he does not have to fire.

His contempt seems justified, on the face of things. These are the same people who, after hooting the Shakespearean efforts of the king and duke, prove ripe for the Royal Nonesuch hoax. The duke, in his estimate of them, agrees with Sherburn. He prints at the foot of his handbill "LADIES AND CHILDREN NOT ADMITTED," remarking, "There . . . if that line don't fetch them, I don't know Arkansaw!" It does. But the deeper point is not explicitly stated here, or anywhere else in *Huck Finn,* nor is it fully understood, we may suppose, by either Sherburn or the duke. They see well enough that the people are ignorant, cowardly, and gullible; they do not see that the reason for that fact is the apparently opposite fact that an aristocracy is in power. Clemens, however, was aware of it and well convinced that poverty, both of the flesh and of the spirit, is the mirror image of aristocratic splendor and that universal cruelty is inevitably characteristic of any society divided into rigid classes with hereditary inequalities of function, privilege, and status. /98/

This principle is explained more clearly in *A Connecticut Yankee.* The Yankee is shocked at the way poor peasants in Arthurian England rush out, heedless of right or justice, and help each other hang their neighbors in their lord's behalf, apparently unable "to see anything horrible about it." His comment is almost a direct reference to the satire in *Huck Finn.*

> It reminded me of a time thirteen centuries away, when the "poor whites" of our South who were always despised and frequently insulted by the slave-lords around them, and who owed their base condition simply to the presence of slavery in their midst, were yet pusillanimously ready to side with the slave-lords in all political moves for the upholding and perpetuating of slavery, and did also finally shoulder their muskets and pour out their lives in an effort to prevent the destruction of that very institution which degraded them. And there was only one

> redeeming feature connected with that pitiful piece of history; and that was, that secretly the "poor white" did detest the slave-lord, and did feel his own shame.

The Yankee also remarks that "it is enough to make a body ashamed of his race to think of the sort of froth that has always occupied its thrones without shadow of right or reason," and what Clemens obviously means is that any respectable race would blow such froth to the moon before letting it settle into power.

Huck, whose background is about as purely poor-white as it could be, is given almost exactly the same words—"It was enough to make a body ashamed of the human race"—to describe his feelings about the next incident. The king and duke are having a fine run of initial success in playing their confidence game on the Wilks girls and most of their neighbors. It is a game that Huck perfectly understands, and he becomes so much ashamed of himself for being involved in it, though unwillingly, that he takes the risky measure of telling the truth in order to break it up. The most painful aspect of the affair applies directly to the theme of slavery, being the inhumanity of the fake aristocrats in the sale of the Wilks family slaves, "the two sons up the river to Memphis, and their mother down the river to Orleans." Huck says again that "it most made me down sick to see it. . . . I can't ever get it out of my memory, the sight of them poor miserable girls and niggers hanging around each other's necks and crying. . . ." The reader is likely to recall, as Clemens must have done, that this is not something only fakers do; it is precisely what Miss Watson does in planning to sell Jim "down to Orleans"; the general truth is that, as the Connecticut Yankee remarks in another place, "a privileged class, an aristocracy, is but a /99/ band of slaveholders under another name." The function of the king and duke is to show this basic identity, and underscore its meaning. Are these two scoundrels the most absurd, unmitigated, bare-faced buffoons of wickedness imaginable? So, Clemens wishes us to feel and understand, are all aristocrats. Kings, dukes, pirates, robbers, confidence men, and slaveholders are the same, and all sorry. Anyone who respects them is a fool, anyone who fears them is a coward, and anyone who supports them or submits to them is a slave himself.

Huck is none of these things, though he is almost infinitely good-natured and accommodating. He goes along with the king and duke as well and as long as he can, and he feels sorry for them when the mob escorts them out of town, in tar and feathers, on a rail. But he spoils their game with the Wilkses, and he leaves them when the king sells Jim into bondage again. For him, their function has been to complete his education in the social realities of slavocracy and to put the finishing touches on his preparation for the final decision he has to make. They have done the job effectively; he is ready now to see Jim through to freedom in spite of anything. Unconsciously, but with deep conviction, he understands the society to which by accident of birth he belongs, and refuses to submit to it.

On this last occasion, Huck sees his problem as being more difficult than it has ever seemed to him before, because it presents itself to him in terms of the religious sanction which the institution of slavery enjoyed in the prewar South. His conscience, unable to win the battle alone, now tells him, in accordance with the Sunday-school teaching he feels he should have had, "that people that acts as I'd been acting about the nigger goes to everlasting fire." Again, Huck is expressing one of his author's ideas. Clemens remarks of his mother in the *Autobiography* that,

> kind-hearted and compassionate as she was, I think she was not conscious that slavery was a bald, grotesque, and unwarrantable usurpation. She had never heard it assailed in any pulpit, but had heard it defended and sanctified in a thousand; her ears were familiar with Bible texts that approved it, but if there were any that disapproved it they had not been quoted by her pastors; as far as her experience went, the wise and the good and the holy were unanimous in the conviction that slavery was right, righteous, sacred, the peculiar pet of the Deity, and a condition which the slave himself ought to be daily and nightly thankful for.[12] /100/

Huck has easily won out over public opinion, less easily over public opinion reinforced by his own conscience. The addition of the Deity to the list of powers with which he has to contend raises his battle to its ultimate pitch of intensity.

His first maneuver is to pray for the improvement of his character, but he realizes at once that the plea is hypocritical. To make it good, he writes a letter to Miss Watson to tell her where Jim is, but he gets to thinking about Jim's goodness and loyalty and kindness, and all the times they have helped each other, and again he makes up his mind.

> I was a-trembling, because I'd got to decide, forever, betwixt two things, and I knowed it. I studied a minute, sort of holding my breath, and then says to myself:

[12] *Mark Twain's Autobiography*, ed. A. B. Paine (New York and London, 1924), I, 123.

> "All right, then, I'll *go* to hell"—and tore it up.
>
> It was awful thoughts and awful words, but they was said. And I let them stay said; and never thought no more about reforming.

With this decision, the middle or river section comes to its conclusion, and the ending of the book begins.

Clemens obviously had difficulty handling the ending. The reason seems to be that once Huck's final decision is made there is no longer any important part for Jim to play. His function in relation to the theme has been to test, or to furnish occasions when events would test, Huck's growing moral strength and mature independence. When that has been done, to the last possible extreme, Jim needs simply to be got out of the book as quickly and as unobtrusively as possible. Instead, Clemens plays up Tom Sawyer's long, elaborate, and almost meaningless escape plot. The final solution to the problem, the disclosure that Miss Watson has died and freed Jim in her will, is all that is needed, and the less said about it the better. And yet the escape plot is not altogether irrelevant. It furthers and completes the satire on sentimental literature, from which Tom draws his inspirations. It caps the ridicule of aristocratic pretensions by identifying Jim, the imprisoned slave, with the noble persons on whose renowned adventures his liberation is modeled. It is an immense expression of contempt for adult society, so easily and so thoroughly hoodwinked by a pair of audacious children; and the more absurd Tom's antics become, the more the satire is built up. It is as much an attack on conventional respectability as Huck's discomforts at the Widow Douglas's, or his observations on the culture of the Grangerfords, or his rebellion against slavery itself. /101/

Huck's attitude at the end is a mixture, full of ironies and reservations of many kinds. Having made the great decision to repudiate society, physically, morally, and spiritually, he can hardly return to it without equivocation. In a sense, his acceptance of the name and status of Tom Sawyer on the Phelps plantation is a return, but it is made on completely false premises. Also Huck is glad in a way to submit to Tom's leadership and direction. The burden of lonely responsibility has weighed long and heavily. But he is not fooled for a minute into thinking that there is any validity in Tom's adherence to bookish or aristocratic authority. "When I start in to steal a nigger," he says, "I ain't no ways particular how it's done so it's done. What I want is my nigger . . . and I don't give a dead rat what the authorities thinks about it nuther." He has arrived at maturity and self-sufficiency, and he is poised at the end in a delicate balance, ready at any moment "to light out for the territory" in order to escape Aunt Sally's threatened continuation of the civilizing process begun by the Widow Douglas.

This aspect of the conclusion is exactly right. It would have been wrong—impossible in fact—for Clemens to bring the story to a stop, as he might have tried to do by having Huck accept the moral values of society and return to it uncritically in a "happy ending." The whole process of his development runs counter to any such result. The impression that Clemens has to leave, and does leave, in the reader's mind and feelings is that Huck will continue to develop. He will escape again, as many times as he needs to, from society and any of its restrictions which would hamper or prevent his growth. He will die and be reborn whenever his character needs to break the mold that society would place upon it. Accordingly, the structure of the story is left open; the conclusion is deliberately inconclusive.

Frank Baldanza, who has made the most direct attack so far on the problem of structure in *Huck Finn,* believes that the basic principle can be defined as rhythmic repetition, with variation and development, of many thematic motifs, which have the effect of stitching the book together internally. He further suggests that each recurrence "was impulsive on Twain's part, and that any pattern we find in the repetitions is either unconsciously or accidentally ordained." [13] My analysis would seem to bear out the observation that rhythmic, varied, and developmental repetition is important. It is not basic to the structure, but it certainly does support it and supply /102/ it with a texture of rich and complex harmony. However, this effect is not and cannot possibly be accidental; it fits too well with the larger thematic repetition of Huck's decision. And I suspect very strongly too that Clemens must have been aware of it, in some way, as being appropriate to the pattern of the work he meant to make. A close examination will show that the motifs most often repeated are those most intimately concerned with the aristocracy-slavery-sentimentalism relationship. Moreover the variations add up to a steady intensification of Huck's and the reader's awareness of the injustice, the hypocrisy, and the general moral ugliness and weakness of Southern society before the war. This intensification provides the milieu and the measure of Huck's development through the death-and-rebirth pattern from irresponsible boyhood to moral maturity.

The total result of these thematic, structural, and symbolic workings is a novel which has a remarkably high degree of consistency, coherence, and unity. Its theme is the growth of an individual personity. Its crisis is the moral decision, repeated three times, to repudiate

[13] Baldanza, p. 353.

the conventions of society and do the individually, humanly right thing. Its rising interest is given by the sharply increasing complexity of the individual awareness of the implications of such an action. Its structure is defined by the extinction of the old childish organization of mind and feelings, the symbolic death of the individual as he was, his withdrawal from society into nature, and his reconstitution, or symbolic rebirth, on a higher and more mature level of organization, as a better, more capable person. The theme and structure are concretely embodied and related in the texture, which reinforces both with a rhythmically repeated and varied pattern of appropriate motifs and images. The functional, organic interrelations of all these factors must have something to do with the effect of unity which readers generally feel in *Huckleberry Finn*, but which we are now only beginning to understand and be able to explain. /103/

QUESTIONS FOR DISCUSSION AND WRITING

1. Do you agree with Adams and Cox that "repeated deaths and escapes" keep the reader's attention focused on the death and rebirth pattern? What are some of the deaths and escapes Adams and Cox refer to?
2. Adams asserts that Huck grows from youth to manhood in *Huckleberry Finn*. Does his assertion square with your impression of the novel? How much maturity does Huck gain in the novel?
3. Discuss *Huckleberry Finn* as a novel in "the tradition of romantic literature." Is Adams' meaning of "romantic" here synonymous with the meaning other critics have given the word in applying it to *Huckleberry Finn?*
4. Elaborate on or point out disparities in the parallel Adams sees between the boy-gang raid on the Sunday school picnic and the *Walter Scott* episode.
5. Using Adams' discussion of aristocracy in *Huckleberry Finn* as a basis, write a paper on the qualities, positive and negative, of aristocracy as presented in the novel. Use other critics to support your case, wherever possible.
6. Notice the list of violent events which Adams quotes from Twain's *Life on the Mississippi*. Does knowledge of this list make you more or less ready to agree with Pritchett's comments about the violence in *Huckleberry Finn?*

7. Adams is one of the few critics to give much attention to the Wilks episode while he is also one of the many who give much attention to the Grangerford-Shepherdson feud. What are the differences between these two episodes which promote this great difference in critical attention? Do the remarks of the critics themselves give you any clues to the answer?

8. Adams sees *Huckleberry Finn,* it seems fair to say, as an exposure of pre-Civil War Southern culture. Other critics have focused on the Western-ness of the society in the novel. Which side do you think advances the better argument? Which side is right? Or are both sides right?

MARK TWAIN AND THE NOVEL

by Richard Chase

Apart from any and all of its meanings *The Adventures of Huckleberry Finn* (1885) delights the reader first and last by its language. The book makes a music of words which is beautifully sustained and modulated to the very end. The language is original and it has proved to be one of the most important discoveries—for it was discovered and adapted rather than being created out of the whole cloth—that have occurred in American literature. Hemingway's well-known pronouncement that "all modern American literature comes from one book by Mark Twain called *Huckleberry Finn*" states a large truth, even though literally it is untrue. Wherever we find, in writers such as Stephen Crane, Sherwood Anderson, Sinclair Lewis, Faulkner, or Hemingway himself, a style that flows with the easy grace of colloquial speech and gets its directness and simplicity by leaving out subordinate words and clauses, we will be right in thinking that this is the language of Mark Twain. /139/ In the works of these writers we are not asked to accustom ourselves to a version of traditional "literary" English, as we are in reading Cooper, Hawthorne, Melville, or James, writers whose versions of English are sometimes highly idiosyncratic and imprisoned in their own special conventions. And yet, close as it is to the spoken English of rural Southwest America, the language of *Huckleberry Finn* is itself a new literary style which, as the works of Hemingway show, is capable of extreme conventionalization. It is literary because it is sustained beyond the span of spoken language to meet the requirements of a long story and because it is consciously adapted to the purposes of a novel which even those critics who object to the concluding part of the book, where Tom Sawyer takes over, on the ground that this makes a disunity, admit to be in the main a masterpiece of literary form. But it is also literary because, unlike ordinary spoken language, it is always conscious of the traditional English—notably of the Bible and Shakespeare—from which it is departing. The language of *Huckleberry Finn* is a kind of joyous exorcism of traditional literary English, but this ritual act allies it irrevocably with what it exorcises. And half the pleasure of reading the book comes from the alternation of tension and release as the language modulates or, as often happens, shifts with wonderful abruptness from traditional literary English to colloquial American.

This running relation between styles is most easily observed in the passages of burlesque and parody, as when the Widow Douglas tries unsuccessfully to "learn" Huck about Moses and the Bulrushers or in the scene where the Duke is working up to a delivery of Hamlet's soliloquy—

> Hamlet's soliloquy, you know; the most celebrated thing in Shakespeare. Ah, it's sublime, sublime! Always fetches the house. I haven't got it in the book—I've only got one volume—but I reckon I can piece it out from memory. I'll just walk up and down a minute, and see if I can call it back from recollection's vaults. /140/
>
> So he went marching up and down, thinking, and frowning horrible every now and then; then he would hoist up his eyebrows; next he would squeeze his hand on his forehead and stagger back and kind of moan; next he would sigh, and next he'd let on to drop a tear. It was beautiful to see him. By and by he got it. He told us to give attention. Then he strikes a most noble attitude, with one leg shoved forwards, and his arms stretched away up, and his head tilted back, looking up at the sky; and then he begins to rip and rave and grit his teeth; and after that, all through his speech, he howled, and spread around,

> and swelled up his chest, and just knocked the spots out of any acting ever *I* see before.

But a more subtly amalgamated language than that of burlesque is what makes the style of *Huckleberry Finn*. Among innumerable examples, there is Huck's version of the parting words of the woman who befriends him when, dressed as a girl, he stops by at her house: "If you get into trouble you send word to Mrs. Judith Loftus, which is me, and I'll do what I can to get you out." It is a perfect sentence considered either as "correct" English or ordinary speech, except for the incorrectness of "which is me." But the "which is me" is of the essence of Huck's style, the only graceful way of saying what it says. Any of the other possibilities would be awkward or preposterous—such as "which am I" or "who am I" or "who is me" or "that's my name" or "which is my name." The last alternative would be the least false; but it would be too formal and the natural tone of the sentence would have been thrown out of key. Huck's language flows with the effortlessness of the river itself, filling its mold to perfection, and in fact making in its restless energy its own ever new mold as it goes along. "We said there warn't no home like a raft, after all. Other places do seem so cramped up and smothery, but a raft don't. You feel mighty free and easy and comfortable on a raft." /141/

The language of *Huckleberry Finn* is a perfect vehicle for the hard, common-sense realism for which the book is famous and which, as much as the language itself, gives the book its important place as a precursor of modern literature. The author always seems to know when a detailed inventory of objects will be effective, and he sometimes makes these very detailed indeed. He knows too when to suppress detail, as in his descriptions of the raft. He gives a fairly factual account of the raft—how it was built, how it was steered, how Huck and Jim built the tepee on a raised platform, how they cooked fish and coffee. And yet the raft is rather vague in detail, perhaps because it is most important for what people feel about it and what they do and say on it. Pap's cabin in the woods, the "house of death" that floats down the river, the Grangerford house, these are described, particularly their contents, with more factual precision than the raft.

The greatness of *Huckleberry Finn* is in the simple clairvoyance of the truth it tells. Huck Finn, our observer and narrator, sees *everything* with the same impassive clarity and the same total lack of distortion with which he sees the most ordinary stick, stone, or fishhook. Unspeakable violence and cruelty, fraudulence and pretense, sordidness and glory, the sublime and ridiculous, pride and humility—all these are to be seen in the strong, representative episodes that epitomize so much of American civilization as they unfold before Huck on the trip down the river. This realism would not be a triumph if behind the impassive mask Huck remained unfeeling. But his feelings are strong, his reticences sensitive, and his sympathies and resentments plain. Nor do these feelings affect the cool steadfastness with which he sees and reports fact. In later writers such as Stephen Crane and Hemingway we encounter the same impassive clairvoyance, yet at no time do these authors succeed in reporting so much of the essential reality of a civilization. Doubtless this is what Lionel Trilling has in mind when he says that the greatness of *Huckleberry Finn* lies /142/ in "its power of telling the truth" and what T. S. Eliot means when he praises Huck's "vision" of the real world.

But to see truth clearly is to see that it is not always simple or predictable. So Mark Twain himself recognizes in one of the witticisms of Pudd'nhead Wilson's Calendar (in *Following the Equator*): "Truth is stranger than Fiction, but it is because Fiction is obliged to stick to the possibilities; Truth isn't." This aphorism, applied to *Huckleberry Finn,* leads us to see, what is in any case obvious, that Mark Twain's greatest book is poetic as well as realistic, for a part of the truth it encompases is of the sort we cannot even conceive without the intervening illusion of poetry.

Bernard De Voto, a dedicated Mark Twain critic and scholar, had no more than the most elementary understanding of poetic fictions and indeed he seemed not to believe in the virtue and substance of literature at all. He often put himself in the vanguard of those who automatically reject all talk of the "myth," "symbols," and "levels of meaning" literature may contain. Yet, with a rough accuracy, he says this of *Huckleberry Finn:* "Like *Tom* and in much greater measure it has a mythic quality. This is in part the river itself, the Mississippi which had dominion over Mark's imagination and here becomes a truly great symbol. Thus realism, fantasy, satire, mythology, and the tragic knowledge of man, all of them a good many layers deep, united in Mark Twain's masterpiece."

The river is a "symbol" all right, a symbol of nature and of God in nature. Both Mr. Trilling and Mr. Eliot say that in *Huck Finn* the river is "a god" and Mr. Trilling quotes from *The Dry Salvages,* a poem by Mark Twain's fellow Missourian, the lines about the river: "I do not know much about gods; but I think that the river / Is a strong brown god." The river throws off in the mind of Huck Finn an abundance of poetic forms and feelings. It is a poetic symbol, of the sort described above in Chapter IV, and it is analogous, as a symbol, to the whale in *Moby-Dick.* Like /143/ the white whale it has the complex and contradictory qualities of nature as well as of deity, being not only genial, sustaining, and nourishing but also sinister and dangerous.

As for the mythic quality alluded to by Mr. De Voto, this need not concern us at any length. It is present in at least two forms—in the theme of initiation and in what may be called the ritual of exorcism. The departures from and returns to the river as Huck goes through his adventures approximate the *rite de passage* which in religious cult introduces a boy into manhood, so that in this respect one thinks of *Huckleberry Finn* in relation to the book of Cooper's Mark Twain most disliked—*Deerslayer,* as well as in relation to *The Red Badge of Courage,* Hemingway's *In Our Time,* and Faulkner's *The Bear.* Actually, however, this myth is present in *Huckleberry Finn* only dimly, as a kind of abstract framework or unrealized possibility. This is typical of American literature. Generally speaking, it is not a literature in which the classic actions of the soul as traditionally depicted in myth, religion, and tragedy are carried through. Only in *Deerslayer* and *The Bear* is the drama of initiation rendered with any fullness. Characters in American fiction who seem to be, because of their situation and prospects, candidates for initiation do not usually change much under the pressure of what happens to them and when the author ascribes to his character, as in *The Red Badge of Courage,* a new manhood, new courage, new tragic awareness of life, it sounds unmistakably like "the moral"—in short, an afterthought—and we do not feel that the theme of initiation has been dramatically realized. In looking for the typical American candidates for initiation, one finds either that, sensitive, suffering, and intelligent as they may be, they turn out like Christopher Newman in James's *The American* to be impervious to transformation and tragic awareness or, like Huck Finn himself (or Frederic Henry in *A Farewell to Arms*), they are already initiated, they already know the real world with a tragic awareness. There is no real change in Huck Finn during the /144/ course of the book, except that he comes to adopt, as he reflects on his duty to Jim, a morality based on New Testament ethic rather than the convention of his time and place. This is a great achievement but it doesn't make a myth of initiation. What we have is only some of the abstract framework of this myth and some of its poetic awareness of the presence of deity in nature.

Huckleberry Finn is full of exorcism, and exorcism being a kind of magic, it arouses the emotions of awe and of wonder out of which myth grows. Jim teaches Huck a great deal about the magic of hair balls and other objects useful in banishing witches and placating the malign powers of the universe, and his tales and incantations are fertile ground for the sensibility of myth.

Analogous to this superstitious magic, but having nothing ostensibly to do with myth, is what one might call the intellectual exorcism of false forms by the sympathetic magic of parody and burlesque. Huck Finn frees himself of the romance imagination of Tom Sawyer, more or less as Sancho Panza does that of Don Quixote, by saying in various contexts: I don't take no stock in it. He ironically detects and parodies the graveyard romanticism of Emmeline Grangerford. Describing the pictures on the walls of the Grangerford house, Huck says:

> There was some that they called crayons, which one of the daughters which was dead made her own self when she was only fifteen years old. They was different from any pictures I ever see before—blacker, mostly, than is common. One was a woman in a slim black dress, belted small under the armpits, with bulges like a cabbage in the middle of the sleeves, and a large black scoop-shovel bonnet with a black veil, and white slim ankles crossed about with black tape, and very wee black slippers, like a chisel, and she was leaning pensive on a tombstone on her right elbow, under a weeping willow, and her other hand hanging down her side holding a white handker- /145/ chief and a reticule, and underneath the picture it said "Shall I Never See Thee More Alas."

The falseness of conventional religion is burlesqued in a thousand ways, but not often with the irony of the passage that describes the church service just before the ancient feud of the Shepherdsons and Grangerfords breaks out again with bloody cruelty:

> Next Sunday we all went to church, about three mile, everybody a-horseback. The men took their guns along, so did Buck, and kept them between their knees or stood them handy against the wall. The Shepherdsons done the same. It was pretty ornery preaching—all about brotherly love, and suchlike tiresomeness; but everybody said it was a good sermon, and they all talked it over going home, and had such a powerful lot to say about faith and good works and free grace and preforeordestination, and I don't know what all, that it did seem to me to be one of the roughest Sundays I had run across yet.

Had D. H. Lawrence concerned himself with *Huckleberry Finn*, he would doubtless have pointed out, with a measure of plausibility, the book's profoundest, more hidden and most ambivalent exorcism—that of European culture itself.

Mark Twain made himself famous for his enmity to Scott, Cooper, and the Gothic and sentimental novelists. His thrusts at these writers and their imitators are often hilarious. In *Roughing It* he ironically contrasts Cooper's "scholarly savages" with the tribe of mangy and disconsolate Indians which, as he learns on his trip West, are called the Goshoots. In Chapter 51 of *Roughing It* there is a farcical account of the communal composition of a novel, which turns out to be a farrago of Gothic horrors and tear-soaked domestic scenes. And everyone remembers the accusations against Scott in *Life on the Mississippi,* where the author of *Ivanhoe* is accused not only of infecting the Southern mind with "romantic juvenilities" and "windy /146/ humbuggeries" but also with having caused the Civil War. Contrasting *Don Quixote* with *Ivanhoe,* Mark Twain accounts for the superiority of the first by saying that it "swept the world's admiration for the medieval chivalry silliness out of existence; and the other restored it." *Huckleberry Finn* is also a book one of whose functions it is to sweep silliness out of existence.

But Mark Twain's most famous diatribe against the false forms of romance is "Fenimore Cooper's Literary Offenses." One never reads *Deerslayer* quite as one had, after hearing the suggestion that the name of the noble chieftain—Chingachgook—should be pronounced "Chicago." Mark Twain's general indictment of *Deerslayer* is a serious criticism, even though a rebuttal to most of the particulars suggests itself as one reads:

> It has no invention; it has no order, system, sequence, or result; it has no lifelikeness, no thrill, no stir, no seeming of reality; its characters are confusedly drawn and by their acts and words they prove that they are not the sort of people the author claims that they are; its humor is pathetic; its pathos is funny; its conversations are—oh! indescribable; its love-scenes odious; its English a crime against the language.

A writer of fiction, says Mark Twain, should "eschew surplusage. . . . use the right word, not its second cousin. . . . employ a simple, straightforward style." His characters should not behave like "windy melodramatic actors," their actions should be consistent with the personality attributed to them by the author, and their speech should be consistent and not, like that of Natty Bumppo, elevated and rhetorical at one moment and then, for no observable reason, colloquial at the next.

Still, all this is not an attempt to demolish romance and substitute realism. On the contrary, despite its negative approach, Mark Twain's essay is intended to show how romance must be written. He is lecturing Cooper on the "rules /147/ governing literary art in the domain of romantic fiction." He is pleading not for realism as such but for realism as the only way of effectively assimilating the miraculous. A leading rule of fiction is that "the personages of a tale shall confine themselves to possibilities and let miracles alone; or, if they venture a miracle, the author must so plausibly set it forth as to make it look plausible and reasonable."

Huck Finn shares Mark Twain's view of the imagination of romance, as we see whenever Tom Sawyer is present. Tom's head is full of the claptrap of romance, and for him it would be unthinkable to set Jim free from the cabin where in the late chapters of the book he is imprisoned, without doing it as such things are done in "the books," even though this entails an elaborate paraphernalia of moats, coats of arms, mysterious letters, and various impractical instruments of liberation. Tom's insistence on doing it the "right" way, the "regular" way, as specified by the authoritative books, makes the whole procedure, Huck has to admit, "mixed-up and splendid." Still, he can't help finally exclaiming, "I don't give a dead rat what the authorities thinks about it."

In *Huckleberry Finn* Mark Twain's imagination, when it is poetic, is the imagination of idyl and of melodrama. That life on the raft is idyllic and that *Huckleberry Finn* is a pastoral fiction that looks back nostalgically to an earlier and simpler America—this does not need arguing. It is only somewhat less obvious that the book banks heavily on melodrama—and burlesque and farce, which are to comedy what melodrama is to tragedy. T. S. Eliot is correct in saying that neither a tragic nor a happy conclusion would be appropriate for Huck himself. His life simply continues its pattern of unresolved contradictions; he will go on as the impassive observer and participant in abruptly alternating experiences of contentment and horror.

The melodrama in *Huckleberry Finn* is to be seen not only in stagey episodes like that involving the villains aboard the wrecked "Walter Scott" but in the sheer sensa- /148/ tional violence of the Shepherdson-Grangerford feud and the murder of Boggs and in episodes like Pap's wrestle with the angel of death. The dramatic lights and darks of the Calvinism on which Mark Twain was brought up seem mirrored in the very thunderstorms that roll spectacularly through the vast sky above the tranquil river. On aesthetic grounds at least, Jim seems right when he makes the oracular pronouncement that Huck is watched over by two angels, one of them light and the other dark.

There is no doubt that Mark Twain's imagination was profoundly affected by the doubleness of his personality and the contradictoriness of his feelings and opinions. He was a gay *farceur* and a saddened cynic, a romancer and a pessimistic determinist, a raffish westerner and a "candidate for gentility," a radical democrat and a hobnobber with Standard Oil executives, a disinterested genius and a commercial opportunist, an author who liked to project his own divided character by portraying twins and dealing in mistaken identities. All of his critics and biographers seem agreed on Mark Twain's doubleness, whether they go on to say, with Van Wyck Brooks, that his inner contradictions thwarted and ruined a literary genius or to say, with Mr. De Voto, that they did not. Probably all his critics agree too that Mark Twain's habit of mind was originally derived from the small-town life on the river that he knew as a boy and from his later feelings about it. When Mark Twain invoked Hannibal, Mr. De Voto says, "he found there not only the idyl of boyhood but anxiety, violence, supernatural horror, and an uncrystallized but enveloping dread." To know experience in this form is to prepare oneself for the imagination of *Huckleberry Finn*. /149/

QUESTIONS FOR DISCUSSION AND WRITING

1. Discuss one way in which the language of *Huckleberry Finn* delights the reader.
2. Using Chase's discussion of the style of *Huckleberry Finn* as a starter, discuss the prose style of the novel in detail.
3. Define and illustrate the "hard, common-sense realism" which Chase finds in the novel.
4. In what way may the "truth" that is in *Huckleberry Finn* be described as "simple" and "clairvoyant"?
5. Apply Twain's aphorism, quoted on page 143, to *Huckleberry Finn*.
6. What does Chase mean by saying *Huckleberry Finn* is "poetic as well as realistic"? (p. 143)
7. Write an essay demonstrating the applicability of the adjectives Chase uses to describe the river. (p. 144)
8. How much evidence can you find in *Huckleberry Finn* of a ritual which "introduces a boy into manhood"? (p. 144)
9. "There is no real change in *Huckleberry Finn* during the course of the book . . ." (pp. 144–145) What have other critics said about this? (Note Chase's qualification at the end of the above-quoted statement.)

10. Chase says that Huck "detects and parodies the graveyard romanticism of Emmeline Grangerford." (p. 145) What critics disagree with Chase? With whom do you agree?

11. What kinds of "silliness" does *Huckleberry Finn* help to "sweep . . . out of existence"? (p. 147)

12. What has been the critical consensus on the balance of romance and realism in *Huckleberry Finn?*

[STYLE AND POINT OF VIEW IN *HUCKLEBERRY FINN*]

by John C. Gerber

The most significant decision Mark Twain makes in beginning to write *Huckleberry Finn* is to have Huck tell the story. By this one decision he provides himself with a point of view that offers both the curbs and the detachment that his imagination needs for its best efforts. Almost magically it discourages him from doing the things he does badly and encourages him to do the things he does best. What is most important is not simply that Huck is a boy, though that is important; it is the kind of boy that Huck is.

Huck is a serious boy. From the very first, Twain makes him the straight, almost solemn reporter, with little or no sense of humor. Fog on the river, Pap's drunkenness, Miss Watson's piety, and the Royal Nonesuch, these are all solemn facts of life to Huck, no one of them to be regarded as less serious or more trivial than another. His own statements he takes as equally solemn facts, no matter how ludicrous they may be to the reader. He can report with sober admiration that Uncle Silas Phelps "never charged nothing for his preaching, and it was worth it too." This is the poker-face style elevated and made sincere.

From John C. Gerber's "Relation between Point of View and Style in the Works of Mark Twain," in *Style In Prose Fiction: English Institute Essays*, Columbia University Press, New York, 1958.

Having created such a character as narrator, Twain can hardly use him for his usual plunges into Washoe-type humor. Huck, who in a sense becomes stronger than Twain, won't be a party to such foolishness, though he is willing to report it as he hears it from others. So Twain is forced either to tone down his exaggerations and burlesques or to parcel them out to other characters. He does both, and in either case they get toned /158/ down, because in parceling them out he causes them to become revelations of character as well as means of evoking laughter. Consider, for example, what happens to an old Western chestnut as it gets told by Huck:

> . . . I've always reckoned that looking at the new moon over your left shoulder is one of the carelessest and foolishest things a body can do. Old Hank Bunker done it once and bragged about it; and in less than two years he got drunk and fell off of a shot-tower, and spread himself out so that he was just a kind of layer, as you may say; and they slid him edgeways between two barn doors for a coffin, and buried him so, so they say, but I didn't see it. Pap told me. But anyway it all come of looking at the moon that way, like a fool. (chap. 10)

Here the story becomes in part a revelation of Pap's character. More than that, as filtered through Huck's consciousness—his worry over new moons and his concern that the implausible details not be attributed to him—the original hilarity gets transmuted into something almost tender. Nothing of this sort has happened before, even in *Tom Sawyer*.

In like manner Huck's simplicity forces a new subtlety on Twain's satire. (I use the term *simplicity* here to indicate what is possibly more accurately suggested by the expression "the folk mind": a mind which is at once limited in knowledge and inept in abstract speculation but which is still deeply and profoundly aware of those elementary principles which give life meaning and make it tolerable.) Patently Huck does not know enough about politics, economics, and such to serve as satirist. What is more, he would make an implausible one even if /159/ properly informed since his inclination is to accept life rather than to denounce it. Substantially, therefore, the method of direct satire is closed to Twain.

But the indirect method is richly open and Twain makes the most of it. He gives to Huck those simple folk insights which in the end are the basis of his own mature reflection. Like Twain, Huck values what is useful, what is comfortable, and what is kindly. There is an obvious falsity about attaching grand labels to Huck, but it may be worth noticing that bundled up in him are the most elementary principles of utilitarianism, hedonism, and humanitarianism, and that when these principles clash the humanitarian principle prevails. Thus in Huck Twain has created a character perfectly equipped for direct or implied satire. Huck's standards are so uncomplicated and so indisputably praiseworthy that his very presence becomes a rebuke to conventional values and behavior. His practicality makes Tom's flights of fancy completely ridiculous; his hedonism makes the materialism of the Mississippi valley seem petty and futile; and his humanitarianism makes the mores and institutions of his time seem unspeakably hypocritical and cruel. To achieve his satirical intent in *Huckleberry Finn*, therefore, Twain need only show Huck acting in accord with his principles.

The most readily apparent effect on the style of this shift to indirect satire is that the narrative flow is no longer repeatedly interrupted for ridicule or denunciation. When it *is* interrupted, as when Twain stops to burlesque the artistic accomplishments of Emmeline Grangerford, there is still a general relevance. The rhetoric of direct satire which is inappropriate to Huck is either dropped, toned down, or put into /160/ the mouths of other characters, like Colonel Sherburn, where (as with the humor) it becomes primarily a revelation of character. In short, because of Huck's nature the satire, like the humor, becomes more restrained, more subtly contrived, and in the end more compelling.

Seeing the world through Huck's eyes also forces Twain into a more consistently pictorial style than he has used before. Huck is a boy, as every reader knows, of remarkable sensory perception. His concern is primarily with the facts of experience and not with generalizations drawn from the facts. And his mind, largely uncluttered with adult preconceptions, sees every experience as something fresh and new. It sees it realistically, too, for Huck is just as aware of the dangers as he is of the beauties. As Edgar M. Branch has put it, "Sensuous delight and apprehension are the twin overtones of his perception." [1] Such a viewpoint forces upon Twain an undeviating concern with the specific and concrete. The result is a style in which—and I do not exaggerate—almost every subject has a concrete referrent and in which the verbs are exploited for their connotative power even more spectacularly than before. Notice a few of these verbs: "It looked late and it *smelt* late. . . . They *swarmed* up in front of Sherburn's palings. . . . The racket stopped and the wave *sucked* back. . . . The crowd *washed* back sudden and then *broke* all apart and went tearing off every which way."

Whatever other effects Huck has on Twain's style, however, easily

[1] *The Literary Apprenticeship of Mark Twain* (Urbana, Ill., 1950), p. 209.

the most important is that he forces Twain into the vernacular. Having Huck tell the story in anything but his own dialect would be preposterous. /161/

What strikes one first about the dialect in *Huckleberry Finn*, I suppose, is its colloquial authenticity. This is, of course, no accident. Twain had an extraordinary ear for dialect and had been practicing with it in writing, if we want to be literal, ever since he sent in his first piece to Shillaber's *Carpet-Bag* in 1852. As he composed in dialect, he frequently spoke many of the lines over and over until he was quite sure that he had them right. The result in *Huckleberry Finn* is that he not only discriminates between dialects but between modifications of the same dialect. And within the speech of a single character he indicates sound differences due to stress and the position in the sentence. Just as important, he catches the drawling rhythms of his characters with uncanny effectiveness. The sentences are the shortest that he uses anywhere. About half of them in the narrative passages begin with the subject. The great majority of the others begin with words that have primarily a coordinating effect, such as *and, but, so, then, well,* and *anyways*. Fewer than one-tenth begin with an introductory clause or phrase, and most of these are phrases indicating time or place. Very rarely do sentences in dialogue begin with an introductory clause or phrase, though a number begin with nonsense words like *why* and *well* or with imperative verbs.

What must be clear is that Twain's rhythms are dependent primarily upon parallelism—parallelism of sentences as well as of elements within the sentence. He regulates tempo by varying the length of the elements and the complexity of the parallelism itself. In so doing he not only effects a difference in tempo between dialogue and narrative but a difference within the narrative itself. George Mayberry has made a detailed analysis /162/ of Huck's description of the circus and has discovered that the sentence rhythm is adapted to the gait of the horses and the activities of the performers. The sentence elements first come in twos, then in threes; then there is a quick acceleration to a climax followed by a drop to a spondaic ending.[2]

Although the writing of *Huckleberry Finn* has an authentic colloquial ring, it is not simply the recording of actual talk. Twain himself, in writing to Edward Bok, remarked on the difference between writing and speaking: "The moment 'talk' is put into print you recognize that it is not what it was when you heard it; you perceive that an immense something has disappeared from it. That is its soul." What is left, he continues, is "a pallid, stiff, and repulsive cadaver." [3]

[2] "Reading and Writing," *New Republic*, CX (May 1, 1944), 608.
[3] *Mark Twain's Letters*, II, 504.

No one would call Huck's talk cadaverous. It is casual, to be sure, but its casualness is so heightened that some are willing to call it folk poetry. This almost magical blend of the casual and the poetic, which avoids flatness on the one hand and mannered intensity on the other, is easier to illustrate than to describe. In the following passage, however, we can see at least some of the elements that make the blend possible.

> Once or twice of a night we would see a steamboat slipping along in the dark, and now and then she would belch a whole world of sparks up out of her chimbleys, and they would rain down in the river and look awful pretty; then she would turn a corner and her lights would wink out and her pow-wow shut off and leave the river still again; and by and by her waves would get to us a long time after /163/ she was gone and joggle the raft a bit, and after that you wouldn't hear nothing for you couldn't tell how long, except maybe frogs or something. (chap. 19)

Pushing the style toward the poetic are elements like these: the richly suggestive imagery, the connotative verbs, the economy of statement, the combination of introductory adverbial expressions and carefully molded parallelisms which create a slow, sustained, and quiet rhythm; and the over-all unity of effect which is so appropriate to the material. Holding the style to the casual are elements like these: the semi-local idioms, the phonetic spelling and the mistake in grammar, the shift from "we" to "you"; and, especially, such imprecise expressions as "whole world of sparks," "awful pretty," and "except maybe frogs or something."

In forcing Twain to find dialect locutions Huck causes him to abandon his bookish expressions. The "pretty" wording of the conventional nature description, beginning to die out in *Tom Sawyer*, now disappears altogether. Twain now observes through Huck and reports what he sees in Huck's words, not in the words of a chromo lover. Happily one misses, too, the hackneyed phrasing that has to some degree blunted the style of all Twain's books up to this one. Huck's dialect simply will not accommodate the old clichés. And the "soft" wording of the sentimental scenes almost disappears. In *Tom Sawyer*, Tom, peeking in on grieving Aunt Polly, hears her pray for him "touchingly" and "appealingly." He "lingers" over her while she is asleep and finally bends and kisses her "faded lips." When Huck says good-bye to Mary Jane Wilks, however, about all /164/ that happens is that his eyes "water a little." Even when she promises to pray for him, he reacts admiringly but nonsentimentally:

> Pray for me! I reckoned if she knowed me she'd take a job that was more nearer her size. But I bet she done it, just the same—she was that kind. She had the grit to pray for Judas if she took the notion—there warn't no backdown to her, I judge. You may say what you want to, but in my opinion she had more sand in her than any girl I ever see; in my opinion she was just full of sand. (chap. 28)

There is no need in this paper to get tangled in the controversy over whether the last ten chapters contribute to the value of the book or lessen it. There is the possibility, however, that one point about these chapters might be relevant here. *Huckleberry Finn* is a modified frame story, with Tom the major character in the first three chapters and the last ten and Huck the major character in the large central portion. Technically the point of view does not change since Huck tells the entire story. But in effect it exerts less control over Twain in the frame elements where Tom, as the focal point, makes it relatively easy for Twain to carry the story into parody. Likewise the style *per se* does not change, but it is not so impressive in the frame elements since it is expended there upon material of less consequence.

We hardly need go back and labor the main point again. Huck, at least in the central part of the book, provides Twain with precisely the kind of detached and limited point of view that his imagination needs, and the result is his finest stylistic /165/ achievement. Indeed, if we are to believe Ernest Hemingway it is the most influential prose style in American literature.[4]

At first glance Hank Morgan seems to offer a point of view for *A Connecticut Yankee* that is about as detached and sharply restricted as the one Huck gives to *Huckleberry Finn*. Hank is not a boy, to be sure, but on the other hand he is not a man of broad education and sophistication. When he first wakes up in Camelot he is in his thirties; he has been a blacksmith, a horse-doctor, a mechanic, and finally a superintendent in a Connecticut arms factory; he has apparently read little and traveled not at all. By his own admission he is so practical that he is "nearly barren of sentiment." Twain's initial intention, then, is to view the arch-romance of "sixth-century" England through the eyes of a character as unromantic as one can imagine. But he does not write four chapters before he bursts through his persona and takes over the story himself. Hank Morgan remains as the narrator, but the point of view, the basic attitudes, and the language are Twain's.

[4] See his much-quoted passage in the first chapter of *The Green Hills of Africa*: "All modern American literature comes from one book by Mark Twain called *Huckleberry Finn*."

This happens partly because Twain does not understand or even respect his narrator. All the elements that gave Huck reality and individuality are lacking here: a knowledge of the lore of his own religion; the local idioms, allusions, and slang; the regional pronunciation. Huck knows the jargon of the river and uses it; Hank Morgan, despite his background, employs /166/ almost no shop talk. As a matter of fact, Hank's humor and general orientation are more Western than Eastern.

Twain seems to be able to conceive of the Yankee only as a stereotype, not as a flesh and blood Connecticut mechanic. What is more, it is a stereotype that he does not especially admire. In the book itself he attacks the excessively practical and moralistic person, and to Dan Beard, his illustrator, he confided that his Yankee was an "ignoramus."

Even if Twain had understood and respected his narrator, however, it is still doubtful that he would have maintained the identity, for his purposes in writing the book were too diverse and confused. At first the story was to be only a genial, tall-tale farce based on the Arthurian legend; then it was to be a satire on English traditions and institutions; finally it was both of these plus a commentary on America and mankind in general. It seems doubtful that any narrowly focused or detached point of view could have been accommodated to all that Twain wanted to jam into the book with a pen, as he said, "warmed up in hell." In any event, the result was almost inevitable: despite the Yankee narrator *A Connecticut Yankee* turns out to be closer in both point of view and style to *Innocents Abroad* than to *Huckleberry Finn*.

Like *Innocents Abroad*, such uniformity as the style of the *Connecticut Yankee* possesses it gains from its basic colloquialism, but it is a badly battered colloquialism before the book comes to an end. According to the role that Twain forces the Yankee to play, the narration displays the exaggerations, raciness, and wild climaxes of the western raconteur; the over-obvious contrivances of the burlesquer; the silly solemnities of the buf- /167/ foon; the terse aphorisms of the crackerbarrel philosopher; the soggy emotion of the sentimentalist; and the sarcasm, broad irony, and vituperation of the satirist.

To take one of these roles, consider those passages in which the Yankee serves as raconteur. In these his style is at its liveliest. The incidents are molded for climax, and the words—especially the verbs—are dynamic. For sheer movement, vigor, color, and climax, some of the dramatic incidents in the book represent the finest in the western tall story tradition. And this despite the fact that even these passages are weakened by the clichés that plague the book as a whole. The climax of the restoration of the fountain in the Valley of Holiness is typical:

> Then I touched off the hogshead of rockets, and a vast fountain of dazzling lances of fire vomited itself toward the zenith with a hissing rush, and burst in mid-sky into a storm of flashing jewels! One mighty groan of terror started up from the massed people—then suddenly broke into a wild hosannah of joy—for there, fair and plain in the uncanny glare, they saw the freed water leaping forth! The old abbot could not speak a word, for tears and the chokings in his throat; without utterance of any sort, he folded me in his arms and mashed me. It was more eloquent than speech. And harder to get over, too, in a country where there were really no doctors that were worth a damaged nickel. (chap. 23)

Twain seldom allows the Yankee to serve as raconteur very long. Invariably he turns him into a satirist and the narration into anything from gentle spoofing to angry denunciation. The satire takes many forms: aphorisms, incidents, essays, sermons, /168/ and bits and pieces of vituperation. But whatever the form, the style is almost always characterized by emotional excess. When Twain attacks a character he beats him (or her) to a literary pulp. Morgan le Fay, for example is Satan, Vesuvius, and an ass; she is "loaded to the eyeballs with cold malice"; she is "hypercritical, murderous, rapacious, and morally rotten." Similarily, when he becomes sympathetic with a character the style grows maudlin. One young woman condemned unfairly to be hanged is "friendless" and her case "piteous." As the noose is adjusted around her neck she "devours" the baby in her arms, "wildly kissing it and snatching it to her face and her breast and drenching it with her tears, and half moaning, half shrieking all the while." She implores one more kiss: "it is the dying that begs it." She gets it and almost "smothers" the child. At the last minute a priest promises to look out for it.

> You should have seen her face then! Gratitude? Lord, what do you want with words to express that? Words are only painted fire; a look is the fire itself. She gave the look, and carried it away to the treasury of heaven, where all things that are divine belong. (chap. 15)

What is probably more disconcerting about the satire than its emotional excesses is that it almost always dissolves into buffoonery. The narrator is forced to lay aside his lance and put on the cap and bells. The attack on medieval cruelty in the Morgan le Fay chapters is blunted because Hank Morgan himself suggests the hanging of the orchestra that played *In the Sweet Bye and Bye.* ("A little concession, now and then, where it can do no harm is the wise policy.") The pathetic toothless prisoners released from the dungeon are pursued by Sir Madok /169/ selling Peterson's Prophylactic Toothbrushes. And any indignation which develops over the wanton hanging of the slaves (and almost of the king and the boss) is dissipated by the arrival of Sir Launcelot and his followers on bicycles. The style in such passages shifts as abruptly as the role of the narrator. One moment we are treated to an obviously contrived attempt to produce concentrated horror:

> There was a jerk, and the slave hung dangling; dangling and hideously squirming, for his limbs were not tied.

Within a few lines, however, Hank is sounding exactly like Tom Sawyer:

> "On your knees, every rascal of you, and salute the king! Who fails shall sup in hell tonight!"
>
> I always use that high style when I'm climaxing an effect.

Sometimes the buffoon and the satirist blend together with astonishing results. At one point in the story, in three consecutive paragraphs the Yankee narrator sounds like a Malory ("he lightly took his spear and gat him hence"), a sentimental novelist ("They could remember him as he was in the freshness and strength of his young manhood, when he kissed his child and delivered it to its mother's hands and went away into that long oblivion"), an American rustic ("when you can say that of a man, he has struck bottom, I reckon"), and an essayist gifted with erratic literary elegance (". . . all gentle cant and philosophizing to the contrary notwithstanding, no people in the world ever did achieve their freedom by goody-goody talk and moral suasion").

Taken as a whole, the writing in *A Connecticut Yankee*, despite its basic colloquialism, is just about as patchwork a /170/ production as the ill-defined point of view should lead us to expect. Its appeal is in its profusion, in the variety and extremes of its effects. It is not dull but it is tiring. And as the book proceeds it grows progressively less interesting and effective. Like the other books discussed here, therefore, *A Connecticut Yankee* indicates that Twain's style is extraordinarily responsive to his point of view. More specifically—and here I return to my central proposition—it leads one almost inevitably to conclude that Twain's style flourishes only to the extent that his point of view is both detached and sharply restricted. /171/

QUESTIONS FOR DISCUSSION AND WRITING

1. Can you make a case for Huck as possessing a sense of humor?
2. Why is there "an obvious falsity about attaching grand labels to Huck" (p. 160)?
3. Explain where and how the most elementary principles of utilitarianism, hedonism, and humanitarianism are bundled up in Huck. Do other critics also find these in Huck?
4. Find a passage in *Huckleberry Finn* which serves to illustrate Gerber's statements about the connotative powers of Twain's verbs. Analyze the effect of each verb, and then, if possible, the cumulative effect of the connotations in the whole passage.
5. How many dialects and modifications of dialects can you find in *Huckleberry Finn?*
6. Your composition instructor has probably warned you against the dangers of monotony in a style that fails to use devices for variation, particularly those which are connected with sentence structure. Yet Gerber points out that Twain rarely uses introductory dependent clauses or other devices for changing sentence structure. How does he get away with it? Are there other methods of achieving variation that he employs?
7. Cite a passage similar to that Gerber presents in page 163, and analyze it as he does.
8. What is "a modified frame story" (p. 165)? Why does Gerber call *The Adventures of Huckleberry Finn* a modified frame story?

HUCK FINN ONCE MORE

by Eric Solomon

". . . the episodes of a tale shall be necessary parts of the tale, and shall help to develop it."

Mark Twain, "Fenimore Cooper's Literary Offenses."

". . . there is a way . . . the one right way, the sole form for *you*, the other forms being for men whose line these forms are . . ."

Letter to Howells, August 16, 1898

"Persons attempting to find a motive in this narrative will be prosecuted; persons attempting to find a moral in it will be banished; persons attempting to find a plot in it will be shot

By Order of the Author."

Mark Twain's threats against critical evaluators of *Huckleberry Finn* have been fruitless. Without the fear of being banished or shot by Twain, commentators have relentlessly analyzed his novel, and most of their disapproval has been aimed at the final quarter of the book, the episode of Tom and Huck at Phelps Farm. Even sympathetic supporters of the novel's structure have labored in vain to account for the closing section. Ignoring the author's "Notice," most critics have searched for the moral of the plot. We may avoid the more serious crimes that Twain would punish by exile or death and merely venture to risk prosecution by an attempt to "find a motive" in Twain's narrative. As in all great novels, the theme of *Huckleberry Finn* supplies the inner structure of the work. A judgment of the validity of the novel's ending depends in large part upon the book's motive; if art is an attempt to cast the raw materials of life into a suitable form, the author's motives, conscious or unconscious, should be taken into consideration.

All the attempts to fit the last section into the basic framework of the novel seem to lack conclusiveness. The attacks and defenses alike have one element in common—the belief that Twain's motive in writing *Huckleberry Finn* was either to show Huck's growth to ma-

Reprinted from *College English* XXII, 3 (December 1960), by permission of the publisher and Eric Solomon.

turity, to hail the joys of freedom on the river, or to depict the escape from civilization and slavery. All these elements are present and prominent in the novel. If we consider only these themes, we must see the ending of the novel as failure. By approaching *Huckleberry Finn* from another angle, we may comprehend how Twain does supply his book with a thematic unity that explains the apparent flaws of farcical tone in the final quarter of the novel.

That Twain was not usually in search of the formal perfection of orderly plotting and consistent tone in his fiction is /172/ obvious. Nevertheless, *Huckleberry Finn*, for all Twain's haphazard approach, does have a consistent theme, a theme that is emphasized throughout the novel and most heavily underlined at Phelps Farm: the novel is about a boy's search to find his identity through a satisfying family life. T. S. Eliot has touched upon this topic in passing: "Huck Finn is alone: there is no more solitary character in fiction. The fact that he has a father only emphasizes his loneliness . . . ."[1] In spite of the author's customary vigorous freedoms with unity of structure, Huck's search for a family gives Twain's novel a unity of dramatic meaning. We may concede the presence of other motives in the book; still, the idea of family is deeply imbedded in the novel's texture, and this theme makes the ending fit the essential aim of *Huckleberry Finn*.

Lies, disguises, hidden identities run through Mark Twain's fiction like an obsession. The plots of *The Prince and the Pauper, Pudd'nhead Wilson, The American Claimant,* "A Double-Barrelled Detective Story," "The Man Who Corrupted Hadleyburg," to name but a few, treat the discrepancy between appearance and reality. All these stories deal with perversions of the truth. Impostors substituted for true heirs, the claims of bastard lines, long-standing feuds, willingness to cheat for family honor—indicate how Twain's fiction betrays the author's fascination with the two subjects of lies and families.

In no work does Mark Twain stress lies as heavily as in *Huckleberry Finn*. From the boys' first trick on Jim through Huck's shattering experience when he learns how a cruel lie can hurt even a Negro to the time when Huck discovers that he can't pray a lie, the novel is punctuated by Huck's elaborate disguises and fabrications. An examination of these rich and enthusiastic prevarications reveals Huck's deepest preoccupations. We see that family relationships provide the motivations for these lies.

There are six major deceptions practiced by Huck in the novel (as well as one by Jim who does not tell Huck of his father's death). In five of these lies the boy, to all purposes an orphan and outcast,

[1] T. S. Eliot, "Introduction," *The Adventures of Huckleberry Finn* (London, 1950), p. ix.

invents elaborate family patterns for himself. When Huck is seeking information from Judith Loftis, he first identifies himself as Sarah Williams, a girl whose mother is sick and who is on her way to get help from her uncle, Abner Moore. After being discovered in this lie, Huck calls himself George Peters, a run-away apprentice whose parents are dead. But Uncle Abner Moore is retained as the object of the orphan's quest.

Huck makes his next dissimulation [2] to the watchman of a ferryboat in order to save from drowning the gang on the *Walter Scott*. Again he invents a substantial family for himself, pap and mam and sis and Uncle Hornbeck. Later, to save Jim from the slave hunters, Huck invents another full family—the smallpox-ridden pap, mam, and Mary Ann. Thus, just as in most of Twain's serious fiction, the invention of family relationships is a recurrent situation in *Huckleberry Finn*.

A further pattern is noticeable in these distortions. Huck's inventions show not only families, but families coming to death and destruction. Among the Grangerfords Huck becomes George Jackson and recounts the decimation of a large family on a farm in Arkansaw. /173/ First Mary Ann runs off and marries, then Bill goes off to hunt for her, then Tom and Mort die, and finally pap expires. Lying to the two master-prevaricators, the Duke and the Dauphin, Huck invents another full family, this time in Pike County, Missouri. All his relations die except "me and Pa and my brother Ike," [3] and the last two have recently drowned.

The pattern of Huck's lies is threefold. The lonely Huck, the boy who could not at first join Tom Sawyer's gang because he had no visible family to sign over as hostages, the youth whose only genuine family is an ignorant drunkard of a father, this boy in the first place invents large families for himself, then he brings them to shocking and untimely deaths. Thirdly, these lies are the result of a positive desire in Huck to protect Jim. They are, as it were, moral lies, the immoral lies—such as Huck's trick on Jim after the storm—have no family basis. Villains like the Duke lie from self-interest, betray Jim, and seek to harm families.

After his pattern of lies is fully established, Huck arrives at last at Phelps Farm. Once again Huck finds himself a family. But there is

[2] The raft passage from *Life on the Mississippi*, originally intended for *Huckleberry Finn*, shows the hero first pretending to be Charles William Allbright—a child supposedly murdered by his father. Caught in this lie, the boy calls himself Aleck James Hopkins and refers to his pap to justify the boy's presence on the raft. See Appendix A, *Adventures of Huckleberry Finn*, edited by Henry Nash Smith (Boston, 1958), pp. 257–258.

[3] Mark Twain, *The Adventures of Huckleberry Finn* (New York, 1956), p. 126. All subsequent references to this edition will appear in the text.

an important difference in this sixth dissimulation. Huck does not invent this family. It already exists, and the lie is forced upon him by eager Aunt Sally. Yet Huck's becoming Tom Sawyer is a culmination of his dreams, of the subconscious desires that formed the motifs of his earlier inventions. "I went right along, not fixing up any particular plan, but just trusting to Providence to put the right words in my mouth when the time come; for I'd noticed that Providence always did put the right words in my mouth if I left it alone" (220). We see that there is a special quality about the Phelps family, as Huck's narrative stresses the providential aspect of his arrival in their midst. Here is a kindly providence taking care of the wanderer, giving him in the sojourn at Phelps Farm rest from the toil of his hectic adventures. To be sure, Huck's relief at his acceptance is an immature feeling. But we must not forget that Huck is still a boy, no matter how mature, self-reliant, and cynical he may appear in times of stress. The boy who can believe in a circus clown's antics can relish playing the role of Tom.

As Huck acts out his most elaborate deception, indeed, as he pretends to the limits of Tom's vivid imagination, Huck learns that there are times when he cannot tamper with the truth—even to help Jim. The true climax of Huck's moral development comes not when he learns to respect Jim, not when he learns that he can't pray a lie, but when he discovers that the essence of loyalty to the genuine familial affection displayed by Aunt Sally is to be true to his promise. Huck does not sneak out to search after Jim and Tom, despite the ease with which he could deceive Aunt Sally. "I wouldn't never do nothing to grieve her any more" (283). Huck has learned the nature of responsibility to a family. The Phelps Farm episode is long because it supplies the necessary time for Huck to use the family relationship to work out his attitudes towards truth and deception.

Huck's lies are only one indication that a substantial basis for the novel is the boy's search for a family. In his perceptive essay "Huck and Jim," Kenneth Lynn catches the importance of this theme in *Huckleberry Finn.* Although his indication that the novel is concerned with the entire problem of parenthood is accurate, Lynn seems to push his conclusion too far when he nominates Jim as the father for whom Huck has been searching. Yet the /174/ theme and structure of the novel are predicated on the need for family ties. For, as Lynn says, ". . . in Twain loneliness almost without exception takes the form of alienation from the family." [4] We have only to recall the numbers of childless couples and estranged children that fill the pages of the

[4] Kenneth S. Lynn, "Huck and Jim," *Yale Review* XLVIII, 422 (Spring 1958).

Twain canon to see the truth of the statement. Such a search for a family, of course, is a fundamental fictional theme. Twain was influenced not only by his own interests but also by a tradition of loss and discovery as old as the Homeric epics. American fiction, from Cooper to Stowe, concentrated on broken familial ties; indeed the American dream of success usually commenced with a boy leaving home and mother to make his own way and family in an alien world.

A glance at the position of Huck in the earlier *Tom Sawyer* indicates Huck's role in life. To be sure, he is free, and the boys envy his outcast condition. Huck's prototype, young Sam Clemens' friend Tom Blankenship, was also free: "He was the only really independent person—boy or man—in the community, and by consequence he was tranquilly and continuously happy and was envied by all the rest of us." [5] Clearly Twain draws from his memories of the Hannibal drunkard's son the sense of freedom reflected in the portrait of Huck Finn. But part of Huck's characterization, the loneliness, comes from another source, the author's own view of the darker aspects of life. Where Tom Sawyer can rejoice at his return from a supposed watery grave to the arms of his Aunt Polly, poor Huck Finn finds no one to greet him. When he first hears the word "welcome," "He could not recollect that the closing word had ever been applied to his case before." [6] *Tom Sawyer* ends on a note of temporary triumph. A grateful Widow Douglas takes in the homeless boy who had been accustomed to sleep in lofts and empty hogsheads. How real was this adoption? Was it the genuine Huck Finn who found a welcome in the Widow's genteel home or was it her romantic vision of the heroic youth who had saved her from Indian Joe's revenge and who had gained the respectability of $6000? The opening of Huck's own novel shows that he is still lacking a proper family.

Huck's attempt to join the gang after he has found a home with the Widow is met by Ben Rogers' retort: " 'Here's Huck Finn, he hain't got no family. What you going to do 'bout him?' " (8). They make an adjustment for Huck, but there is no doubt in the mind of the gang that his is a special case.

The diction and imagery, the references and subplots of the novel emphasize family. The orphan child Moses in the Bulrushers, Sollermun's lack of sympathy for children, the tragedy that strikes the Wilks' slaves when two sons are sold up river to Memphis and the mother down river to New Orleans—such familial relations make up the substance of *Huckleberry Finn*. Jim runs away rather than be sent

[5] Charles Neider, ed., *The Autobiography of Mark Twain* (New York, 1959), p. 203.

[6] Mark Twain, *Tom Sawyer* (London, 1956), p. 203.

down river away from his family. Huck strives to understand why a Negro could feel so strongly about his wife and children that he would threaten to steal them out of captivity. The main moments of pathos in the book come when Boggs' orphaned daughter weeps over her father's corpse and when Jim recounts his unintentional cruelty towards his deaf child. Huck's adventures on the shore, like his lies, follow a family pattern. The Grangerfords fight out old family feuds with the Shepherdsons. /175/ Faked heirs defraud the Wilks family, and Huck protects the orphans. The Duke and the Dauphin stress their descents from the ducal Bridgewaters and the regal Louis XVI. And, of course, Huck escapes from a cramped and over-civilized adoption (despite the widow's humanity, the harsh religiosity of Miss Watson rules the establishment) and a savage, murderous father. He is an orphan in truth by the time he and Jim start their journey, although only Jim knows that Pap is dead.

Each family Huck contacts is a little better than the previous one; still, all the possible family relationships fail for him. Miss Watson's moral rigidity gives way to Pap's moral laxness—and physical repression; the Grangerford's warmth, respectability, and sentiment disappear in the bloody, destructive feud that wipes out the family; the Wilks girls are idealized and innocent, but Huck cannot find a suitable role in their midst. Finally, Huck meets the Phelps family. Here, at last, he has a role—as Tom, a blood-relative—and in a decent family. The Phelps are sentimental like the Grangerfords, but without their proud sense of honor. Aunt Sally and Uncle Silas are religious like Miss Watson, but without her strictness. The Phelps, to be sure, are not perfect: they are gullible, at times irascible, bigoted in their unthinking cruelty to Negroes. Yet there is no question but that the Phelps and their farm present one of the few favorable portraits of the family institution in Mark Twain's fiction.

Silas is "the innocentest, best old soul I ever see" (227), "a mighty nice old man" (255). Silas Phelps is patterned on Twain's uncle John Quarles. "I have never come across a better man,"[7] said Twain of Quarles. Twain was quite sure that he spent the happiest days of his boyhood on the Quarles farm; here was the good, free life as opposed to the strict household of Judge Clemens. "It was a heavenly place for a boy, that farm of my uncle John's."[8] What more inevitable climax for a novel of search for family than this recreation of the place Twain recalled in association with the lyric joy of his glorious childhood summers? To be sure, Huck spends one-fourth of his adventure at Phelps Farm. Rather than an artistic flaw, the farm is the

[7] Dixon Wecter, *Sam Clemens of Hannibal* (Boston, 1952), p. 29.
[8] Neider, *The Autobiography*, p. 4.

proper objective correlative for the happy family of Huck's dreams. Here are the kindly, unworldly uncle, the sweet, honest aunt, the children and the dogs that represent what Huck has been searching for. Note the prose rhythm in Huck's description of the farm:

> A rail fence round a two-acre yard; a stile made out of logs sawed off and upended in steps, like barrels of a different length, to climb over the fence with, and for the women to stand on when they are going to jump onto a horse; some sickly grass-patches in the big yard, but mostly it was bare and smooth, like an old hat with the nap rubbed of; big double log house for the white folks—hewed logs, with the chinks stopped up with mud or mortar, and these mudstripes been whitewashed some time or another; round-log kitchen, with a big broad, open but roofed passage joining it to the house; log smokehouse back of the kitchen; three little log nigger cabins in a row t'other side of the smokehouse; one little hut all by itself away down against the back fence, and some out-buildings down a piece the other side; ash-hopper and big kettle to bile soap in by the little hut; bench by the kitchen door, with bucket of water and a gourd; hound asleep there in the sun; more hounds asleep round about; about three shade trees away off in a corner; some currant bushes and gooseberry bushes in one place by the fence . . . (219)

This sentence, surely one of the longest /176/ Twain ever wrote, moves on with the flow of unleashed emotion, despite the objectivity and bareness of the description. Here Huck finds peace.

Providence brings him a family. "But if they was joyful, it warn't nothing to what I was; for it was like being born again, I was so glad to find out who I was" (224). This statement, of course, is made in the negative context of Huck's relief at the face-saving discovery that he is supposed to be Tom. Nevertheless, the statement also has a positive meaning. Huck has been on a journey of freedom; he has learned to worship the river-god; he has committed himself to humanity in the person of Jim—and he has found a family. We need not insist that Twain's primary purpose in *Huckleberry Finn* was to find Huck a family. Yet we must note that the last chapters of the book emphasize heavily this theme that is extremely important to the entire novel.

Huck's response to his acceptance by the Phelps' is stated in deeply moving terms. He is indeed born again, as a boy into a family, after his struggles in the man's role of Jim's protector. Certainly, Huck becomes a boy again. After all, he *is* a boy. Twain's interpreters have assumed that Huck is becoming mature; thus the horseplay at Phelps Farm is a reversion. All picaresque novels, however, need not trace the development from innocence to maturity. Since the novel is the work of Mark Twain, who would scarcely place maturity over childhood in the scale of success, we are justified in considering as integral to the development of the book the aura of safety existing at the farm that enables Tom and Huck to play at releasing Jim from bondage.

As in his lies which are pleas for the sympathy owing to a child, at Phelps Farm Huck can rejoice in a boy's freedom from responsibility. The genuine goodness of Uncle Silas and Aunt Sally provides a feeling of security. There is a comfortable frame for the light irony that satirizes Tom's romantic notions. Indeed, this part of the plot fits the structure particularly closely; since Jim actually has been freed by Miss Watson's will, his "escape" is only the formal working-out of the act of freeing a slave. In addition, for the first time Huck acts positively to free Jim, actually stealing him from slavery instead of going along with a *fait accompli*. Thus Huck makes his most distinct commitment to the idea of freedom. Therefore, this ending helps to supply a logical climax to the themes of freedom and individual rights.

Although the farce is still at times forced and awkward, by attending to a reading of the book that sees Huck finding a family, we can understand why Twain concentrates much of his novel at Phelps Farm, why the mood reverts to happy farce, and why such a shift does not destroy the formal perfection of the novel.

One problem remains. Huck seems to repudiate the warmth of the Phelps Family at the close of the book when he plans to set out for the territory ahead of the others. Twain leaves the reader with a pleasing note of ambiguity. Huck can speak lightly of being civilized because he possesses the security that will enable him to escape and then return home—as a boy should, as Tom Sawyer could do in his book when he and Huck hid on Jackson's Island. Now Huck, too, having gained his family, can head "for howling adventures amongst the Injuns, over in the territory, for a couple of weeks or two" (293). In other words, this last phrase indicates that Huck wants to continue his youthful adventures—and then return after a few weeks. This passage, at least, which has long been taken as an indication of Huck's disgust with the Phelps' and civilization, is hardly that. After all, /177/ Tom and Jim are supposed to accompany Huck, and surely they will return to civilization.

Yet Huck ends his book with the words, "But I reckon I got to light out for the territory ahead of the rest, because Aunt Sally she's going to adopt me and civilize me, and I can't stand it. I been there before" (293). Again Twain's critics have been inclined to understand Huck's words as a denial of the workability of his relationship with the Phelps' since he evidently equates Aunt Sally with the Widow Douglas. Two points must be taken into consideration, however. While Huck's last remark may seem to find the Widow and Aunt Sally similar, the tone of the book, as revealed in the whole sense of nostalgia evoked by the loving care given to the description of the Phelps establishment, displays Aunt Sally in a far more motherly light. Then we must remember that here, at the very end of the book, Huck resumes his role as boy-author, in a chapter entitled "Nothing More to Write." Essentially Twain reminds us that Huck is now consciously posturing, taking the part of manly adventurer who is more inclined to the free ways of Pap than the civilizing ways of the Widow or Aunt Sally. Huck, it can be submitted, like his creator, is ambivalent. Huck's words as self-conscious author praise freedom from society. His actions as a boy reveal his desire for a home. In similar fashion, Twain was torn between the ideals of rough individualism and genteel respectability.

The theme of the search for security accompanies the more obvious themes of the novel. The boyish ideal of independence within the restraint of family love, the ideal that Mark Twain firmly subscribed to, is attained by Huck through his long stay at Phelps Farm. Huck's story, like Mark Twain's own, tells of the effort to remain a boy despite external conditions that force adulthood. /178/

QUESTIONS FOR DISCUSSION AND WRITING

1. What have the critics found the "moral of the plot" to be? What does Solomon think of this disregarding of Twain's "Notice"?

2. What does Solomon mean by "inner structure of the work"? (p. 172) What do you suppose the "outer structure" is?

3. Solomon asserts that the "true climax of Huck's moral development comes not when he learns to respect Jim, not when he learns that he can't pray a lie, but when he discovers that the essence of loyalty to the genuine familial affection displayed by Aunt Sally is to be true to his promise." How much does this assertion vary from what other critics have said about Huck's maturing? If Solomon is not correct in this assertion, how much is his entire argument weakened?

4. Solomon notes "six major deceptions" by Huck in *Huckleberry Finn*. Examine each. In what sense is it "major"? Are there other lies you consider equally important? Do they concern themselves

with inventing a family? Write a full evaluation of this part of Solomon's argument.

5. Can you add to Solomon's list of things in the novel which emphasize family?
6. Why can't Huck "find a suitable role" (p. 176) in the Wilks family?
7. Discuss with your instructor (or look up in a dictionary of literary terms) "objective correlative" (p. 176), and apply it to the Phelps farm.
8. Comment on Solomon's explanation of the conclusion of the novel.

THE BEST AUTHORITIES

by Carson Gibb

The last nine chapters of *The Adventures of Huckleberry Finn* have been deplored almost as generally as the whole book has been praised. According to Andrew Lang, "The story . . . ends by lapsing into burlesque, when Tom Sawyer insists on freeing the slave whom he knows to be free already, in a manner accordant with 'the best authorities.'" Newton Arvin speaks of "the dreary elaboration of Tom Sawyer's rescue of Jim."[1] Brander Matthews uses the rescue as an example of "passages where the interest falls off."[2] Dixon Wecter calls this part "shallows of burlesque and extravaganaza."[3] And Lionel Trilling sums up: "In form and style *Huckleberry Finn* is an almost perfect work. Only one mistake has ever been charged against it, that

[1] See *Mark Twain: Selected Criticism*, ed., Arthur L. Scott (Dallas, 1955), p. 40 & p. 233.

[2] Harper's Classics edition of *The Adventures of Huckleberry Finn* (New York, 1948), p. xvii.

[3] "Mark Twain," *Literary History of the United States*, ed., Spiller, Thorp, Johnson & Canby (New York, 1948), II, p. 933.

Reprinted from *College English*, XXII, 3 (December 1960) by permission of the publisher and Carson Gibb.

it concludes with Tom Sawyer's elaborate, too elaborate, game of Jim's escape. Certainly this episode is too long—in the original draft it was much longer— /178/ and certainly it is a falling off, as most anything would have to be, from the incidents on the river."[4]

The usual explanation is that this is an egregious example of Twain's defective taste and inability to criticize his own work. Wecter and Trilling offer additional explanations, which are much alike. Trilling says that the ending is a "device . . . needed to permit Huck to return to his anonymity, to give up the role of hero, to fall into the background which he prefers. . . ." Wecter says, "The story thus closes on the farcical note with which the Hannibal cycle has begun, in the whitewashing episode."

The judgment is hardly disputable. But the explanations are apt to leave one wondering why a man who (though "unequal" and "never keen at self-criticism") could write "an almost perfect work" should nod so violently that the last fifth of that work uniformly depresses critics. Was Twain perhaps doing something more than mechanically ending a book or a cycle, something more than indulging his predilection for fun?

Is the rescue really fun? It is fun when Tom and Huck raid the A-rabs, swear dark oaths, and trick Jim. But is this sort of foolery the same after Huck has assisted mountebanks and swindlers, out-maneuvered murderers, witnessed the butchery of a feud, and learned how filthy it is to trick Jim? Is it fun to confront A-rabs when the A-rabs are not a Sunday school class (primer) but men armed with rifles? When the booty is not "some doughnuts and jam . . . a rag doll . . . a hymnbook and a tract" but Jim? Tom may still think it is fun when he gets a bullet in his leg—he shows real pluck. But Huck discovers it was not really much fun when he sees how "grieved" Aunt Sally is:

> . . . I wished I could do something for her, but I couldn't, only to swear that I wouldn't never do nothing to grieve her any more. And the third time I waked up at dawn, and slid down, and she was there yet, and her candle was most out, and her old grey head was resting on her hands, and she was asleep. (283)

If it is not fun, or at least not merely fun, what is it? It is the pranks of two boys—one accustomed to danger, the other intoxicated by fantasy—who believe niggers and people are two different things.

[4] Rinehart edition of *The Adventures of Huckleberry Finn* (New York, 1948), p. xv–xvi. Page numbers (in parentheses) refer to this edition.

When lying to Aunt Sally about how he happened to arrive as he did, Huck tells her he was in a steamboat accident, and she reacts with characteristic humaneness:

> "Good gracious! anybody hurt?"
> "No'm. Killed a nigger."
> "Well, it's lucky; because sometimes people do get hurt." (222)

And she rattles on about a Baptist who had been "crippled" by an explosion in a boat Uncle Silas was aboard. Neither Aunt Sally nor any other decent person would reproach a boy for having his fun at a nigger's expense. Tom and Huck's attitude toward niggers is standard—the attitude of the rich and the poor, of the prim and the disreputable, even of the niggers themselves. And all the fun of the prolonged emancipation of Jim depends on this attitude, just as Huck's accounts of Colonel Sherburn's murder of Boggs and the Grangerford-Shepherdson butchery depend on Southern chivalry. The point is the same: custom brutalizes.

But if Twain wished to end the book with a burst of spleen, why did he aim it at two likable youngsters? Huck does his best to free Jim—his best, that is, without challenging Tom's established superiority. Huck never forgets that Tom has the support of "the best /179/ authorities"; even when alone on the river, Huck never faced a difficult situation without wishing Tom were with him and wondering what he would do. Tom's grip on him is so strong that Huck, loving Jim as he now does, can only feebly protest against Tom's fantasies and humbly offer his own common sense—which, of course, Tom always demolishes with scorn. Not even love can make Huck, the outcast, doubt Tom, who has book-learning, respectability, wealth—all the best authorities. Tom alone is *responsible* for playing with Jim's life in order to indulge in fantasy. And Tom knows all the while Jim is legally free.

Compared with Huck, Tom looks shabby. Still, he is all good nature, and when his fantasy suddenly turns real, his courage does not falter. Absurd and outrageous as his behavior is, Tom comes off well; he is as good as it is possible for one of his breeding to be. Tom is not under attack, but the world that created him is.

Not long before Tom appears, Huck becomes conscious of how sinful he has been in "stealing a poor old woman's nigger that hadn't ever done me no harm." First he tries to excuse himself.

> Well, I tried the best I could to kinder soften it up somehow for myself by saying I was brung up wicked, and so I warn't so much to blame; but something inside of me kept saying, "There

> was the Sunday-school, you could 'a' gone to it; and if you'd 'a' done it they'd 'a' learnt you there that people that acts as I'd been acting about that nigger goes to everlasting fire." (213)

Since he had a choice, he cannot blame circumstances for his sinful conduct. Then he finds he is so steeped in sin that he cannot pray, and decides to cleanse himself by writing a letter telling Miss Watson where Jim is. The act has the effect he hoped for: he feels he can pray. But before praying, he starts "thinking—thinking how good it was all this happened so, and how near I come to being lost and going to hell. And went on thinking. And got to thinking over our trip down the river; and I see Jim before me all the time. . . ." And all he can remember is how grateful, generous, and forgiving Jim always was. He notices the letter.

> "All right, then, I'll go to hell"—and tore it up.
>
> It was awful thoughts and awful words, but they was said. And I let them stay said; and never thought no more about reforming. I shoved the whole thing out of my head, and said I would take up wickedness again, which was in my line, being brung up to it, and the other warn't. And for a starter I would go to work and steal Jim out of slavery again. . . . (214–215)

Huck's heart is too black for even the church—the best of all possible authorities—to cleanse. Custom brutalizes and perverts. It could not be plainer.

Huck is not too depressed by his new commitment to sin to be delighted when Tom turns up a little later. As soon as he has convinced Tom he is not a ghost and Tom has planned how to fool Aunt Sally, Huck blurts out his intention to free Jim. Tom is surprised, but he sizes up the situation and says:

> "I'll *help* you steal him!"
>
> Well, I let go all holts then, like I was shot. It was the most astonishing speech I ever heard—and I'm bound to say Tom Sawyer fell considerable in my estimation. Only I couldn't believe it. Tom Sawyer a *nigger-stealer!*
>
> "Oh, shucks!" I says; "you're joking."
>
> "I ain't joking, either."
>
> "Well, then," I says, "joking or no joking. . . . (226–227)

Ignorant that Tom *is* joking in a way different from what he supposes, Huck is not to be convinced by any number of words that Tom could be guilty of anything more heinous than concealing his knowledge of an attempt to steal /180/ a nigger. But before long, by committing himself to the theft, Tom succeeds in convincing Huck that he too is on the side of the Devil.

> Well, one thing was dead sure, and that was that Tom Sawyer was in earnest, and was actuly going to help steal that nigger out of slavery. That was the thing that was too many for me. Here was a boy that was respectable and well brung up; . . . and yet here he was, without any more pride, or rightness, or feeling, than to stoop to this business, and make himself a shame, and his family a shame, before everybody. I *couldn't* understand it no way at all. . . . (234)

To tell Huck the truth would spoil the game; so Tom simply asserts his authority, which has behind it all the best authorities—in fiction and in life. Tom will do many outrageous things, but he wouldn't really steal a nigger. So he must grasp this unique opportunity to pretend to steal one; he must use Huck and Jim for his amusement.

Here on this farm peopled by obedient Huck and Jim, gullible Aunt Sally and Uncle Silas, and proportionally simple-minded niggers, Tom —the comparative sophisticate—uses his opportunity like a truly civilized man. As soon as he has sized up the situation, he is dissatisfied.

> "Why, drat it, Huck, it's the stupidest arrangement I ever see. You got to invent *all* the difficulties. Well, we can't help it; we've got to do the best we can with the materials we've got. Anyhow, there's one thing—there's more honor in getting him out through a lot of difficulties and dangers, where there warn't one of them furnished by the people who it was their duty to furnish them, and you had to contrive them all out of your own head." (239)

Having displayed his ability to observe accurately and make reasonable deductions by locating Jim, Tom proceeds spectacularly "to invent *all* the difficulties" consistent with the principles laid down by such best authorities as "Baron Trenck," Casanova, "Benvenuto Chelleeny," and Henry IV. He does not make so much of *honor* as would a Grangerford, a Shepherdson, or a Hotspur, but he disdains the ignoble expedient of raising Jim's bed and slipping the chain off in favor of sawing off the bed leg, and at one moment he is prepared to amputate Jim's leg for the sake of honor (240). This, of course, is only the beginning of his invention of fantastic difficulties. A truly sophisticated mind.

Tom's purpose is the epitome of civilized man's purposes: to escape boredom (damn the cost!) by inventing high adventure. In a few years he will be ready to attack Mount Everest, take off for the moon, or fight a war over something of no concern to him. His shrewdness in finding and seizing the opportunity for adventure is remarkable; his shrewdness in calculating just how long he can extend his game without having it spoiled is even more so. He is able to foresee what steps Uncle Silas will take to find Jim's owner and how long they will take, and therefore, to manipulate the complex preparations so they are complete at exactly the right moment. When Tom's purpose is evident, so is the expedience of his actions.

Once he has plunged into his fantasy, Tom's reasoning and behavior are the *reductio ad absurdum* of the adult precepts and practices—the best authorities—that have stamped him. Once it is granted that fiction and history are properly a means of escape from the boredom of every day, that absurdity is justified by appeal to precedent ("the regulations") and authority, and that a nigger is not a human being, his behavior is reasonable and understandable. Now that he is in a world in which common sense is irrelevant, he logically abandons it. Though Jim could easily be let out through the door, Tom deter- /181/ mines to dig him out. Huck accepts this absurdity on Tom's authority and reminds Tom of "them old crippled picks and things" in the lean-to against Jim's prison. Tom "turns on me, looking pitying enough to make a body cry."

> "Well then," I says, "if we don't want the picks and shovels, what do we want?"
>
> "A couple of case knives." . . .
>
> "Confound it, it's foolish, Tom."
>
> "It don't make no difference how foolish it is, it's the *right* way—and it's the regular way. And there ain't no *other* way. . . ." (244)

When it becomes obvious, even to Tom, that the case knives will not do, he disgustedly adopts the picks and shovels.

> "I'll tell you. It ain't right, and it ain't moral, and I wouldn't like it to get out; but there ain't only just the one way: we got to dig him out with the picks, and *let on* it's case knives." (246–247)

And he refuses to explain further or call the picks and shovels anything but "case knives." "He was always that particular," comments Huck, "Full of principle." Always the man of principle, Tom never admits the folly of a plan; he simply calls things by other names.

For a while the combination of Tom's fancy, his half-consciousness of his own absurdity, and Huck's salty common sense is comically satiric. It is hard not to laugh at Tom even when he is explaining why it might be a good idea to cut off Jim's leg.

> "Well some of the best authorities has done it. They couldn't get the chain off, so they just cut their hand off and shoved. And a leg would be better still. But we got to let that go. There ain't necessity enough in this case, and, besides, Jim's a nigger and wouldn't understand the reasons for it, and how it's the custom in Europe; so we'll let it go. . . . (240)

Even if the reference to Jim's subhuman status recalls what is at stake in this game, there is no anger. And when Tom's fancy is no longer funny, Huck's objections and comments sustain the joke. While they are planning to dig Jim out, Tom tells Huck that it took one of the prisoners thirty-seven years to dig his way out of the "Castle Deef" and that at the end he found himself in China. Huck says, " '*Jim* don't know nobody in China.' " When, on account of his scraped and blistered hands, Tom cannot climb the lightning rod back to the bedroom, he asks Huck, " 'Can't you think of no way?' 'Yes,' I says, 'but I reckon it ain't regular. Come up the stairs, and let on it's a lightning-rod.' So he done it" (248). Huck has caught on to the game, and were his common sense not dulled by admiration of Tom, his attitude toward the whole game would be like Jim's toward the plan for him "to keep a journal on the shirt with his blood, and all that. . . . Jim he couldn't see no sense in the most of it, but he allowed we was white folks and knowed better than him; so he was satisfied, and said he would do it all just as Tom said" (249).

Later, when he has described Jim's coat of arms, Tom gives up explaining, for the simple reason that he has not the slightest idea what a coat of arms signifies. But as he knows the words, he is still an authority.

Bringing in the grindstone (which Jim has to be temporarily freed to accomplish) ends the part of the rescue that is substantially independent of the real challenge—to alarm and outwit Jim's captors. The possibilities of Tom's fantasy in a vacuum are exhausted; the humor and wit—and satire—of Tom's schemes and Huck's and Jim's reactions have been worked for (at least) all they are worth.

Tom is probably becoming bored again, and is certainly apprehensive that word will arrive that Jim is free before /182/ he and Huck can free him. So he creates new excitement by writing "nonnamous letters." In stealing their equipment—a shirt, sheets, spoons, a candlestick, and six candles—the boys have risked discovery by Aunt Sally and have had some narrow escapes. Now they deliberately alarm

Aunt Sally, Uncle Silas, and the neighbors. With the intrusion of the world of adults comes new emphasis on the plight Tom and Huck have put Jim into during the three weeks of their game.

> . . . you never see a cabin as blithesome as Jim's was when they'd [the snakes] all swarm out for music and swarm [*sic*] for him. Jim didn't like the spiders, and the spiders didn't like Jim; and so they'd lay for him, and make it mighty warm for him. And he said that between the rats and the snakes and the grindstone there warn't no room in bed for him skasely; and when there was, a body couldn't sleep, it was so lively; and it was always lively, he said, because *they* never all slept at one time, but took turn about. . . . He said if he ever got out this time, he wouldn't ever be a prisoner again, not for a salary. (267)

"Blithesome," indeed, but as Tom or Huck might say, "Only a nigger."

Tom's fantasy ends in delirium (285), as the doctor, with Jim's help, extracts the bullet from his leg, and Jim is led back into chains. Later, Tom demonstrates his decency by giving "Jim forty dollars for being prisoner for us so patient, and doing it up so good, and Jim was pleased most to death" (292), and construes the forty-dollar present as proof that " 'signs is signs.' " And when Huck learns that Jim was free all along and that Tom knew it, he feels only relief and delight that Tom did not really have a heart as black as his: ". . . . I couldn't ever understand before, until that minute and that talk, how he *could* help a body set a nigger free with his bringing up" (290).

So Tom is exonerated. In a world where the Devil's party steals niggers out of slavery and the Lord's party puts them in chains, Tom Sawyer—Miss Watson to the contrary notwithstanding—remains among the elect. For all his mischief and adventures, real and fancied, Tom is the creature of the best authorities. Histories, novels, schools, churches, respectable guardians—they have begot, borne, and nurtured him. He is their folly—occasionally glorious—blindness, astuteness, double-thinking, perverted logic, brutality, superficiality; their genius for making the simple complicated, the lucid obscure, the good evil.

From Huck and Jim's point of view he *is* the best authority. Before his voyage down the river with Jim—a long time ago, it seems—Huck thought he would rather go to hell with Tom than to heaven with Miss Watson. This was a juvenile thought. When Huck is faced with a real choice between heaven and hell, against all he has been taught, against his better judgment and conscience, he must choose hell—hell without Tom, but with the Duke and the Dauphin, Pap, Jim, and all the other outcasts. Having damned himself, Huck is still concerned as much for Tom's welfare as for Jim's. He is still obedient to and respectful of Tom as the authority he is, and he does not want to see that authority fall. The denouement is a complete relief: Tom has proved to him that civilization is exactly what he thought it was. Huck has more than Aunt Sally's benevolent oppression in mind when he closes his book:

> But I reckon I got to light out for the territory ahead of the rest, because Aunt Sally she's going to adopt me and civilize me, and I can't stand it. I been there before. /183/

QUESTIONS FOR DISCUSSION AND WRITING

1. Comment on Gibb's explanation that *Huckleberry Finn* ends "with a burst of spleen." (p. 179)
2. Notice Gibb's sentences on page 180: "Huck's heart is too black for even the church—the best of all possible authorities—to cleanse. Custom brutalizes and perverts." Examine as closely as you can the relationship between these sentences and the quoted passage on which they are based.
3. Define "sophisticated," and determine how or whether you would apply it to Tom, as Gibb does.
4. Develop further, or disagree with, Gibb's assertion that "Tom is the creature of the best authorities. Histories, novels, schools, churches, respectable guardians—they have begot, borne, and nurtured him."

SUGGESTIONS FOR RESEARCH

1. Consider Huck's relationship to Jim.
2. Define the role of the Negro in *Huckleberry Finn.*
3. Analyze the character of Huck Finn, noting especially the fundamental disagreements of critics.
4. Describe the environment of Huck, and its effect upon him.
5. Consider the river as a symbol in *Huckleberry Finn.*
6. What is the attitude toward crime and punishment in *Huckleberry Finn?* Would you say that there are attitudes, rather than just one?
7. Discuss the anti-romantic attitude found in *Huckleberry Finn.*
8. Does Huck participate in the anti-romantic attitude? Or can you consider him as a romantic?
9. Reach a conclusion about the end of *Huckleberry Finn;* is it art or artifice?
10. Huck apparently considers himself to be a thoroughly wicked character, and some individuals in the novel agree with him. Present those defects which Huck and others find in his character, and then make your own comment upon his morality.
11. Consider loneliness as a theme in *Huckleberry Finn.*
12. Discuss rascality in *Huckleberry Finn.*
13. Present a history of the criticism of *Huckleberry Finn.*
14. Note the use of superstition: what kinds are there? How do they reflect upon those who practise them? What effect do they have upon the atmosphere of the novel? Does Twain seem to mock or to believe in such superstitions as he shows?
15. Write a careful study of the language of *Huckleberry Finn.* This is a very large topic, so be careful to limit your approach to such aspects as you can handle within the appointed length of your paper.
16. Explore the theme of honesty in *Huckleberry Finn.*
17. Consider the humor of Twain from some angle—for example, its nature, its uses, or its fundamental intention.

18. Would a discussion of comedy in *Huckleberry Finn* differ from the above topic? If so, write a paper on this topic, being careful to distinguish your subject from humor.

19. Discuss responsibility as a theme in *Huckleberry Finn.*

20. Discuss duty as a theme in *Huckleberry Finn.*

21. Is Huck a religious individual? If not, why not? If so, what is his religion? Would you say, for example, that he is a Christian?

22. Consider the revenge motif in *Huckleberry Finn.*

23. Describe social criticism found in *Huckleberry Finn.* What is its method? What are its targets? Where lie its strengths and weaknesses?

24. Evaluate *Huckleberry Finn* as a portrait of America.

TOPICS FOR FURTHER RESEARCH

Though the primary purpose of this text is to provide you with materials for research on *Huckleberry Finn,* the editors here present suggestions for further study. We do this for three reasons: (1) we would not have anyone suppose that a single sourcebook can contain enough material to cover all the problems raised by a great novel; (2) we hope some instructors will supplement the opportunities for research within the text with assignments beyond its confines; (3) we hope and confidently expect that many readers who have carried their pursuit of *Huckleberry Finn* this far will not want to stop, but will look for ways to carry it further. The list below suggests areas into which you may pursue your investigations.

1. *Huckleberry Finn* and *Tom Sawyer:* a comparison of these two novels, assisted by scholarly criticism on each, may be developed through several approaches—for example, the use of point of view, the similarity and/or difference of the environment, the protagonists, and the fundamental approach.

2. Compare the resourcefulness of Tom Sawyer, Huck Finn, and the Connecticut Yankee.

3. Write a careful estimate of Hemingway's statement concerning the influence of *Huckleberry Finn* on American fiction. Fully treated, this could turn into a doctoral dissertation, so you will want either to project a brief investigation of the main problems involved, or limit your study to a few authors.

4. Consider the influence of Mark Twain's prose style. Apply here also the limitations for question 3.

5. Determine to what extent *Huckleberry Finn* is autobiographical.

6. Determine in what ways Twain's training as a journalist contributed to or hindered the writing of *Huckleberry Finn.*

7. Investigate the qualities of the "frontier story" and decide to what extent *Huckleberry Finn* is one.

8. Compare Twain's presentation of Huck to other great characterizations of children in literature. Consider especially Dickens.

9. Write a history of the popular, non-literary opposition to *Huckleberry Finn*—for example, the cases in which libraries have refused to circulate the novel.

10. Place *Huckleberry Finn* in the tradition of the picaresque novel.

We would also like to direct your attention to two areas which we feel would be particularly fruitful; both of these fields are connected with the influence of *Huckleberry Finn* on American literature. The most obvious case of such influence must certainly be Ernest Hemingway, who described Twain's great novel as the fountainhead of American fiction. If you have read Hemingway's novels, several avenues of investigation will immediately suggest themselves. For example, how has the influence of Mark Twain reached Hemingway? Has it come directly and solely from *Huckleberry Finn,* or has it progressed through other authors, each of whom has had his share of influence on the modern author? And what has been Hemingway's total response to this influence—has he accepted it completely, rejected it in part, or struggled to escape it? In what ways has Twain influenced Hemingway? (Consider the fundamentals of the novel: plot, character, style, point of view, theme, atmosphere, etc.) Which of his novels gives strongest evidence of this influence? Which gives the least? Does the influence seem to grow stronger or weaker as one reads Hemingway's novels chronologically? What do you infer from your conclusion? Evaluate the influence: has it been predominantly beneficial? Has it in some ways hurt Hemingway?

These are but a few of the fields you may wish to investigate; the briefest look into these will suggest many more topics. Your instructor will probably want you to find your own source material, but perhaps we may suggest a beginning: consult chapter six of Philip Young's *Ernest Hemingway* (New York: Rinehart and Co., 1952). The notes which accompany this chapter (at the back of the book) will help you on your way to a bibliography.

The second area we suggest is a study of the influence of Mark Twain on J. D. Salinger. Here we hardly need to suggest topics, for a single reading of *Huckleberry Finn* and *The Catcher In The Rye* will open up countless fields of inquiry to you. It is obvious, for example, that the protagonists of the two novels invite comparison, though the comparison (and contrast) itself may prove not so obvious. As you consider Huck and Holden, you will find yourself engaging in the same kinds of problems which we have suggested in connection with Hemingway, and in such others as the fundamental approach of the two novels, the attitude of each novelist toward his protagonist, the use of humor by both authors, the world of Huck and that of Holden (the nature of these two worlds, their influence upon their protagonists, the method the authors employ to present them, their relative importance in the novels), or such specific problems as the employment of idiom, the use of point of view, or the structure of the novels.

In connection with Salinger there may be some justification for helping you with a brief bibloigraphy, because criticism is just beginning to catch up with this novelist. We suggest you begin, then, with the following:

Branch, Edgar. "Mark Twain and J. D. Salinger: A Study in Literary Continuity," *American Quarterly*, IX (Summer 1957), 144–158.

Gwynn, Frederick L., and Joseph L. Blotner. *The Fiction of J. D. Salinger*. University of Pittsburgh Press, 1959.

Heiserman, Arthur, and James E. Miller, Jr. "J. D. Salinger: Some Crazy Cliff," *Western Humanities Review*, X (1956), 129–137.

Kaplan, Charles. "Holden and Huck: Odysseys of Youth," *College English*, XVIII (November 1956), 76–80.

Wells, Arvin R. "Huck Finn and Holden Caulfield: The Situation of the Hero," *The Ohio University Review*, II (1960), 31–42.

The following articles do not make specific comparisons of Salinger and Twain, but they may be of use in your attempt to command Salinger for the purposes of comparison.

Costello, Donald P. "The Language of *The Catcher in The Rye*," *American Speech*, XXXIV, 3 (October 1959), 172–181.

Jacobs, Robert G. "J. D. Salinger's *The Catcher in The Rye*: Holden Caulfield's 'Goddam Autobiography,'" *Iowa English Yearbook*, Fall (1959), 9–14.

Jacobsen, Josephine. "The Felicity of J. D. Salinger," *Commonweal*, LXXI, 22 (February 26, 1960), 589–591.

Leitch, David. "The Salinger Myth," *Twentieth Century*, CLXVIII, 1005 (November 1960), 428–435.

Levine, Paul. "J. D. Salinger: The Development of the Misfit Hero," *Twentieth Century Literature*, IV, 3 (October 1958), 92–99.

Light, James F. "Salinger's *The Catcher in The Rye*," *Explicator*, XVIII, 9 (June 1960), Item 59.

Mizener, Arthur. "The Love Song of J. D. Salinger," *Harper's Magazine*, CCXVIII, 1305 (February 1959), 83–90.

Steiner, George. "The Salinger Industry," *Nation* (November 14, 1959), 360–363.

Wakefield, Dan. "Salinger and the Search for Love," *New World Writing*, XIV (December 1958), 68–85.

Wiegand, William. "The Knighthood of J. D. Salinger," *New Republic*, CXLI, 22 (October 19, 1959), 19–21.

BIBLIOGRAPHY

Studies of *Huckleberry Finn*, 1884—1944

Anon. Reviews in *Critic*, V (November 29, 1844), 257; *Independent*, XXXVI (December 4, 1885), 171; *Christian Union*, XXX (December 5, 1884), 550; XXXI (February 5, 1885), 171; *Punch* (January 4, 1896), 5; *English Journal*, X (September 1921), 403–404.

Beck, Warren. "Huckleberry Finn versus the Cash Boy," *Education*, XLIX (September 1928), 1–13.

Besant, Walter. "My Favorite Novelist and His Best Book," *Munsey's*, XVII (February 1898), 659–664.

Blair, Walter. "Mark Twain, Hank, and Huck," *Horse Sense in American Humor*. Chicago, 1942. Pp. 195–217.

Bolton, Sarah. *Famous American Authors*. New York, 1887. Pp. 384–387.

Buxbaum, Katherine. "Mark Twain and American Dialect," *American Speech*, II (1927), 233–236.

Dickinson, A. D. "Huckleberry Finn Is Fifty Years Old," *Wilson Bulletin for Librarians*, X (November 1935), 180–185.

Emberson, Frances G. "Mark Twain's Vocabulary; A General Survey," *University of Missouri Studies*, X (1935), No. 3, pp. 1–53.

Ferguson, DeLancey. "Huck Finn A-Borning," *Colophon*, n.s. III (Spring 1938), 171–180.

———. *Mark Twain: Man and Legend*. Indianapolis, 1943. Pp. 217–230.

Frank, Waldo. *Our America*. New York, 1919. Pp. 34–38, 129–130.

Harris, Joel Chandler. "Letter on Mark Twain's Semi-Centennial," *Critic*, VII (November 28, 1885), 253.

Henderson, Archibald. *Mark Twain*. London, New York, 1911.

Howells, W. D. "Mark Twain, an Inquiry," *North American Review*, CLXXII (February 1901), 306–321.

Lang, Andrew. "Tribute to Mark Twain," *Illustrated News of the World* (1891) and *Critic*, XIX (July 25, 1891), 43–46.

Lorch, Fred W. "A Note on Tom Blankenship," *American Literature*, XII (November 1940), 351–353.

Macy, John. *The Spirit of American Literature*. Garden City, 1913. Pp. 248–277.

Marshall, Archibald. "Last Century's Literary Favorites: I, *Huckleberry Finn*," *Literary Digest International Book Review*, II (January 1942), 104–106.

Matthews, Brander. " 'The Adventures of Huckleberry Finn,' " *Saturday Review* (London), LIX (January 31, 1885), 153–154.

———. *Aspects of Fiction*. New York, 1896.

———. "Mark Twain—His Work," *Book Buyer*, XIII (January 1897), 977–979.

———. "Introduction" to *The Adventures of Huckleberry Finn*. New York, 1918.

Matthiessen, F. O. *American Renaissance*. New York, 1941.

Moore, Olin H. "Mark Twain and Don Quixote," *Publications of the Modern Language Association*, XXXVII (June 1922), 324–346.

Morley, Christopher. "Introduction" to *Tom Sawyer and Huckleberry Finn*.

Pearson, Edmund Lester. "The Children's Librarian versus *Huckleberry Finn*," *Library Journal*, XXXII (July 1907), 312–315. Included in *The Library and the Librarian*. Woodstock, 1910. Pp. 26–32.

Phelps, William Lyon. "Mark Twain," *North American Review*, CLXXXV (July 1907), 540–548.

Rourke, Constance. *American Humor: A Study of National Character*. New York, 1931.

Sherman, Stuart Pratt. "Mark Twain," *Cambridge History of American Literature*, III, 16–17. New York, 1921.

Tarkington, Booth. "Introduction" to *Adventures of Huckleberry Finn*. New York, 1933.

Van Doren, Carl. *The American Novel: 1798–1939*. New York, 1921. Revised with title indicated here, 1942.

Vogelback, Arthur L. "The Publication and Reception of *Huckleberry Finn* in America," *American Literature,* XI (November 1939), 260–272.

Wagenknecht, Edward. *Mark Twain: The Man and His Work*. New Haven, 1935.

Whiting, B. J. "Guyascutus, Royal Nonesuch and Other Hoaxes," *Southern Folklore Quarterly,* VIII (December 1944), 251–275.

Studies of *Huckleberry Finn,* 1945—1959

Adams, Lucille. "*Huckleberry Finn*": *A Descriptive Bibliography*. Buffalo, 1950.

Allen, Walter. "Introduction" to *The Adventures of Huckleberry Finn*. Camden, Ill., 1949.

Andrews, Kenneth R. *Nook Farm:* Mark Twain's Hartford Circle. Cambridge, 1950. Pp. 210–215.

Auden, W. H. "Huck and Oliver," *Listener,* L (October 1, 1953), 540–541.

Bell, Robert E. "How Mark Twain Comments on Society through the Use of Folklore," *Mark Twain Journal,* X (Summer 1955), 1–8, 24.

Blair, Walter. "The French Revolution and *Huckleberry Finn,*" *Modern Philology,* LV (August 1957), 21–35.

———. "When Was *Huckleberry Finn* Written?" *American Literature,* XXX (March 1958), 1–25.

———. "Why Huck and Jim Went Downstream," *College English,* XVIII (November 1956), 106–107.

Blessingame, W. "The Use of the Lie in *Huckleberry Finn* as a Technical Device," *Mark Twain Quarterly,* IX (Winter 1953), 11–12.

Branch, Edgar M. "The Two Provinces: Thematic Form in *Huckleberry Finn,*" *College English,* XI (January 1950), 188–195. Included in *The Literary Apprenticeship of Mark Twain*. Urbana, 1950.

Brooks, Van Wyck. *The Times of Melville and Whitman*. New York, 1947. Pp. 297–300, 453–457.

Brownell, Frances V. "The Role of Jim in Huckleberry Finn," *Studies in English,* I (1955), 74–83.

Brynes, Asher. "Boy-Men and Men-Boys," *Yale Review,* XXXVIII (Winter 1949), 223–233.

Cady, E. H., Frederick J. Hoffman, and Roy Harvey Pearce. "Notes on Reading *Huckleberry Finn,*" in *The Growth of American Literature,* I, 856–858. New York, 1956.

Canby, Henry Seidel. *Turn East, Turn West.* Boston, 1951. Pp. 132–147.

Cardwell, Guy A. *Twins of Genius.* East Lansing, 1953. Pp. 68–76.

Cox, James M. "Remarks on the Sad Initiation of Huckleberry Finn," *Sewanee Review*, LXII (Summer 1954), 389–405.

DeVoto, Bernard. "Introduction" to *The Portable Mark Twain.* New York, 1946.

———. "Those Two Immortal Boys," *Woman's Day* (November 1947), 38–39.

Eliot, T. S. "Introduction" to *The Adventures of Huckleberry Finn.* London, New York, 1950.

Elliott, George P. "Wonder for Huckleberry Finn," *Twelve Original Essays on Great American Novels.* Detroit, 1958.

Fadiman, Clifton. "A Note on *Huckleberry Finn,*" *Party of One.* Cleveland, 1955.

Faust, Clarence. "Introduction" to *The Adventures of Huckleberry Finn.* Chicago, 1950.

Fiedler, Leslie. "Come Back to the Raft Ag'in Honey!" *Partisan Review*, XV (June 1948), 664–671. Reprinted in *An End to Innocence.* Boston, 1955.

Foner, Philip S. *Mark Twain: Social Critic.* New York, 1958. Pp. 204–210.

Frantz, Ray William, Jr. "The Role of Folklore in *Huckleberry Finn,*" *American Literature*, XXVIII (November 1956), 314–327.

Friedrich, Otto. "Mark Twain and the Nature of Humor," *Discourse: A Review of the Liberal Arts*, II, 2 (April 1959), 67–86.

Fussell, Edwin. "Hemingway and Mark Twain," *Accent*, XIV (Summer 1954), 199–206.

Gordon, Edward J. "What's Happened to Humor?" *English Journal*, XLVII (March 1958), 127–133.

Gullason, Thomas Arthur. "The 'Fatal' Ending of *Huckleberry Finn,*" *American Literature*, XXIX (March 1957), 86–91.

Harrison, James G. "A Note on the Duke in 'Huckleberry Finn': The Journeyman Printer as Picaro," *Mark Twain Quarterly*, VIII (Winter 1947), 1–2.

Hemingway, Ernest. *The Green Hills of Africa.* New York, 1935.

Hinz, John. "Huck and Pluck: 'Bad' Boys in American Fiction," *South Atlantic Quarterly*, LI (January 1952), 120–129.

Hunting, Robert. "Mark Twain's Arkansaw Yahoos," *Modern Language Notes*, LXXIII (April 1958), 264–268.

Hutton, Graham. "Hawkeye, Huck Finn and an English Boy," Chicago *Sun Book Week*, IV (May 4, 1947), 2.

Jones, H. E. "Mark Twain and Sexuality," *Publications of the Modern Language Association*, LXXI (Summer 1956), 595–616.

Jones, Joseph. "The Duke's Tooth-Powder Racket," *Modern Language Notes*, LXI (November 1946), 468–469.

Kanapa, Jean. "Preface" to *Les Aventures d'Huckleberry Finn*. Paris, 1948.

Klotz, Marvin. "Mark Twain and Socratic Dialogue," *Mark Twain Journal*, XI, 1 (Summer 1959), 1–3.

Krause, Sydney J. "Twain's Method and Theory of Composition," *Modern Philology*, LVI (February 1959), 167–177.

Krutch, Joseph Wood. "Speaking of Books," New York *Times Book Review* (May 23, 1954), p. 2.

Lane, Lauriat, Jr. "Why *Huckleberry Finn* Is a Great World Novel," *College English*, XVII (October 1955), 1–5.

Leary, Lewis. "Tom and Huck: Innocence on Trial," *Virginia Quarterly Review*, XXX (Summer 1954), 417–430.

Lynn, Kenneth S. "Huck and Jim," *Yale Review*, XLVII (Spring 1958), 421–431.

McGraw, William C. "Pollyanna Rides Again," *Saturday Review* (London), XLI (March 22, 1958), 37–38.

Morris, Wright. *The Territory Ahead*. New York, 1957. Pp. 79–90.

Moses, W. R. "The Pattern of Evil in *Adventures of Huckleberry Finn*," *Georgia Review*, XIII, 2 (Summer 1959), 161–166.

Percy, Walker. "The Man on the Train," *Partisan Review*, XXIII (Fall 1956), 478–494.

Podhoretz, Norman. "The Literary Adventures of Huck Finn," The New York *Times Book Review* (December 6, 1959), pp. 5, 34.

Reinfeld, George. "*Huckleberry Finn:* Candidate for Greatness," *Mark Twain Journal*, X (Fall-Winter 1957), 12–14.

Remes, Carol. "The Heart of *Huckleberry Finn*," *Masses and Mainstream*, XIII (November 1955), 8–16.

Rhoades, Sister Mary Teresa. "Was Mark Twain Influenced by the Prolog to *Don Quixote?*" *Mark Twain Quarterly*, IX (Winter 1952), 4–6.

Rubenstein, Gilbert M. "The Moral Structure of *Huckleberry Finn*," *College English*, XVIII (November 1956), 72–76.

Santayana, George. "*Tom Sawyer* and *Don Quixote*," *Mark Twain Quarterly*, IX (Winter 1952), 1–3.

Schwartz, Edward. "*Huckleberry Finn:* The Inward Thoughts of a Generation," *Mark Twain Quarterly*, IX (Winter 1952), 11–16.

Scott, Arthur. "The Century Magazine Edits *Huckleberry Finn*, 1884–1885," *American Literature*, XXVII (November 1955), 356–362.

———. "Introduction" to *Mark Twain: Selected Criticism.* Dallas, 1955.

Slater, Joseph. "Music and Colonel Grangerford's," *American Literature,* XXI (March 1949), 108–111.

Smith, Henry Nash. "Origins of a Native American Literary Tradition," *The American Writer and the European Tradition.* Minneapolis, 1950. Pp. 70–77.

———. "Mark Twain's Images of Hannibal," *University of Texas Studies in English,* XXXVII (1958), 3–23.

———. "Introduction" to *Adventures of Huckleberry Finn.* Boston, 1958.

Spacks, Barry B. "The Thematic Function of the 'Rescue' in *Huckleberry Finn,*" *Mark Twain Journal,* XI, 1 (Summer 1959), 8–9.

Spiller, Robert Ernest. *The Cycle of American Literature.* New York, 1955. Pp. 150–162.

Stallman, R. W. "Huck Finn Again," *College English,* XVIII (May 1957), 425–426.

Suhnel, Rudolf. "Huckleberry Finn," *Anglo-Americana,* LXI (1955), 150–156.

Torchiana, Donald T. "Will Huck Hang?" *Mark Twain Journal,* X (Winter 1956), 5–8.

Wagenknecht, Edward. *Cavalcade of the American Novel.* New York, 1952. Pp. 117–120.

Wasiolek, Edward. "The Structure of Make-Believe: *Huckleberry Finn,*" *University of Kansas City Review,* XXIV (December 1957), 97–101.

Weber, J. Sherwood, Jules Alan Wein, Arthur Waldhorn, and Arthur Zeigler. "Twain: *The Adventures of Huckleberry Finn,*" *From Homer to Joyce: A Study Guide to Thirty-Six Great Books.* New York, 1959. Pp. 244–248.

Wecter, Dixon. "Mark Twain," *Literary History of the United States,* II, 930–934. New York, 1948.

———. "One Word More," in *The Adventures of Huckleberry Finn.* New York, 1948. Pp. xix–xxvi.

West, Ray B., Jr. "Mark Twain's Idyl of Frontier America," *University of Kansas City Review,* XV (Winter 1948), 92–104.

Wiggins, Robert A. "Mark Twain and the Drama," *American Literature,* XXV (November 1953), 279–286.

Williams, Stanley T. "Introduction" to *The Adventures of Huckleberry Finn.* New York, 1953.

Wouk, Herman. "America's Voice Is Mark Twain's," "This World," San Francisco *Chronicle* (August 5, 1956), p. 18.

Young, Philip. *Ernest Hemingway.* New York, 1952. Pp. 181–212.

Studies of *Huckleberry Finn*, 1960—March, 1961

Blair, Walter. *Mark Twain and Huck Finn.* Berkeley and Los Angeles, 1960.

Drake, Robert Y., Jr. "Huck Among the Doctors," *National Review*, IX, 20 (November 19, 1960), 320–322.

Eby, Cecil D. "Mark Twain's 'Plug' and 'Chaw,'" *Mark Twain Journal*, XI, 2 (Summer 1960), 11, 25.

Fiedler, Leslie A. "Duplicitous Mark Twain," *Commentary*, XXIX, 3 (March 1960), 239–248.

———. "*Huckleberry Finn:* Faust in the Eden of Childhood," in *Love and Death in the American Novel.* New York, 1960.

Gargano, James W. "Disguises in *Huckleberry Finn*," *University of Kansas City Review*, XXVI, 3 (March 1960), 175–178.

Gross, Seymour. "Sherwood Anderson's Debt to *Huckleberry Finn*," *Mark Twain Journal*, XI, 2 (Summer 1960), 3–5, 24.

Hoffman, Daniel G. "Jim's Magic: Black or White?" *American Literature*, XXXII, 1 (March 1960), 1–10.

Jacobson, Dan. "Mark Twain and the Calm Squatter," *Spectator*, No. 6893 (August 5, 1960), 219–220.

Karl, Frederick R. "Joseph Conrad and *Huckleberry Finn*," *Mark Twain Journal*, XI, 2 (Summer 1960), 21–23.

Loomis, C. C., Jr. "Twain's *Huckleberry Finn*," *Explicator*, XVIII, 4 (January 1960), Item 27.

Loomis, Edward W. "Three Notes on Plot," *Spectrum*, IV, 2 (Spring-Summer 1960), 94–99.

Robinson, E. Arthur. "The Two 'Voices' in *Huckleberry Finn*," *Modern Language Notes*, LXXV (March 1960), 204–208.

Yates, Norris W. "The 'Counter-Conversion' of Huckleberry Finn," *American Literature*, XXXII, 1 (March 1960), 1–10.

For articles comparing *Huckleberry Finn* and *Catcher In The Rye*, see "Topics for Further Research."

NOTES ON THE CRITICS

Richard P. Adams, who teaches American literature at Tulane University, is especially interested in the Romantic tradition in American literature and has published work on Emerson and Whitman as well as the essay included in this volume.

Frank Baldanza, Jr., professor of English at Bowling Green State

University in Ohio, has taught also at Louisiana State University; he is a specialist in American literature.

Gladys C. Bellamy received her undergraduate and graduate degrees from the University of Oklahoma, where she also taught from 1944 to 1949. In 1949, she became professor of English and head of the language arts department at Southwestern State College in Oklahoma. *Mark Twain as a Literary Artist* is her major work.

Robert Bridges (1858–1941), editor and author, was a graduate of Princeton University. He was associated with several newspapers and magazines during his lifetime, and from 1883 to 1900 he was literary critic for *Life*. His best-known books include *Overheard in Arcady* (1894), *Bramble Brae* (1907—a volume of poetry), and *The Roosevelt Book* (1904).

Van Wyck Brooks is an important American critic. During his life, he has taught at Stanford University, worked on *Collier's Encyclopaedia*, participated in the translation of some thirty books from French to English, and written important works on the history of literature in America. His *Ordeal of Mark Twain* has been a highly influential work.

Richard Chase, professor of English at Columbia University, is a specialist in American literature. A graduate of Dartmouth College, he received his graduate training at Columbia University and has taught also at Connecticut College, Kenyon College, and Indiana University. His writing, other than *The American Novel and Its Traditions*, includes studies of Melville, Whitman, and Dickinson.

Alexander Cowie is a teacher, critic, and scholar in American literature. He received his graduate training at Yale University and taught at several institutions before going to Wesleyan University where he has taught since 1924. His most important work is *The Rise of the American Novel*.

Bernard DeVoto (1897–1955), American novelist and critic, led a varied literary career. Son of an Italian father and Mormon mother, he was graduated from Harvard, taught as assistant professor of English at Northwestern University, edited the *Saturday Review of Literature*, and conducted the "Easy Chair" department in *Harper's Magazine*. He regarded *Huckleberry Finn* as the greatest novel written by an American.

John Erskine (1879–1951), minor American novelist, poet, and essayist, was educated at Columbia University to which he returned to teach from 1909 to 1937. Though he wrote ten novels and three books of poetry and was co-editor of *The Cambridge History of American Literature,* perhaps his greatest contribution was as a teacher. As a man of varied talents, he was also a well-regarded concert pianist.

James T. Farrell, American novelist, was born and reared in Chicago, which is the setting for his most famous work, the *Studs Lonigan* trilogy. Other well known works of his are *No Star Is Lost* and *A World I Never Made.* In years past he has been a radical of the left in politics and economics.

John C. Gerber is a professor of English at the State University of Iowa. He took his doctorate at the University of Chicago and has taught at the University of Pittsburgh, University of Chicago, and State University of Iowa. A specialist in American literature, he is particularly interested in, and has published several works on, Mark Twain.

Carson Gibb, a specialist in American literature, formerly taught at Lafayette College, Pennsylvania, and now teaches at Longwood College, Virginia.

Leo Marx, professor of English at Amherst College, received his graduate training at Harvard University. Before going to Amherst, he taught for several years at the University of Minnesota. Professor Marx is a specialist in American literature and intellectual history.

William Van O'Connor, critic and teacher, took his Ph.D. degree at Columbia University and now teaches at the University of California, Davis, where he is a professor of English. A prolific critic of American literature, he has written, among other things, book length studies of Wallace Stevens and William Faulkner, and a collection of short stories on academic life.

Albert Bigelow Paine (1861–1937), a man-about-letters, of New England parentage and reared in the Midwest, ended his formal schooling at the age of fifteen, and subsequently tried his hand at many literary tasks. His name lives today because of his biography of Mark Twain, although he wrote about forty books in all.

Vernon L. Parrington (1871–1929), American literary historian and critic, was born in the Midwest, educated in the East, and spent the remainder of his life as a professor of English at the University of Washington. Although he wrote articles for magazines and for standard reference works like the *Cambridge History of American Literature* and the *Encyclopedia of Social Sciences,* his Pulitzer Prize-winning volumes of *Main Currents in American Thought* were his lifework. This work revealed Parrington as an extreme liberalist in his views, brought "the new history" into the literary field, and marked an epoch in its classification.

Thomas Sergeant Perry (1845–1928), author, teacher, lecturer, and scholar, led a life of varied literary interests. A graduate of Harvard, he taught there for several years. His best-known works are *English Literature of the Eighteenth Century* (1883) and *History of Greek Literature* (1890). Oliver Wendell Holmes called him "the best-read man I have ever known."

Victor Sawdon Pritchett, British author and critic, is current director of *New Statesman and Nation*. His publications include *The Spanish Virgin, Shirley Sanz, Nothing Like Leather, Dead Man Leading, You Make Your Own Life, In My Good Books, It May Never Happen, The Spanish Temper*, and *Collected Stories*.

Eric Solomon, who teaches English and American literature at Ohio State University, is a specialist in American fiction, on which he has authored several articles. He has also edited *The Faded Banners: An Anthology of Nineteenth Century Fiction*.

Lionel Trilling, professor of English at Columbia University, is an important literary critic and a novelist of note. His three best-known works represent the range and importance of his contribution to literature: his *Matthew Arnold* is highly regarded as literary biography; his novel, *The Middle of the Journey*, has been very well received; and *The Liberal Imagination*, a collection of literary essays, is a minor landmark in American criticism.